Polynesian love

"Love in these islands has a simplicity, a spontaneity, a kindness that we Westerners have lost," the Frenchman explained. "Here a man can live the life he was supposed to live: the life of the body, the life of the mind, the life of the heart."

Maori love

"During the night I awoke slowly," the white man wrote. "There was a hand in my lava-lava. It was the hand of a girl who was crouched down beside me, smiling. She was perhaps thirteen years old . . . for a moment my European conscience rebelled. Then I took her and it was sheer pleasure. She made love in *Maori* style; quick, savage, silent."

THE BLUE OF
CAPRICORN

Eugene Burdick

▲ PYRAMID BOOKS • NEW YORK

THE BLUE OF CAPRICORN

A PYRAMID BOOK

Published by arrangement with the Houghton Mifflin Company

Pyramid edition published November 1971

Portions of The Blue of Capricorn originally appeared, in somewhat different form, in the October 1960 issue of Holiday, under the title "Journey Across the Pacific." © 1960 The Curtis Publishing Company. Chapter 18, "The Aborigine," has appeared in Harper's; Chapter 10, "The Black and The White," in Cosmopolitan.

Library of Congress Catalog Card Number: 61-14728

Printed in the United States of America

Pyramid Books are published by Pyramid Communications, Inc. Its trademarks, consisting of the word "Pyramid" and the portrayal of a pyramid, are registered in the United States Patent Office.

Pyramid Communications, Inc., 919 Third Avenue, New York, N.Y. 10022

Foreword

BLUE, pure undiluted blue, is the rarest color in nature. Yet in the South Pacific, in the deep waters about the Tropic of Capricorn, blue is everywhere and in the most startling hues and intensities. Pick up a handful of Capricorn water, however, and it is colorless. The blue water is artificial, a trick of refraction, the mischief of optics. Each particle of water is neutral, but between the great depths and the violence of the sun the water is made to look blue. This is a marvelous accident, for the blue forms a vast background for the white sand and coral of the atoll and the dense green and brown of the high island. No other color would frame it quite so well. The blue water is close to perfect.

The area covered by this book is not, however, confined to the Tropic of Capricorn. Indeed it sweeps as far north as the Tropic of Cancer. It also reaches as far east as Easter Island and as far west as the mainland of Asia.

This is not a travel book. Nor is it meant to be exhaustive. It is an impression of the Pacific and the people who live there. Several chapters are fiction; that is, they are an attempt to interpret what went on in the minds of others. I have attempted to be as factual as possible, but for pure fact we have encyclopedias. When one grapples with emptiness, silence, vastness and passion, facts, just facts, can be feeble and a disservice.

The idea for a book, the word or episode or thing

that began it, is seldom remembered correctly. The beginning of this book is long forgotton, but it took shape in conversations and correspondence with Harry Sions and Ted Patrick of *Holiday* Magazine. They were patient firm critics and sensitive friends. I am also grateful to Sterling Hayden and Bill Mullahey who have wiped a good deal of Pacific brine from their faces; to Carlos García-Palacios and his Agnes; to Marlon Brando who sees the place with a fine eye; to Hugh Kelley of Moorea and Jack Russell from, and of, everywhere; and to Bill Lederer who walked over many of the islands with me.

To Carol, my wife, I am specially indebted. Knowing that a book can be suffocated by too close attention she exercised a studied and heroic indifference. Her simulated boredom made it possible to write the book.

Contents

1. The Far Limits

THERE IS a place where the Pacific coldly smokes. Sometimes it is only a thin razor-sharp tendril of steam. Other times there is a great churning wall of vapor: gray, dense, impenetrable, ominous. Abruptly the temperature drops twenty degrees. This is the northern boundary of my Pacific. It occurs at about 46°N. Beyond this smoking line one is technically still in the Pacific, but it is, somehow, a different ocean. Northward are the chilled fog-bound Aleutians, tundra, ice, Eskimos, seals, great lights in the sky and, more recently, the plastic domes of radar sets. But it is a different place, a different personality, a different adventure. It is not my Pacific.

The Pacific is enormous, plural, contradictory. One aches for limitations, for boundaries that reduce the sensation of awe. For each person the limits are differ-

ent. For some people the Pacific is no larger than a
tiny village, a strip of white sand, a reef. For a tiny
group, that inquisitive body of oceanographers, the
Pacific is illimitable. So great is their curiosity that
their Pacific runs from the Bering Strait to the glittering ice cliffs of Antarctica.

My northern limit, the place where the ocean
smokes, is really the place where the warm Pacific
ends and the cold North begins. It is a place of
enormous silent battle. From the Mindanao Deep, off
the Philippines, and the Tonga Trench far to the
southeast, from the heavily salted waters of the equator, great streams of warm water slide slowly north.
Inexorably they gain in weight and volume and velocity and finally blend into the Kuroshio Current.
When the Kuroshio is at its fullest strength and begins
its invasion of the cold North it is bigger than a
hundred Mississippis. Its waters are a deep uniform
indigo, almost black, color. It barges northward at a
steady three knots. This quiet avalanche, gigantic
beyond knowing, seems invulnerable. In fact it is
doomed to an inevitable mechanical defeat. Poised in
the North, waiting for the mass of the Kuroshio, is the
cold dark-green immensity of the Oyashio, that body
of icy water which comes down from the Sea of
Okhotsk and the Bering Sea. The cosmic battle
between warm and cold is joined soundlessly. There
is a slow roiling, an encoiling of waters, a meeting of
pressures, a straining and a resistance. And the only
sign of battle is the smoke of condensation that rises
above the surface of the Pacific.

Occasionally there is a sound beneath the smoke.
This occurs when the fish within the Kuroshio tear
into the planktonrich water of the Oyashio. There is a
snapping and rending, the sound of attack and flight,
tiny skitterings and evasions blend into a gurgling
sound. Sometimes the water is littered with torn

bodies, devastated clouds of egg and sperm, small streaks of blood. But as sounds go it is a diminutive signal for such a gigantic struggle.

The Kuroshio wins occasional skirmishes, but they are tiny; a coconut thrown up on an Aleutian island, a Polynesian canoe discovered by an Eskimo (and giving him the only wood he will ever see), a scattering of ignored litchi nuts along a frosty shoreline. But in the end the Kuroshio loses, turns in an immense arc and begins to curl down along the Pacific Coast; bringing rain to Seattle and fog to San Francisco and, by some climatic irony, leaving Los Angeles desertlike and clear. Then it curves again and begins the long 9000-mile return sweep back to the deeps off the Philippines.

The southern limit of my Pacific is a far reach. One must go southward through endless minutes and degrees of latitude, through long deserts of water, past shoals, over archipelagoes, through the Calms of Cancer and the equatorial calm and the Calms of Capricorn, through the horse latitudes. Finally one ends up in a bit of Angle-Saxon prettiness and order. For me the southern limit of the Pacific is Port Arthur on Tasmania, the island which hangs pendant beneath Australia. Here is an unbelievable bit of English countryside—neat cottages, the bright red of apples on carefully tended trees, pubs, Cockney accents, even the crumbling ruins of an old fort. There it stands, flatly untypical of the rest of the Pacific: controlled, civilized, prosperous. But it is the end of something, for below Port Arthur one moves into the grip of the West Wind Drift which makes of the Antarctic a cold, slowly revolving nightmare. In the latitudes below there is a constant huge cyclone of cold wind, tortured waters, icebergs, sea leopards, the comic waddling stiffness of penguins, and finally, ageless windswept ice which is utterly devoid of life. This is not my Pacific.

The western and eastern limits of my Pacific are easier to define. The eastern limit is Easter Island, once dense with huge simple stone faces and a majestic pattern of avenues, but now a shabby pile of potsherd.

My western limit is ambiguous. It includes the Outback and aboriginal parts of Australia, but not the westernized cities. Nor does it include Japan, which is in the Pacific but not of it, a land deeply complex, glazed over with intricate custom and long tradition, subtle almost to the point of rigidity, with a culture different from the others of the Pacific.

In fact, my Pacific includes only what is known as Oceania plus the great archipelagoes of Indonesia, New Guinea and the Philippines. There are, I think, good reasons for drawing the lines where I have.

Asia is not the Pacific. It supplied some of the people that went in sampans, dugouts, planked canoes, rafts or merely swam to the Pacific islands. But a sea change took place among those that left Asia. The Asian mainlander is a continental type, aware of land and locality, marvelously sensitive to tradition, a worker in stone, a villager, artful with land, clever at trading and manufacturing. The Asian developed a rich sense of history and religions of the most delicate subtlety. He learned to fight serious organized wars and to build dynasties and to read and write and to use gunpowder.

One has only to look at the wonder of Angkor Wat, in Cambodia, to realize how different is the Asian from the Pacific man. There is nothing like Angkor in the Pacific. It would be impossible. Cambodia was once ruled by a river: the Mekong. The Mekong meandered over the land, shooting out branches here, depositing tons of rich mud in one place and starving another, flooding one village and providentially leaving another intact. A monsoon culture prevailed; everything depended on the rain and what it did to the Mekong. Men hung on to a thin listless life, lived in an oppressive and electric-charged humidity, threatened by everything. But at some point the traders from India arrived, and with them they brought "civilization" and the ability to read, to write, to calculate.

Then the Cambodians did a thing which seems very American but was actually very Asian. They conquered the land. They dug an incredible system of drainage canals, an elaborate linkage of sewers, formed huge artificial lakes which are the largest fish preserves in the world. Little slips of canals gave everyone a share of the Mekong's rich silt. The country became rich enough to afford wars, clashes between dynasties, religions of extravagant splendor. Angkor Wat was built in the hills of Cambodia to celebrate this triumph of man over nature. The place is immense. There are great avenues of stone so intricately carved, so beautifully patinaed that they seem to be of cloth. There are cyclopean avenues lined with passive Buddhas, and even where chunks of a stone nose or a lip have fallen away they cannot flaw the serenity which is just short of contempt, the placidity which is almost living death. Angkor is a great monument to man's domination of the land, of his secret pride over coming to terms with nature, a record of his back-looking obsession with ancestry and blood and history. It is a tribute to everything in man that is purposeful, confident, dominant, assured. It is the superb work of city people, a thing of sophistication so subtle that we have not yet equaled it in the modern world.

In just two fields, for example, there is a yawning gap between Angkor and its people and anything that can be found in the Pacific. First, the people of

Angkor could measure. Even after untold centuries and the assault of nature and shifting earth there are moats many kilometers long which have a skew of *only one centimeter*. There is still a canal over sixty miles long which runs in a dead straight line. Secondly, they understood the anatomy of the human body. In Angkor there is the gigantic *garuda* of Prasat Thom; a fantastic sculpture of a winged man. One stares at him for hours before one realizes the fascination: the body actually seems to be in motion, to be straining up on its wings, to be struggling for release. And every muscle is accurately portrayed, is acting precisely as a man's muscles might act if he were to have wings. The knowledge of anatomy is so exquisite, the rendering so faithful that it is uncanny.

With the exception of some of the Malays you will find nothing like this in the Pacific. Measuring was done carelessly, with lengths of coconut fiber or sticks, which were worn down by constant use so that they never became a standard. Most Pacific art is primitive, gross, sharply angular demonstrating no comprehension of what lies beneath the skin of man.

There is nothing in the Pacific to compare with Angkor. In the Pacific, history is short, memory is family-wide and almost entirely verbal. There are politics, but they are raw and unpolished, lacking the elegant quality of style and intricacy which continental Asians have given them. There is cruelty, but great battles are infrequent. More often battles are *bouffe* affairs: great preparations, feverish excitement, frenzied dancing, a beating of chests, a rattling of spears—and when the first drop of blood is shed the whole thing is called off and marvelous stories are invented.

In the Pacific there is envy and suspicion and hatred, but these sentiments do not find institutions to house them. A man will smash another's brains out with a stone and be unable to recall the reason and say in court at Papeete "He urinated close to the taro patch and he gave me a bad look and it was a hot day" and wait for judgment with a childlike lack of excitement. Everywhere there is thievery, it is the most common crime, but in every Pacific language there is a word which makes it a joke rather than a crime.

In the Pacific there are no dynasties. There are no complex economic patterns. There is almost no manufacturing. There is an art, but it is curiously flat and everywhere the same; it is an act of memory, almost a social reflex, rather than something creative. There is little madness, almost no suicide, many murders. There is no logical system of thought, but there is an uncanny use of experience. This means that there is very little innovation, but a most beautiful use of the past.

The Pacific man does not see the ocean as implacable and hostile. He is incapable of weeping on the beach as do Portuguese fisher folk when their boats put out. He has none of the dread of the sea that is found in the bitter-sweet regard of the Scotch and the New Englanders. The Pacific man sees the ocean as Olympian . . . outsized and majestic, capable of enormous power, but also capable of foolishness and mistakes. It gives his life all the tension it needs.

There is, I think, a reason for this. Throughout Oceania, in the great archipelagoes with their vast sweeps of salt water and their tiny specks of islands, men have not yet dominated nature. Nature is lived with gingerly, delicately, sometimes with zest and daring, but always with awe and sometimes with a crawling eerie fear. Not having measured nature, the man of Oceania has little desire to master other men. His art, his politics, his manners, his religion, his industry all seem miniature and bleached and diminished because of a looming presence: the Pacific.

The thing a man first glances at when he leaves his house in the morning is generally a thing he values. In Asia, a man will generally hurry to a shrine or he will join a group of gossipers. Later he will meander to his shop or fields. In Oceania a man will step from his nipa hut and if the Pacific is in sight he will look at it. He will study the waves, the drift of currents, the wind. The ocean around him is more important than any person, natural or supernatural. Good and evil, life and death, plenty or famine, everything is formed by the Pacific.

The physical power of the Pacific is visible and unsurprising. Its currents cut islands and continents into various shapes; its winds determine climate; its waters deliver a surfeit of fish to some areas and starve another. But the Pacific also cuts deep into the personality and soul of man. For example, the sin of pride is impossible in the Pacific native. And so is a highly developed notion of private property, of a single vengeful God, excessive egotism. Because the Pacific is so inhumanly vast, so brooding, so puckish wherever men can live they come to value sociability ... the ultimate punishment is enforced estrangement from other men.

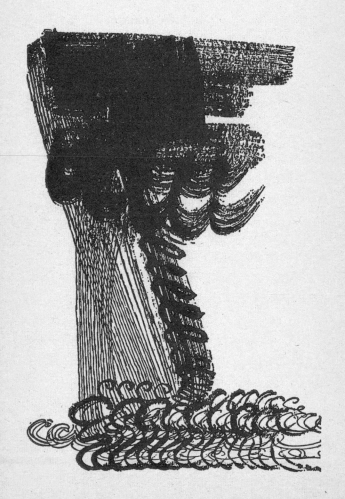

2. The Skin of the Pacific

DESPITE the horrendous sea stories told about the Pacific it really is, by and large, the most pacific of oceans. The massive but gentle cyclone system which moves air about the Pacific gives it a consistent and predictable pattern. The skin of the Pacific, the only thing the naked eye sees, has an endless regularity. From Diamond Head one can see the Kaiwai Channel behave precisely the same way for months; dead calm in the morning and then ruffled by a spanking breeze in the afternoon. From the mountain plantations of Borneo one can look over the Sulu Sea and for an endless reaching away of days it will look like a pool of molten lead, light green in patches, hazed over by the unbelievable heat. On Tongareva, east and north of Samoa, the Pacific will appear as an infinite procession of waves which all "feather" at the same point and then foam softly to their death against the reef. The trade winds off the ocean will hold the trunk of a coco palm frozen in position for months.

Once on an ocean, any ocean, all that one can see is a perfect horizon. It surrounds the ship in the fateful 360 degrees and appears always the same distance

away. It may be obscured in bad weather, one may
be distracted by clouds in the sky or the sight of an
albatross. But one seems to be moving in the same
circle of water. The illusion persists until a landfall is
made.

One would think that all oceans would be the
same. But the Pacific is different. After awhile the
sheer passage of time starts to produce a taste of
uniqueness. At first it is merely a sense of fatigue,
eyes aching from the bright sun, something visceral.
The sensation deepens, however, and the mind begins
to ask: how much longer? Time and monotony work
on a person until at some point they change into a
conscious intuition of immense size. This immensity at
first is merely boring, but boredom can be pushed to
the edge of cruelty. It can also be terrifying.

There is no word that is the antonym of "claustro-
phobia," but there should be. It is an affliction of the
Pacific, one that is becoming obsolete. It occurs only
on sailing ships or slow-moving ships. The sailor
learns to keep this awesome sense of immensity by
reducing it to manageable proportions. On a sailing
ship every hand will wait for the noon and evening
sights to see how the hugeness has been chopped into
miles. In the crew's quarters as well as on the bridge
the chart, with its x's and short lines marking a day's
run, is more diverting than any piece of literature.
The one inevitable conversation is about distance and
time. This is why crews make bets, that get increasingly large and desperate as time passes, about the
day's run, the time of first landfall, the time when the
anchor pin will be knocked loose. By these devices,
trivial and time-worn, the sailor manages to survive
the Pacific and its reaches.

There is a limit to even a sailor's patience. I once
saw the crew of a big seagoing tug which had hauled
two obsolete Liberty ships, in tandem, from Panama

to Japan. There they would be turned into scrap. The high freeboard of the Liberty ships made them difficult to handle in any kind of wind and their weight and that of the towing cables forced the tug to travel at a dead slow speed. They had twice altered course to avoid reported typhoons. The trip had taken sixty-seven days. During that passage every day was identical: clear, hot, cloudless. They had not seen another ship nor had they made a landfall. By some rare freak of weather rain had not once cooled the tug.

This was in the year of Our Lord 1956 and the tug was fitted out with movies, frozen food and tons of magazines and books. Even so the veteran crew stumbled off the tug as hollow-eyed and quarrelsome as the sailors of Bligh or Tasman or Magellan. Two of them said they would never again sail the Pacific although they were old Asian hands and the sea was their life. The rest were inarticulate; mute with some unspeakable rage or anger.

"I begged the skipper to cut the tows loose and start making time," one of the Asian hands said. "Me, who's been at sea for forty years. When he wouldn't do it I really considered killing him. We talked mutiny in the crew's quarters." He laughed shakily as if recalling a persistent nightmare. "I even got to aching for a typhoon. I prayed we would hit a reef."

When it came to reasons they were incapable of words. Their hands made traceries in the air of hugeness, of vast boring spaces. Anything as large as the Pacific should have more faces, show more of its personality. They hated the Pacific as if it were a person.

Regardless of how much you see of the Pacific it conveys an impression not of bigness but of massivity, of reaches so great and powers so illimitable that we have no precise word for them. All one can do is make traceries in the air.

By a staggering amount the Pacific is the biggest ocean of the world. Its waves have the longest fetch of open water in which to travel. The two deepest "deeps," the Mindanao and the Marianas, are in the Pacific, and so are the next four deepest "deeps." There is no other body of water which seems so empty, in which distances loom so depressingly great. In the early days of exploration, sailors dreaded the Pacific because its vast distances made it certain that many of the crew would die of scurvy, heat, suicide and assorted afflictions which seem to grow simply out of the bigness of the place. Today, when it is possible to barrel cleanly across the whole expanse in fifteen hours, in a jet at 35,000 feet, passengers arriving in Hong Kong have the slight gnawing sensation that they have defied something by making the trip so swiftly. Everywhere, among everybody in the Pacific, there is this shared sense of awe at the brutal cosmic size of the place.

The intuition that the Pacific is different from other oceans is not a pure act of imagination. Scientists are agreed that the Pacific originated in a quite novel manner. Indeed the scientific theory of the creation of the Pacific is so weird that it sounds as if it were taken from mythology.

Geophysicists have known for some time that the floor of the Pacific is basalt, a substance generally found only in the middle layer of the earth. Other oceans have a floor of granite. Rachel Carson is among those who argue that the great basin of the Pacific was formed by the tearing away of an enormous fragment of the earth which orbited away into space and became the moon.

According to the theory there was a time when the earth was made up entirely of molten liquids. These white hot liquids responded to the tidal pull of the sun. Having no land masses to break their build-up the molten mass formed into huge tidal sweeps which roared endlessly around the earth. Each time the tides became larger and larger, responding harmonically to the pulse of the sun and the utter absence of physical restraint. At some point these tides became so rageful and monstrous that a great chunk of the earth was thrown, flaming and wild, into the firmament. Instantly, however, it was subject to the physical laws. It was whipped into a ball-like shape and commenced an orderly orbit around the earth. It rapidly cooled.

Actually the water of the Pacific is never still. Even when it is as flat and glistening as poured lacquer it is in motion. The surface waters sometimes move with considerable speed so that a coconut or a drifting boat, even on a windless day, might travel as much as seventy-five to one hundred miles. Unless there is a landmark in view this movement is invisible for a simple reason: the whole horizon of water moves simultaneously. There is no sensation of movement because one's whole world is moving. The deep cold waters also move, but in a much slower fashion. They creep rather than flow.

The Russells are a group of magnificent little islands in the Solomons. Once I was ashore there during the equivalent of a doldrum. I noticed a coconut in the water and slowly became aware that it was moving as fast as I was walking although the water was dead still and as motionless as quicksilver in a plate. The coconut was held in a sharp grip so that its upper side was dry and blackened by the sun. It did not roll or bob, but it moved. In fact the whole body of water I could see was in slow invisible motion. The coconut moved into shore, almost beached itself and then slid out into deeper water. I watched it move down one complicated channel after another and finally it was free of the islands and rapidly became a dot and then vanished.

In a crude sense the Pacific currents are dominated by massive movements of surface waters, so huge that they are called "drifts" rather than currents. The equator divides the two. The North Pacific Drift moves in a great sweeping clockwise manner, flowing west along the equator, turning north and forming the Kuroshio, is turned back by the cold waters of the Oyashio current, spins off a minor current that is called the California. Below the equator the South Pacific Drift moves in a counterclockwise direction, spinning off minor currents as vast as all the rivers of the world, but perfectly invisible to the eye.

There was a time when the Pacific dwellers, especially the Polynesians, knew these big currents and also the smaller eddies and backwashes and peculiarities around their own islands. Today because of interisland steamers and power-driven schooners they have lost much of their old knowledge of the ocean currents. But the sea around their islands they still know well. I have been fishing in an outrigger with a Melanesian and had the experience of suddenly realizing as we started for land that we were making no progress. The Melanesian instantly shrugged his shoulders and stopped paddling. In pidgin he explained that two men could not make headway against the current at that moment. Wait for two hours, he said, and the tide would overcome the current and we would be swept back. For two hours the island grew smaller until it was only a dark line on the horizon. Then without any change in the surface of the water the dark line began to thicken. Instantly we started to paddle. Then the current was with us and the island came up quickly. In an hour we were back ashore.

The consistent direction and velocity of these currents suggests that the waters of the Pacific are autonomous, are almost comparable to the circulation of the human body. In fact the currents work in a delicate balance with the prevailing trade winds and the rotation of the earth. It is the trades from the northeast in the North Pacific and from the southeast in the South Pacific that start these gigantic eddies. But at the same time the cold upwelling of masses of water and the distribution of land masses determines how the winds will blow. The result is that neither wind nor sea is autonomous, both are locked in a timeless mechanism, utterly dependent upon one another. The eastern part of the Pacific is dominated by the monsoons. With an almost perfect regularity the monsoon blows from the continent of Asia out to sea in the winter and then reverses itself in the summer. Generally the summer monsoon brings with it the unending warm rains that can stretch a white man's nerves to the breaking point. When the rain stops for a few moments the earth steams and something about the Occidental physiology is sickened. This is the time when American and European mothers, their faces pale and damp, herd miserable children into the hill stations and resorts or, if that is impossible, to the seashore.

I, for one, do not believe that the monsoon is necessarily as enervating as British colonials, Maugham and missionaries would have us believe. Sea Bee officers have told me that Americans during the war worked through the monsoon season, putting in almost the same hours they did in the States and with almost precisely the same output. They did sweat more and learned to take salt pills. But when they were not down with malaria or fungus infections or ennui they worked without regard for the weather.

It is true, however, that the monsoon wears at the nerves of Occidentals. First, it outrages our sense of fastidiousness. It is somehow indecent to be sweating day and night; to change a shirt and have it rimed with sweat in a half hour, to go to sleep on a fresh sheet and find it slippery by midnight. Secondly, hot wet winds are somehow foreign to the American and European personality. Our bodies unconsciously anticipate that a wind will be bracing . . . and when it comes steady, unending and hot it rapidly becomes more than just boring. It becomes maddening.

The calm revolving mass of the Pacific is cut directly down the middle by a band of dead air called the doldrums. This band varies somewhat in width, and is generally a bit north of the equator and parallel to it. It is a kind of still buffer between the gigantic eddies of the North and South Drifts. In the sailing days it was an area of pure torture. The sea goes flat and glassy. Rain squalls appear and drop a gray curtain of rain straight to the ocean, the edges so sharp that they seem to have been cut by a machine. It looks cool and gray, a refuge from the sun. But when the squall falls upon your ship it is warm, small-dropped, tea-like. The sun moves close and burns red, but with a lemon aura.

Sailing vessels must wait until they drift out of the doldrums or pick up a vagrant breeze. Even today on sailing vessels that have refrigerators and ice and scotch and frozen meat it is a deadly time. The ship shrinks in size, the horizon expands, one feels diminished as if he is sweating away his body. But oddly enough you are more aware of other people and the ship which seemed empty and almost lonely when running before the trades is now squalid and jammed. A sailing vessel is a self-ventilating affair; she is not designed for standing still under a lemon-colored sun. Tiny smells, of shoes and dirty shorts and toothpaste, hang invisibly and persistently in the air . . . annoying.

Garbage thrown overboard floats beside the ship and as the days pass the mess grows.

Today most sailing vessels, unless racing, turn on their auxiliary and power through the doldrums. But in the days of pure sail, when ships were loaded with enormous crews and the food was chiefly salted meat and hardtack and the water quickly grew green slime over each barrelhead it must have been agony. It was in the doldrums that mutinies were hatched, where marginal men ran amok, where the cat whistled before smacking flesh, where suicides occurred, where the weak perished out of crushing futility.

I have heard that dying by freezing is a blissful relief, a kind of pleasant letting go after great pain and stress. Suicide in the doldrums must be much the same thing ... to cut through the brassy refracting surface, to go deep with bubbles and spray and coldness about one. I am not a professional yachtsman, but I have noticed that among ocean racers, who will talk endlessly about anything to do with yachting, there is a curious silence, a mutual embarrassment, which comes up when the doldrums are mentioned. Those that have been through it would like to forget it.

But if the sailor talks and writes little about the doldrums the opposite of the doldrums, the typhoon, arouses a kind of fierce poetry in every sea-going man, even those that have never seen one. Joseph Conrad, avoiding the pitfalls of describing the indescribable, showed the power of the typhoon by telling of a hold full of Chinese whose bags of silver dollars were tossed and split by the heaving of the ship and then showed the wild scrambling of seasick people in a chaos of vomit and debris and bodies clutching for their dollars. The story told more, however, about human character than about typhoons.

No one is certain how a typhoon starts. But once

begun it is quickly recognized. For unknown reasons
the hot air of the tropics begins to spin and begins to
feed on surrounding air until it is a vast whirlpool of
wind ranging from twenty to a thousand miles in
width. The revolving mass is pulled along by the
upper winds and the typhoon moves in a great curve
until it mysteriously expends its energy or hits a mass
of land or cold air. The winds within the typhoon
commonly reach 75 miles an hour and have been
measured at 150 miles an hour. Part of the destructive
power of the typhoon wind is due to its pulsing
character: one moment the winds will drop to nothing, an instant later in a gigantic puff they will roar
by at incredible speeds.

This odd rhythm can do immense damage to certain kinds of objects. I was on a destroyer during a
typhoon and was standing on the bridge. Our inclinometer rolled regularly back and forth as the ship
rolled with the waves . . . no one cares about pitch on
a destroyer, the fore and aft motion of the ship, and
there is not even an instrument to measure it. Pitch is
not fatal. A high pitch will often send the nose of the
ship deep into the water and make it shudder along
its entire length or throw the screws into the air
where they accelerate wildly for a few seconds, but a
ship recovers from these blows. But a degree too
much of roll and a ship will turn turtle. For this
reason everyone on the bridge was watching the
inclinometer. We had filled the empty fuel tanks with
salt water as ballast and had trimmed for maximum
stability and still we were rolling between 35 and 40
degrees. It was exciting, but not dangerous.

Then there was a curious lull and the wind almost
died. The action of the waves continued our roll, but
the air was calm. A young quartermaster opened the
hatch on the windward side and peered out.

"It's calming down . . ." he started to say when the

typhoon hit again. It was a burst of wind travelling at well over 125 miles an hour. It snapped the hatch shut, slicing the quartermaster's thumb off neatly at the first joint. It caught us on a roll and everyone on the bridge sensed we were in trouble . . . even the quartermaster did not bother to look at the blood jetting softly from his thumb. He swung his eyes to the inclinometer. It went to 45 in a steady, even swing and without stopping went to 53, then slowed but continued to climb to 58. It paused there and all of us, standing at impossible angles, stared. There was nothing to do and each of us knew it. The inclinometer went higher to 60 and there it hung for perhaps two seconds . . . a 2000-ton hull being held over by the invisible flow of wind. Then it let go. With an awesome compensating lurch we rolled 52 degrees in the other direction. Strange noises came from below, but we were out of danger. The quartermaster suddenly began to whimper, looking down at his thumb. That single roll cost us six broken wrists, a broken leg, a man scalded by a coffee urn, the quartermaster's thumb and hundreds of shattered glasses, plates and cups.

I have never been strapped to a coconut tree during a typhoon, but many a person living on a low atoll has. It is a relatively safe place, for the roots of the coconut tree are as deep and tough as any in the world. It will remain standing while concrete piers are being torn into chunks, tin roofs are torn from wooden buildings which are themselves later reduced to matchwood. But there is an art to survival on a coconut tree in a typhoon. Position yourself too low and you might be caught by high waves. Go to the top of the tree and you run three risks. First, coconuts that are torn loose by the high winds will travel in a straight, fast horizontal line like projectiles. Natives have been cut down from trees with their bodies

beaten to death by flying nuts. Secondly the lull and
gust rhythm of a typhoon will set a coconut tree to
waving in a strange harmonic. At the top of the tree
this can become a fierce whiplash which either breaks
the lines securing a person or beats him senseless.
Thirdly, the palm frond itself offers so much wind
resistance that it will occasionally snap off and take
the top few feet of the coconut tree with it.

And, when all is said and done, even the most
experienced of old hands may choose the wrong tree.
For in some typhoons coconut trees are wrenched
loose and no one can foresee which they will be. The
biggest and thickest tree may be the oldest and its
roots the closest to death. It is a maddening choice. I
should not like to have to make it.

One of the weirdest stories of atoll survival during
a typhoon is what occurred to the famous Frisbie
family. Robert Frisbie had taken his children, aged
two to ten, to the atoll of Suwarrow. When the
typhoon struck in full force almost simultaneously
three things happened: the tin roof was torn from
their shack, half of the coconut trees on the *motu*
were felled and waves started washing over the
motu. After the first frenzied minutes Frisbie decided
to take refuge in a clump of five giant tamanu trees.
Although the tamanu does not have the lasting power
of a coconut tree it was the only place he could keep
the children together.

He describes the episode in *The Island of Desire*:

> I tied Elaine on my back again and this time took
> Nga under my arm, for the tamanus were to wind-
> ward, and Johnny could not carry her sister against
> the wind. We crawled past the tank on our hands
> and knees, seeming to force our heads and shoulders
> into a solid substance, feeling our bodies too light to
> grip the ground. It was slow work and it was des-
> perate work, for constantly we were haunted by the

knowledge that we might not reach the trees before the next sea came. Even now it makes a cold sweat start from my skin when I recall that laborious half hour's struggle when the five of us wormed painfully through the solid body of wind, desperate but not despairing. Brave children! They dug their toes and fingers in the sand and pushed forward like draft horses hauling a heavy load. And the seas! The seas! Would another comber rage through the clearing before we made the tamanus?

The Frisbies survived, but Suwarrow was swept bare and the motus were nothing more than sand cays. They survived until the boat arrived because of their knowledge of reef life and their ability to find and eat birds, crabs, fish . . . all raw.

Almost every typhoon leaves some atoll swept clean. The surviving natives abandon the island. In a surprisingly short time, however, coconuts will have drifted ashore and begun to grow, seeds come floating in on the winds or in the droppings of birds and the atoll will come back to life.

The swath of destruction a typhoon cuts is generally confined to a twenty or thirty mile wide path surrounding the "eye" of the typhoon. Weather planes have photographed the eye of a typhoon from above. It is like looking down into a huge whirlpool of clouds, tulip-shaped at the top, but quickly narrowing to a thin empty stem which reaches to the surface of the earth. The eye itself is a tall tube of quiet air, a pillar around which the winds revolve. But the closer the eye the more savage and fast are the revolutions. When the eyes passes close to fruit trees it will wipe them clean of mangoes and papayas. In some cases it will even strip away leaves and tiny tough twigs and finally will jerk the entire tree free.

A rubber plantation that falls within the typhoon's eyes is a tragedy to see. Wherever a twig has been broken away the tree begins to "bleed"; long white streams of latex that flow down the bole and represent ruined tons of rubber. And the wounds are rapidly infected by fungus. Many is the rubber planter who has cast an eye over his plantation as a typhoon passes and knows he is ruined.

For reasons which are not clear to me the pandanus roof of a nipa hut is better able to withstand typhoon winds than the tin roof . . . which is really made of sheet iron. Perhaps it is because the wind can pass through the spaces in the pandanus and thus is unable to get a solid purchase. But a tin roof can be ripped off without effort and go whirling off like some odd, clumsy and fantastic sword . . . slicing through trees, wooden houses and human bodies without the slightest diminution of speed.

A Fijian once showed me a dent in a kauri tree which had the precise shape of a scotch bottle. It looked exactly as if a bottle had been pressed into a soft material, except that kauri is very hard. The Fijian said the bottle had been slammed against the tree by a typhoon. It is possible, I suppose. I do know that the bark of the tree was unbroken so that the shape had not been carved into the tree.

Pacific typhoons are accompanied by unbelievable deluges of rain. The average rainfall throughout the United States is probably around thirty inches a year and it is hard for an American to comprehend that a typhoon can produce that much rainfall in a *single day*. Rain as we know it is a gentle thing, occasionally rising to a sharp intensity. Typhoon-driven rain comes in solid heavy torrents; it seems not to be made up of drops, but to come with the smash and force of a fire hose. Such a rain will chew into plowed land like a monitor washing gold-bearing dirt from California hills and leave a torn and leached-out landscape behind it. Flying over an archipelago like the Philip-

pines after a typhoon one will see great ugly red-
dish-brown splotches reaching out into the ocean
wherever a river empties. They are the thousands of
tons of top soil blasted loose from the earth by the
typhoon rains. The splotches look oddly like blood.

The storm waves of a typhoon also seem to work
themselves up rhythmically and harmonically. During
the peak of a typhoon at sea the waves become quite
invisible for spume is torn from the tops of the waves
and travels like a solid layer of froth just above the
wave tops. In the typhoon which I mentioned earlier,
our destroyer was escorting five small Army river tugs
from Manila to Okinawa. As the weather closed in we
kept tabs on their movements by radar . . . they appeared as five small white blips on the screen. As the
wind rose and the white froth began to fly the tugs
were literally submerged in the creamy water and the
radar signal began to bounce back from the almost
solid layer of spume. One by one the tugs disappeared from the screen. We cleared the area to avoid
collision.

The tugs were manned by Army sergeants who in
some cases had never taken a tug to sea before, but
were trained to work in rivers and seaports. When the
typhoon passed us by, we began to search for the
tugs, with the dread feeling that they would not
survive. We were wrong. Not only had they survived,
but they had managed to hold together and were
sailing towards the Chinese mainland in a straight
line . . . not one of the sergeants knew how to navigate and all had lost their compasses during the blow.
As we came alongside they grinned wanly up at us.
Their only request was for ice cream, for they had
eaten nothing but crackers for three days.

Later I talked to one of the sergeants and he said
that the tugs were never in any real danger of capsiz-
ing. But beneath the layer of spume it had been

oppressively hot and the noise was unending. He was not a demonstrative man, but he had been shaken.

"I never really thought I would sink after the first couple of hours," he said. "But I really thought that I was going crazy. There I was, skinned down to skivvies, soaking wet from sweat and rain and just a few feet above me was this white stream of water going by at a hell of a speed and making a noise like a railroad train. When we came to the top of a wave the spume would hit us. The glass in the deckhouse had blown out the first hour and the water hit me right in the back of the head. Then we'd drop down into the trough and everything would be a dark green color. Somehow I kept thinking there wasn't enough air to breathe and I'd be taking big sucks of it each time we went down into the trough." He held up his hands, his thumb and forefinger separated by a tiny slit of space. "I came that close to going nutty. Really, that close."

Typhoon storm waves have been known to work up to heights of close to fifty feet and waves of this size will batter constantly at whatever land is in their way. Not only can waves like this destroy solid concrete quays and piers, but they will tear pieces of coral as large as a house loose and roll them from the oceanside of a reef into the lagoon. Typhoon waves can leave a luxuriant, green atoll as bare and white as a bone with only a few battered spikes of coconut stumps sticking into the air.

Among the most awesome catastrophes of the Pacific is the *tsunami*, a tidal wave caused by a submarine earthquake. The traveler on the Pacific will not even be aware of the passage of such a wave. It will appear on the ocean as only another, perhaps slightly larger wave, among others. But in hard fact, the tsunami radiates out from the submarine disturbance at a very high speed, traveling ten times as fast as ordinary waves.

Actually a tsunami should not be dangerous to humans on land for it gives ample warning of its arrival. There is usually a brief time when the water pulls from the land as if pulled by an excessive low tide. Anchored boats are suddenly on the bottom, fish flounder in the reef, coral heads are exposed. But even with this warning Hawaiians, for example, will rush to the reef to gather fish or to stare at the new seascape, confident that they can outrun the tsunami when it comes. They never can. The tsunami of 1946 which hit the Hawaiian Islands killed more than 150 people and did $25 million damage. By 1959 an elaborate pattern of tidal wave detection devices had been placed around the Pacific and the Islands had hours of advance warning. Even so, there were deaths when a summer tsunami struck. Curiosity seems to be in delicate balance with fear.

Before that tidal wave struck, a clever used car dealer quickly moved his cars behind a waterfront super-market to protect them from the rising water. When the tsunami hit, those cars parked by exits were bombarded with cans of tomato sauce and soup and fruit juice which reduced them to ruins. On the backwash of the wave the remaining cars were smashed against the building. The used car dealer quietly went out of business. The supermarket was rebuilt on the same spot.

The most destructive tsunami known to man occurred in 1883 when the volcanic island of Krakatoa in the Strait of Sunda was blown apart by a series of explosions that were not to be equaled until hydrogen bombs were detonated. The dust from that explosion was carried around the world in thick gray clouds. Faster than the dust, however, were the waves. Some of them reached 100 feet high and swept silently down on unsuspecting coast dwellers thousands of miles away. In some fishing villages the only survivors were those who were at sea. These survivors, innocent of what had happened, returned to find villages scoured from the earth, great slashes cut into the jungles, the coastal waters dense with bodies and debris. Over 30,000 people lost their lives.

There are three hundred active volcanoes in and around the rim of the Pacific. No one is certain if another Krakatoa is possible and volcanologists are among the most cautious of scientists . . . partially because they are not yet sure of their science.

One thing is certain, however, and that is the fact that the Pacific is the most active, unpredictable, mercurial and surprising of our oceans. At the same time it is so vast that it accommodates these natural catastrophes with the complacency with which a caraboa endures its small perpetual cloud of insects. The capacity of the Pacific to endure is almost limitless. Although there are about one hundred and thirty typhoons a year in the Pacific most of them spin themselves to death over empty waters and go virtually unnoticed. Volcanos will slowly shoulder their way to the surface, erupt in steam and heavy yellow sulphur smoke, live for a few days and then fall beneath the surface unseen by a human eye. Fathometers will indicate shoals where charts show only deep water and other ships will confirm the finding . . . and a month later the fathometers will record only deep water. The highest wave ever authenticated was 112 feet high and no sailor was surprised that it was in the Pacific.

The log entry "Beaufort: 12" means a wind speed of over seventy-five miles an hour, and nowhere is it more frequently recorded than in the Pacific. Such winds, combined with the great fetches of the Pacific, produce not only great waves, but a sound one can

neither forget nor accurately describe. Every pro-
tusion on a ship, even the rivet heads, will sing or
howl or hum depending on its shape. Signal lanyards,
which have been hanging loose for months, will draw
tight as violin strings and give off a dangerous fierce
humming. When they break, one by one, they instantly snap out into the wind and become as stiff as rods.
At some point the ocean itself starts to give off a
sound: the great fundamental clash of wave trains
colliding with one another, the soft unendurable suck
of foam, the hiss of wave tops converted into stinging
liquid shrapnel. The sight of the Pacific lashed into a
kind of Brobdingnagian madness, at war insanely with
itself, is chilling.

The vastness of the Pacific and its weather have
made it a devourer of ships. Each ocean takes its toll
of ships, but the Pacific often does it in novel ways.

In 1819 an Owen Chase first mate of the whaler
Essex was witness to a unique event. The captain and
most of the crew were in boats harpooning whales
when a large spermaceti whale, about eighty-five feet
in length, surfaced close to the ship.

> His appearance and attitude gave us at first no
> alarm [Owen wrote]. But while I stood watching his
> movements, and observing him but a ship's length
> off, coming down for us with great celerity, I in-
> voluntarily ordered the boy at the helm to put it
> hard up: intending to sheer off and avoid him. The
> words were scarcely out of my mouth, before he
> came down upon us with full speed, and struck the
> ship with his head, just forward of the fore-chains;
> he gave us such an appalling and tremendous jar as
> nearly threw us all on our faces. The ship brought
> up as suddenly and violently as if she had struck a
> rock, and trembled for a few seconds like a leaf. We
> looked at each other with perfect amazement . . .

The *Essex* was already doomed, but the whale did

not appreciate that fact. He rolled and threshed, snapped his jaws in rage and moving with twice the normal speed of a whale bore down again on the *Essex*. "The surf flew in all directions about him, and his course towards us was marked by a white foam of a rod in width . . . He struck her to windward, directly under the cathead, and completely stove in her bows," Chase wrote.

Not only was this episode to become great literature in *Moby Dick*, but it was followed by an epic small-boat voyage twice as long as that of Captain Bligh and infinitely more gruesome. Sailors ever since have been puzzled by two things: first, if the whale had possessed the knowledge of a master shipbuilder he could not have chosen a more vulnerable area in which to strike than the bows of the *Essex*; secondly, whales do not fight in such manner. They fight with tails and jaws. But this whale acted with a deliberation which seamen believe was intelligent.

Take a more recent time. There are thousands of sailors alive today who watched a World War II destroyer try to maneuver in waves which, pushed by high winds, gradually increased their "length" (the distance from crest to crest) until finally there came a wave which lifted the destroyer high, poised her on a crest of salt water and broke her back. There was a splinter of time when the sailors from other ships could see both halves of the destroyer falling through mid-air. Only a handful of her men survived.

Last year a carefully outfitted Japanese fishing boat ventured into the South Seas on a tuna-fishing expedition. It had the most modern of equipment, was considered extremely stable, was equipped with radar and radio and a fathometer. It picked up a few Samoan crewmen and departed for the fishing grounds. It was never heard from again. Not a radio SOS or a life jacket or an oil slick. It simply vanished. There was no bad weather at the time.

Recently in the Solomons a brand new radar- and radio-equipped government ship disappeared without a trace. There was regret, an inquiry, conjecture, gossip about underwater volcanos and uncharted reefs. There was almost no surprise.

Despite all of this, the Pacific is largely a calm and orderly place. Some sailors have spent a lifetime in it and never seen anything except even trade winds, a hot sun, predictable clouds, manageable seas. Over such a sweep even the most appalling catastrophes are made to seem small. A typhoon, a mushroom cloud at Bikini, a ship sinking, an atoll drowning . . . all are pinpricks. This, I suppose, is what is meant by the word "oceanic."

3. The Puzzle of the Ninety-Eight

THIS STORY is nine-tenths true. The ninety-eight died, and they died in the circumstances which I depict. These facts are as accurate as the records of a military court-martial can make them. But no court-martial knows what goes on in the minds of ninety-eight men who lived the most isolated life of any prisoners of World War II. That must be the task of imagination.

Wake Island is a V-shaped atoll which rises about twelve feet above the water. The land above water is tiny, no more than two and a half square miles. It is also miserable; coral rubble and sand so porous that it will hold no fresh water. Few plants can live on such land, but the morning-glory vine, a shrub called desert magnolia and a dwarf Buka tree supply patches of green color.

The open end of the V-shaped atoll is closed by a barrier reef. The great sea waves rage at the reef incessantly and their booming can be heard over the entire atoll.

Wake is one of the most solitary islands in the

world. It is no part of a friendly archipelago. The closest islands, and they are tiny, are far distant. It is thousands of miles from ports like Honolulu or Tokyo. There are no signs of Pacific peoples there and there is nothing to stay a person ... no water or vegetation or shelter. The water around Wake is an endless reach of virgin waves. They surge against Wake and then go on for thousands of miles more before touching land. It is lonely beyond the telling.

The waters immediately around the atoll and within the lagoon are magnificent. On the lee side of the island the water is utterly pellucid. One can see the details of a brain coral at depths of over a hundred feet. In the lagoon and about the reef, there is an abundance of barracuda, yellow tuna, mackerel, shark and giant ray. On land the only living indigenous creatures are great swarms of birds, a multitude of small land crabs and that is all. Rats have escaped from ships wrecked on the reefs of Wake and have grown huge and sleek. These living creatures, all of them, play an important part in the story.

Wake would be valueless, uninhabited, bleak and forgotten except for one thing: the airplane. Its very loneliness, its isolation in the midst of empty ocean, made it an invaluable piece of land. It provided a place where planes, to and from Asia, could land and fuel. It was also a place where the military apparatus of the United States could put an advanced outpost ... not a strong outpost for it was too small for that, but a sort of military eye to sweep the emptiness. It was an outpost that was necessarily without muscle. Even the mechanical ingenuity of Americans could do little with such a tiny area.

On the morning of December 8, 1941, Wake Island (it is across the international date line and in Pearl Harbor it was the morning of December 7) bustled with activity. A total of 516 servicemen and 1216 civilians were at work. An airstrip had been laid out and was in primitive operating condition. The three small islands of the atoll, Peale, Wilkes, and Wake itself, were jammed with dumps of ammunition, gasoline, unmounted guns, big water distilleries, small mountains of food. A Marine squadron of twelve F4–F wildcat fighters had just been flown into the island. The Pan American plane, the China Clipper, was at anchor in the lagoon. There was no aircraft detection apparatus of any kind on the island.

At 11:58, eighteen Japanese two-engine bombers, hidden by clouds and unheard because of the booming surf, barreled down on the island in power dives, dropped fragmentation bombs, made a long graceful curve in the sky and came back to strafe.

It was the beginning of a short, bloody and ferocious battle. On Christmas Eve, Colonel Devereux did what few Marines have ever been called upon to do. He left his command post with a white bag tied to a broom handle and began negotiations for the surrender of Wake. There was no humiliation in the surrender. The defenders had fought well. The Marine fliers, working under unbelievable difficulties, and overwhelming odds, feverishly cannibalized each plane as it was destroyed until their last plane was literally a mechanical mongrel made up of the parts of six other planes. Then it, too, was lost. The ground defenders fought off one Japanese assault force. The civilians tried to enlist in one or another of the Armed Forces, but were turned down for their own good. If they stayed civilians they would be treated as noncombatants. With a fine disregard for international law the civilians "attached" themselves to various units. They hauled ammunition, set up guns, fired them, dug trenches, fought fires, repaired planes and died. But none of this could turn aside the inevitable.

When the Japanese returned they returned in numbers so vast that the issue was never in doubt.

With the surrender, the Japanese faced a difficult choice. They were determined to build Wake into one of a powerful link of fortified islands from which they could continue their strikes eastward. The hundreds of Americans on the islands were merely a hindrance to this and the Japanese decided to evacuate them as soon as possible. However, they also wished to use the equipment which the Americans had installed on the island. It was intricate and strange machinery. They needed American help to maintain it and they knew that.

The Japanese made a fateful choice. All of the American military personnel was to be evacuated and most of the civilians. The evacuees were sent to Shanghai and most of them survived the war. But 100 Americans stayed behind.

Not one of the hundred selected Americans was alive after October 7, 1943. Two of them died ordinary deaths. One succumbed to septicemia and was buried. Another, a confirmed alcoholic, displayed great ingenuity in stealing liquor from the Japanese. The third time he was caught he was ordered to apologize and to agree never to steal alcohol again. With the strange lunatic courage of the absolute alcoholic, he looked his captors in the eye and refused. The next moment he was beheaded.

The remaining ninety-eight Americans were to die in one of the most eerie, lemminglike, mysterious and courageous episodes of that or any other war. Or, perhaps, it was simple madness.

The Japanese, aided by the captive Americans, began an amazing fortification of Wake. Almost literally they dug deep into the coral and then pulled it over themselves. They built hundreds of coral and concrete pillboxes, underground magazines, and carefully dispersed command posts. Most of these were "bomb-proof" and were connected to one another by a complex pattern of tunnels and trenches.

Above ground they laid down a fantastic array of defenses. The entire length of the oceanside of the atoll was protected by huge tank traps. Seaward of the traps was a system of slit trenches with steel and concrete pillboxes scattered among them. At the very edge of the sea there was a low hummock of barbed wire entanglements with land mines placed underneath them. The raised parts of the island bristled with cleverly concealed guns of every description. Anything that could be damaged was buried. Every jeep had its own revetment, every barrel of fuel was buried deep. The island was one vast honeycomb which housed 4500 Japanese and their ninety-eight American helpers.

They busily dredged the channel between Wilkes and Wake to permit submarines and ships to enter the lagoon. They started to dredge a turning basin for submarines off Wilkes and a channel which would allow submarines to come alongside shoreside quays for replenishing and repairs.

But the Japanese had made a terrible strategic miscalculation. Their vast row of defenses, aimed at Australia and all of Oceania, was stopped short. Midway remained in American hands. Kwajalein and Eniwetok became available to American forces. Also American cruisers could lie safely out of range and lob shells onto the island. Wake became a "milk run." Cruisers and battleships returning to Pearl Harbor emptied their magazines on the island. Task forces going west used Wake as a practice target, but were given careful instructions not to hinder the dredging of the submarine turning basin ... it would be valuable when the Americans repossessed the island. In any case the American air cover over Wake was so intense that no Japanese sub could use the basin. In the midst of a holocaust of bombs and shells the dredge working the turning basin operated with perfect immunity. Carrier planes, and later landbased planes, were almost constantly overhead. It soon became impossible to reinforce or supply Wake by surface vessels. Instead of being a redoubt in a massive defense line, Wake had become an isolated and tortured island, under continuous siege.

The last attempt at surface reinforcement came in 1943. The *Suwa Maru* of 10,000 tons came to Wake with supplies. A patrolling American submarine torpedoed her twice just as she came to her moorings. In desperation, her skipper ran her onto the reef where her rusty carcass can be seen today. Now for long months and then years the empty horizon around Wake was broken only by hostile ships which came in quietly, but brazenly, lobbed in their devastating bombardments and then vanished.

The ninety-eight Americans were, under the circumstances, given remarkably good treatment. The Japanese, knowing that they were essential for the maintenance of the island's intricate communication and distilling systems, gave them better rations than the Japanese soldiers received. Even so, the ninety-eight lived in a queer and dreamlike world. In those scattered hours when it was possible to be above ground they worked for the Japanese to repair bomb and shell damage. At night they crowded back into their two shelters and talked. They were all highly skilled craftsmen and it is safe to assume that their intelligence was a cut or two above average.

What do men do in such utter isolation? They talk, they conspire, they form cliques, they engage in irritable arguments, and they exchange rumors. Indeed, rumors become the staff of their psychic life. This is true of all prison and concentration camps. But most prisoners, by one means or another, have a contact with the outside world. Even in the most closely guarded of Nazi concentration camps, there were clandestine radios and fairly accurate reports of what was happening on the "outside." Guards could be bribed for information, the progress of the war could be charted, escape committees could be formed, hope could be nourished. But on Wake there was not the slightest possibility of contact with the outside. The Americans did not speak Japanese and the Japanese themselves had only the most meager radio contact with Japan. There was also the stunning and always present realization that they were surrounded by hundreds of miles of open sea. The Pacific, the sheer immense bulk of water, was their most efficient guard, kept them in the most perfect isolation. The Japanese knew this too and the actual guard maintained over the prisoners was slight.

There is no other group of prisoners I know of during World War II which lived in such complete physical and psychological isolation. Anything that the ninety-eight "knew" must be manufactured from whole cloth.

Psychological and social anarchy cannot be endured for long. We can assume that at some point the ninety-eight men, consciously or unconsciously, formed themselves into some sort of social hierarchy. Natural leaders emerged; some men became identified as comics; other became chronic complainers; some withdrew into themselves. But one thing is certain, the group could feed only on itself. Slowly it began to manufacture a "reality" about the outside world. Some men more imaginative and persuasive and glib than the others made guesses as to what was happening outside. Just as in primitive societies the unknown is made known by oracles so the ninety-eight invented a mythology. As it was passed from man to man it lost the quality of myth; it became a form of reality. When it was repeated back to the original oracles they also believed it. All of them believed for a simple reason: in such awesome isolation man must have something to believe or go mad.

The tiny world of Wake became increasingly bizarre. The water distillers still worked and rainwater was carefully gathered, but food soon came into short supply. The Japanese made heroic efforts to supply the island. Surface ships being out of the question, they attempted to send in food by submarine. These supply submarines made a hazardous and slow passage from Japan. In daylight hours they submerged and stopped their engines. At night they came to the surface and went ahead at full speed. They carried a curious cargo. Hundred-pound bags of rice were surrounded by crude latex rubber and made into a waterproof and floatable package. Hundreds of these were strapped to the open decks of the submarines.

When a submarine arrived off Wake, it was still in mortal danger. American submarines constantly patrolled the island and the chances of being detected were high. To surface during the day, even for a few moments, was to commit suicide. The Japanese submarines and the garrison developed a peculiar technique. At a prearranged time, chosen so that the tide would be favorable and the night at its blackest, the submarine would surface for a few moments. Lining the windward edge of the reef would be hundreds of Japanese soldiers, peering into the darkness. When the submarine surfaced, picked men ran down the decks, cutting the bindings which held the rice bags to the submarine. The submarine skipper then gave a single guarded flash of an Aldis lamp towards the shore. Then he closed his hatches and submerged. As the submarine sank, the rice bags floated from her decks and bobbed on the water.

For the Japanese lining the reef, it was a desperate time. Quite beyond their control their very life was bobbing about in the dark water. The Japanese soldiers, their eyes sharpened by hunger, studied each of the unending procession of waves. There would be a tormented period when they did not know whether tide and wind were favoring them. Then, with luck, the heavy yellow packages would come surging up onto the reef. The soldiers were too desperate to cheer. They fought the bundles free of the surf and trotted them to a central storehouse. The next morning, every foot of the periphery of the island would be searched to see that no bags had been missed. Occasionally, the tides would play a cruel trick and in the morning they would see a dozen of the bags that had worked around into the lee of the island. They might sit there for days, only a hundred yards offshore, but the Japanese did not dare to put a boat into the water. At night, the more skillful swimmers would venture into the dark waters to try to retrieve the bags. Occasionally, they were successful. Sometimes the swimmers merely disappeared forever into the ocean.

The ninety-eight Americans were aware of a successful submarine delivery only because of the sudden spurt of optimism and good cheer among their captors. Admiral Sakaibara, the officer-in-charge of the island, was too orderly a man to permit an increase in rations. He had some inkling of how far the food had to be stretched. The Americans began to feel the pinch. Their food rations were cut. Ribs began to show on men who had always been fat; thin men became gaunt. When food was divided they gathered and watched quietly, only their burning eyes revealing their intensity.

Very soon, however, even the submarine trips became too hazardous. They were discontinued and the island was on its own. Everyone, including the Americans now realized that they had to subsist on their accumulated stores plus whatever food the island and its surrounding waters could supply. There commenced one of the most ingenious and thorough efforts ever made to find and husband food. Rat hunting, for example, became an organized activity. The orderly Japanese records indicate that they caught and devoured over 54,000 rats. The thousands of birds on the island were carefully stalked, slaughtered and eaten. Every crevice, however small, was searched to see if it might contain bird eggs. Land crabs were hunted with a ruthless intensity.

By the end of 1944, there was not a single bird, rat or crab left on the island.

Nothing was wasted. The Japanese discovered that the leaves of the morning-glory vines were edible and the island was soon bare of these. Too late there was the realization that the very thoroughness of the search was a mistake. By killing *all* of the birds and eating *all* of their eggs they had assured that no new generations of birds or eggs would appear. By killing *all* of the rats they assured that no new rats would appear. By eating *all* the morning-glory vines they assured that no future vines would grow. It was a bitter discovery. It was also irreversible.

Their wits sharpened by desperation the Japanese set about to build truck gardens. But how does one build a garden on an island which has no soil? The Japanese extracted the soil from their own bodies. They carefully gathered the night soil, their own excrement, mixed it with sand and dumped it into great boxes made of brass and iron. This compost was then planted with tomato and squash and melon seeds which came in by submarine. Never were gardens so carefully tended and so carefully watched. The pre-

cious water, now in short supply, was sluiced over
the plants by the helmetful. Full captains were given
formal responsibility for guarding the tiny plots. Occasionally during a strafing spray bullets would tear
into the gardens, tearing plants to pieces, spraying
excrement over the containing walls. After a raid
each plot was carefully surveyed and salvagable vines
were replanted. Bits of scattered excrement were
gathered and returned to the plot. Hopelessly shattered plants were used in soup.

The Japanese were used to eating seaweed and the
reef and lagoon were denuded of edible seaweed to
the depth that the Japanese could dive.

At first the fish along the reef and inside the lagoon
were caught in abundance. But the Japanese made a
crucial mistake. They used hand grenades which
could be thrown into a school of fish and the explosion stunned the fish long enough for them to be
gathered. The Japanese did not know, however, that
the explosion also killed the billions of fish eggs that
accumulated invisibly in the crevices of the reef and
lagoon. After a short while, the fish were also extermi-
nated and there were no new generations to replace
them.

The ninety-eight Americans watched all of this
with a horrified fascination. At some point in 1943,
they began to realize that the bombings and the
disruption of the island life were making their skills
unnecessary. They spent less and less time doing
useful work. More and more they talked and watched
and returned to their talking. They were torn between hoping that the Japanese would find food in
which they would share and satisfaction in seeing
their captors grow weaker. For a time they specu-
lated on whether the Americans would reinvade before all of them starved or whether the island would

merely be by-passed. Such ambiguity became impossible. They came to the conclusion, and no man dared or wished to oppose it, that the invasion would occur first. In so hermetic an isolation, with hunger beginning to make tempers sharp and rationality difficult, they all sensed that their survival depended on unanimity. A minority view, even a well-considered minority view, was impossible. Those that doubted were silent and, finally, even they came to share the view.

The disruption of Wake continued. Once the entire garrison had been tightly bound together by an elaborate communication system. It was gradually destroyed. Now little clots of Japanese soldiers huddled around their gardens, stared hollow-eyed at the ocean, dragged themselves to cover when American planes approached. Once, when soldiers had died, their bodies had been cremated and the ashes returned to Japan. Now they were carefully buried beneath the garden to add nourishment to the soil. There was also a time when the various groups of men had visited with one another. Now this called for too great an expenditure of energy. They beat out signals to one another by banging wrenches against empty CO_2 bottles. Where once the island had teemed with busy men it now became more roomy. The Japanese were beginning to die from hunger. Eventually half of them starved to death . . . over 2000 bodies went beneath the garden plots to enrich them. By day the survivors did a minimum amount of repair work. By night they slept. The certainty of doom became a vapor in the air. The private diaries which the Japanese kept were long messages of farewell, written by men who were certain of their death.

But somehow the Americans lived. Not well, but they lived. They grew thinner. Their desperation grew sharper.

The weird life around them drove them into an ever more intense solidarity. They were called upon to do almost no work and knew they were expendable. Their boredom, their ignorance, their shared desperation, their proximity, their gossip made them oddly identical. Rumors became more important than food, were hashed and rehashed, re-examined from different points of view, taken as rumor at first, but quickly hardening into "facts." There was still a hierarchy among them, but what they thought, the inside of their minds, came to be strangely similar.

They discussed the possibility of capturing one of the boats and trying to escape by night. They debated it endlessly and then one day were given their answer. Three of the stronger Japanese ventured out in the boat to do some fishing. The boat was heavily camouflaged and looked like nothing so much as a piece of drifting seaweed. However, it was no further than a few hundred yards from the shore when a Corsair came hurtling over the horizon, drew a pinpoint bead on the boat and strafed it. All three Japanese were killed, the boat sank. The Americans knew that other boats were buried about and it would probably be easy to steal one, but they knew they would be strafed before they could escape.

They talked again. They racked their brains for solutions. But now the months of isolation, the awareness of the vastness of the ocean about them, and a growing irrationality because of the inadequate diet reduced their perceptiveness. They dared not even argue among themselves any more. Each man sensed that an argument, an act of selfishness, a misunderstanding might set them at one another's throats, snarling like hyenas. They whispered gently to one another.

At one point a B-24 bomber bombed Wake and

then came in low and slow for a strafing attack. By now long experience and a diminshing supply of ammunition made the Japanese AA gunners extremely accurate. They waited and then at the plane's lowest elevation opened fire. The plane was mortally damaged, made a slow burning circle in the sky and finally crash-landed at the edge of Wilkes. The Japanese commanding officer made a decision. The fliers were tried and then killed and parts of their bodies were eaten in a *bushido* ritual. Only the heart, liver and lights were eaten by the Japanese. There were those among them who would have willingly eaten the entire bodies, but they were not given the chance. After the ceremony the remains were given a ceremonial burial.

On the day of October 6, 1943, the tension grew greater, stretching the nerves and rationality of the ninety-eight men to the very limit.

That day, American planes, clearly flying from carriers, made a savage raid on Wake. The dive bombers picked their targets at leisure and then dove. The fighter planes shrieked up and down the atoll shooting at anything that moved or was above the surface. A chance incendiary set one of the buried fuel dumps on fire so that the very coral itself seemed to be burning with an inexhaustible flame.

The Americans peered up at the attacking planes, torn between pride in the bombing and fear of death.

That night the ninety-eight began another, and the last, of their long whispered and very intense conversations. They knew only four facts for certain. First, the fighter planes had stayed so long over the target that the task force from which they came could not be far over the horizon. Secondly, the Japanese were rapidly weakening. Hundreds hung at the edge of starvation. Third, the ninety-eight were now starting to show the signs of malnutrition and starvation was

probably not far away for them. Fourth, they knew
that the only feasible location for a landing was on
the lee side of the island with the best stretch being
at the channel that separated Wake from Wilkes Island. This is all that the ninety-eight could have
known. All other facts were denied to them. The
Pacific, unending and silent, told them nothing and
allowed nothing to be told.

Sometime during the night of October 6, in their
low-pitched but deadly serious conversation, these
four facts fused into a common agreement: they were
to be rescued the next morning, at the juncture of
Wilkes and Wake, by an American task force. So
identical had the ninety-eight become, so smooth
their method of communication, that their unanimity
was as solid as a fused granite boulder. Not a man
doubted that the task force would reach them.

The emaciated men now began to act with an
incredible deadly efficiency. They called to the
guards who, unsuspectingly, opened the doors and
looked in. They were seized by the throat by powerful hands and strangled. Their bodies were thrown
into the barracks and the ninety-eight began to move
across Wake.

With an eerie quality, almost a ghostliness, they
flitted past the innumerable dugouts and posts. When
a Japanese head did appear and question them, the
closest man would simply reach out, and with a
strength of desperation, choke the questioner to
death. In an area which was so crowded with persons, the passage of skilled and trained Marines
would have been a miracle. Also, every Japanese on
the island had become sensitive to even the smallest
sound in the coral: it might be a rat or a land crab.
Contrary to popular belief starving men do not sleep
a deep exhausted sleep. They sleep lightly, restlessly,
nervously. But the ninety-eight filtered past dugouts,

around command posts, past sentries, by a manned radar station and finally came to the last pillbox which overlooked the channel between Wake and Wilkes. Quietly, without a word, they made a vicious silent assault on the pillbox. They captured it and killed every occupant without raising an alarm. Then they waited, gazing out over the ocean with utter confidence for the arrival of the dawn and the American task force.

Dawn came, pink and soft, and then passed into the brassy light of early morning. The sea was empty. Still the ninety-eight did not lose confidence. No one panicked. No one proposed doing anything except precisely what they were doing.

It was at this moment that the Japanese discovered what had happened. They quickly organized several companies into search parties, fully armed and carrying hand grenades. They searched Peale and found nothing. Then they started, in a line abreast, to sweep down Wake. They searched every dugout, every shell hole, behind every rock. As the Japanese skirmish line got to the narrow end of Wake it grew denser and denser. The Americans waited unperturbed. Between them they had six guns and a small amount of amunition. They looked out to sea calmly, and then back at the approaching Japanese. There was no hysteria, no whining, no defection.

The ninety-eight prepared to resist the hundreds of fully armed Japanese. They fought with their six guns, rocks, sticks, and some with their bare hands. It was short, bloody and final. In a half hour, fifty of the ninety-eight had been killed.

The forty-eight Americans that were left stood in the welter of blood and bits of flesh, dazed by the explosion of hand grenades, but curiously calm. As the Japanese surrounded them they still looked out over the ocean, still hopeful that deliverance would come.

It did not. Prodded by bayonets and rifle butts the remaining forty-eight formed two lines and marched back up Wake. They were taken to the north shore. There they were given shovels and ordered to dig their collective grave. They did this calmly and without protest or remorse. Occasionally one of the Americans would stand up, wipe sweat from his forehead, and gaze confidently out at the horizon. The Japanese watched in puzzlement as the Americans quietly went about their last mortal task. When the grave was dug, the Japanese were still suspicious. They bound the Americans hand and foot and then backed cautiously away from them. The Americans gazed impassively at the Japanese, uncomprehending. Then they looked again at the blue encircling Pacific, scanned it as they had scanned it for years. They smiled at one another with confidence, sharing some secret which was denied their captors. They had passed some psychological point of no return and now were ready for whatever consequences followed.

At a command from a Japanese officer, machine guns began to chatter and rifles to crack. The forty-eight were smashed back into the grave by a solid hail of bullets. A few moments later not one of them was alive. The Japanese covered them over with sand and coral.

In 1946, Admiral Sakaibara and Lieutenant Commander Tachibana and fourteen others were sentenced to hang by the military commission which was convened in Kwajalein to investigate the circumstances of the deaths of the ninety-eight. This was done.

4. The Empty Space Above

THE VOYAGER in the Pacific, the surface voyager, has only three things to see. The interior of his ship, the skin of the ocean and the empty space above him. The shipboard view will depend entirely upon the ship that carries him. On some it is elegant and cool. At a cheaper rate it is squalid and not beyond any Chicago slum. Occasionally he will be reminded that there is a life below the surface: the purling wake of a porpoise; the triangular, tender and sunburnt fin of a shark describing a circle; the skittering of a flying fish as it gains speed and its long glide and clumsy fall back into the sea.

The third dimension, the emptiness above him, is a puzzling thing. Polynesians sail with eyes darting from the ocean's surface to the sky and back. Westerners travel with their eyes on the surface. It is, somehow, profoundly wrong. For the land dweller it may be inevitable; he must always watch where his feet land. It is a primitive impulse which even the most sophisticated cannot resist. Look down a ship's rail of tourists and inevitably they will be staring at the waves pushed out by the bow or will be gazing at the wake.

This is sad, for the spaces above the Pacific teem with activity. In order of propinquity they are: bird, clouds and stars.

Take the birds. For some reason they are invisible to Westerners. I started to notice them only when my attention was stirred by Polynesians. The only bird I had noticed was the gull. It lives at the edge of the Pacific, rarely penetrating the vast central spaces. The most beautifully proportioned of birds it is, oddly, the hyena of the sea. It scavenges. The gull will ride the air current made by the wind hitting the side of a ship. For hours it will hover without moving a feather. Sometimes it comes so close that one can see a single unblinking eye ... and watch the hard leathery lid come down over the eye. Its proportions and its soar are flawless. When garbage is dumped it will start a long slow outward spiral, its wings still motionless, and move for the first time only when it has to brake itself and settle into the debris. Then its beak begins to peck with a strange disturbing anxiety.

But beyond the gull the sky teems with birds. Great streams of birds flow up and down the Pacific, veering away from ships and land, remorselessly seeking a single target. The Polynesians have learned to see the birds for two reasons: they are food and they are an aid to navigation. Because they are doomed to fly regular routes (with a few exceptions) they are like pointers in the sky. Harold Gatty, for example, believes that the golden plover led the early Polynesians to Hawaii. The shining cuckoo is also alleged to have guided other argonauts from the Solomons to New Zealand. Western eyes will only be aware of a mote, a beading of black dots in the middle distance, but the Polynesian, driven by iron necessity, has learned to make out the different kinds of birds.

The birds of the Pacific range from the magnificent to the antic and even to the pathetic. There is, for example, the albatross, huge and elegant and somewhat aloof. It flies at a far distance and at a high altitude for the entire day. It hangs at the very edge of visibility. At night it settles on the water to feed on the small squids and fish that come to the surface.

Hawaiian storm petrels, a tiny bird, will skim over the water, their feet touching so that they seem to be walking on the water, taking some kind of nourishment from the water. The few samples that had been caught have had only a slimy substance and bits of pumice stone in their stomach. They lead a solitary life and will approach a ship only at night when they are attracted by lights. Occasionally I have seen them, tiny birds of sooty brown, flash through the aura of a mainmast light, circle it for several minutes and then vanish. There is something ascetic, shy and courageous about the storm petrel. Like an old maiden aunt it hesitates to make a direct approach, lives on a Spartan diet, but cannot resist a sudden gleam of light.

One of the most absurd and satirized of birds is the gooney bird. Actually it is the Laysan albatross, named for an uninhabited island which lies between Hawaii and Midway. It is, despite its reputation, a beautiful bird with a pure white body and black wings. Seen singly it is strikingly handsome. But seen in swarms, as the Marines saw them on Wake and Midway, they become a joke. They are a victim of some internal mechanism which forces them to do identical things in precisely identical ways until they die. Let a building be built on Midway or Wake and when the gooneys return, those that passed over that bit of land will plunge helplessly and at full speed into the building, breaking their necks and falling to the ground in heaps. It is sad to see flights of beautiful birds commit suicide with awful precision. The thuds come with a machine gun rapidity and it is a stout heart that can watch for long.

The gooneys first came to public attention around 1910 when they supplied plumes for ladies' hats. Previously their only natural enemy was shipwrecked sailors. At one time in the 1890's Midway had been wiped clean of gooneys by such crews. By 1940, however, they had returned in great numbers and became an object of ridicule and then of battle as the Marines and Pan American Airways tried to clear them from the runways and to clean up after them. To date no gooney-elimination plan has been entirely successful. Poison, shotgun fire, noise-makers have all failed. Flattening the sand dunes around the air strips has eliminated the precious up-currents of air which help the gooney soar and eased the problem. In all probability nothing will work until the breeding and nesting grounds in Laysan and the Hawaiian Islands are destroyed. By the time this happens no one will much care. Midway and Wake are rapidly becoming obsolete as the new jets overfly them on their way to and from the Far East.

The cycle will then have come full circle and there will be no one to witness the strange mass matings of the gooneys. The mating consists of a gigantic swirling of birds, each clapping its wings rapidly in a drumbeat rhythm. The females whistle and also give off an almost human groan. The males fight one another and keep up an unbroken shrill scream. The groans of the female seem to have a maddening and erotic effect on the males and the fighting and screaming grows to a high pitch ... and then ends in thousands of spontaneous matings.

The bos'n bird is another which travelers will seldom see. It is a graceful pure white bird and it flies hundreds of miles over the ocean with a powerful flapping motion. Oddly enough this graceful bird cannot stand on ground and takes off with a beating motion of the wings which quickly lift it into the air. When it lands it comes in with a bone-crushing thud, the force of which is absorbed by thick breast feathers as well as an air cushion under the skin. Its inability to stand also means that it must mate in the air. The mating is not promiscuous or casual for male and female join together some weeks before the first breeding period and remain together for life.

One of the most beautiful birds in the Pacific is the man-o'-war hawk, with a wingspread of over seven feet. It is a black bird with a metallic gloss of green and purple on its feathers. It has tiny atrophied feet which are useless for anything except perching which it has brought to a fine art. It can perch on the smallest twig and sleep peacefully. The bird cannot swim, run or even stand. As a result it cannot land on the water to fish as do other birds. The man-o'-war hawk has brought soaring to its greatest perfection. It can live almost indefinitely in the air, its great wings incredibly sensitive to any thermal rise or fall, hoarding its energy as it floats without the slightest exertion. I once watched from land as a man-o'-war spied a surface fish and stalked it. It was a miracle of tactical ingenuity. It dropped effortlessly and soundlessly from a few hundred feet, carefully keeping its shadow from falling over the fish. It swept down on the fish from behind, soared only a few inches over the water and then reaching down made a savage slash with its big hooked beak. The beak came out with the fish firmly grasped and only then did the bird move its wings slightly to compensate for the additional weight. Had it miscalculated even inches or ounces it would have touched the surface and probably have been doomed. As I watched it tilted on its side and without a motion went aloft in a long smooth swoop that reduced it to a black dot in moments. Through binoculars I then saw it drop the fish and make a quick dive after it and catch it in mid-air. It did this several times until finally the fish was mangled and torn and ready for swallowing.

Its useless feet have doomed it to a life which is terrifying and mean. In Hawaiian the bird is called

Iwa, meaning "a thief." When it is a chick in its nest it must be constantly protected for others of its species will hover over the nesting ground ready to pounce even on its own kind. They make merciless raids on better equipped birds. In the evening they will flow out to sea in a smooth rippling stream, hundreds of birds dipping and falling, then soaring, each bird motionless yet the whole band moving ahead. They never touch one another and are quite soundless as they move out. At some point they intercept birds coming back from a day's fishing and promptly begin a raid on the full beaks and stomachs of the other birds. They will fall like a plummet past a bird, snatch a fish from its mouth and soar away ... only to have another man-o'-war tear the fish from its jaws. Occasionally they will seem to attack a gorged bird which, in its fright, vomits up the fish it was carrying back for its young. Fish drop like great black raindrops, but none hit the water for each is caught and devoured before it can touch the surface. Back and forth the deadly game goes until the hapless have been entirely looted or the hawks are satisfied.

In this game there are elements of a grisly sportsmanship. But only between the men-o'-war. They will toss a single fish between them for miles, letting it drop, sure that another will swoop in to catch it. Then they dive at the successful bird and hack at the fish until it, in turn, is dropped by the tormented bird. The game goes on and on, sometimes reaching thousands of feet into the sky, other times skimming desperately low over the water. Then, when they have exhausted the fun, they turn back and ravage the more peaceful and less fierce birds of whatever fish they still possess. A man-o'-war seldom goes hungry.

When they return to earth the men-o'-war must land with the greatest care. If they land on level ground they will not be able to take off. But even the slightest incline will allow them to raise their vast wings, as the morning heat creates fugitive and tiny thermal layers, and begin to soar. They land in a gentle silent descent, which is actually a glittering-eyed life-and-death calculation and maneuvering for advantageous spots.

When viewed from an island or the deck of a ship birds seem to lead an effortless life. In fact, they are caught up in a taut circle of too many mouths for too little food. The margin for error is slight. Golden plovers, for example, will fight one another viciously for a bit of food, leaving a tiny circle of feathers to mark their battles. In Hawaii early settlers brought in foreign birds to "beautify" the forests and discovered that the more energetic aliens quickly dominated the food supply. Many of the old Hawaiian birds have now disappeared.

Although the battle for survival is incessant among the wandering birds some manage to survive and the species continues. But those birds which have given up the fight and retreated to the safety of lonely Pacific islands have strange and bitter things happen to them. Some birds, like the kiwi and the dodo, lost the capacity to fly and were forever rooted to the ground. The dodo suffered the worst of nature's penalties: it utterly vanished. Other birds, stupefied by generations of undangerous and languid life, lost their fear of men and landed on the heads and arms of the first sailors they saw . . . and were promptly strangled and eaten. The white man's ships also brought the big black seagoing rat; an animal against which the disarmed island birds had no defense. The rat glutted on their compliant victims and in some cases would decimate a whole clump of trees of its bird population in a single day, eating only the heads of the birds.

The birds that wander, the lonely soarers, the long travelers lead a hard life, but they manage to survive.

No one is quite certain why vast flocks of birds suddenly take to the air for their long migrations. Probably it is some intricate chemical mechanism within the bird that is tripped by changes in temperature or the length of daylight or the mating cycle. Dr. Gustav Kramer of Germany has established that migrating birds position themselves by observations of the sun and stars, automatically compensating their flight with such accuracy that they will make landfalls a thousand miles away with an uncanny precision. Within themselves the birds apparently have a navigational system self-compensating and sensitive, which man has only now begun to equal.

But even with this marvelous navigational system the ocean bird is not fully safe. If the stars are obscured he will become confused and disoriented and fly in meaningless frightened circles. Their capacity for flight is not endless and if the overcast persists too long whole flights may fall to the ocean and die of starvation.

The great typhoon storms of the Pacific are also an enemy of the bird. As the speed of the wind rises and the rain thickens the storm finally reaches a point where the bird cannot fly against it and is buffeted wildly from one layer of air to another. Finally, exhausted, they begin to fall from the skies. Sailors have reported seeing long stretches of water, after a typhoon, covered with the freshly dead bodies of plovers, storm petrels, shearwaters. On breeding islands such as Laysan there will be thousands of bodies of young birds killed during a storm; so thick that they must be scraped aside before vehicles can pass.

The great skies of the Pacific are no limitless heaven of escape. Here too there is an orderliness which is intolerant of mistakes, makes no allowance for individuals, ruthlessly eliminates the weak and the slow.

Most of it takes place out of the sight of man, but it is there.

Except for supplying food to shipwrecked sailors the birds of the Pacific have only two direct economic uses. One of these was the supplying of plumes for ladies' hats in the early 1920's. The Japanese descended on isolated bird islands such as Wake and Laysan and netted birds by the thousands. They also had the annoying custom of eating the cache of food which American warships periodically dropped off on the islands for castaways. With the end of the plume fad the Laysan albatross became freed from one form of enemy although that same enemy was to return a generation later and destroy the albatross for more urgent reasons.

The most valuable economic use of birds is guano. Because of its fish diet the guano of sea birds is an excellent fertilizer. The average bird will drop several dollars worth of guano a year. The volume of guano deposited by the billions of sea birds is staggering. Fortunately most of it is washed out to sea by heavy rains or whipped away by winds. If guano were allowed to accumulate undisturbed some islands such as the Galapagos and Baker and Jarvis would, literally, rise thousands of feet into the air and be natural resources of the first magnitude. They would also be exceedingly unpleasant places to live.

On some islands, such as Ocean and Nauru, the droppings of the birds have been mixed with the broken-down coral sand and been converted into a high grade of lime phosphate. Islands with such deposits are methodically mined, great slashes cut into them by bulldozers and dump trucks. Such islands provide the only truly hideous landscapes in the Pacific.

It is difficult to see a perfectly cloudless day in the Pacific. There will usually be at least a shred of distant dark mist from which rain squalls fall in such volume that it is difficult to believe that so much water could be held in so slight a cloud. Even in the doldrums a distant scud of cloud is usually visible ... sometimes no bigger than a handful of striated cumulus, sometimes a great solid upcurling cloud, pure white except for the upper edges which turn a dangerous black. As you watch, the whole thing will be whipped to shreds by distant winds or will slowly collapse into the hot brazen surface of the doldrum sea.

In the trades there will usually be a sprinkling of cirrus across the sky; low, wispy, insubstantial, occasionally blurring the sun. At night they appear as much more solid for the light of the moon is weaker. If your ship is traveling against the wind they seem to be going at very high speeds and when the moon is full its face will blink jaggedly as the clouds pass. Occasionally a ship and a cloud will move at the same pace for days. At night this is magnificent for at the edges of the cloud the moonlight will seem yellow and intense, made more brilliant by the relative darkness which covers the ship. Low hanging stars have a hot glitter.

There is an architecture to clouds. They do not appear in an infinity of forms and shapes and altitudes. The first man who had the courage to label clouds was a Luke Howard who made the effort in 1803. The classifications have changed, but Howard's mark still remains. Cirrus he defined as all cloud forms which are built up of delicate threads, like the fibers of some sort of marvelous wool. Stratus he applied to all clouds which lie in level, horizontal sheets. And Cumulus was used to name clouds that were knobby, lumpy, bunched. No self-respecting meteorologist would content himself today with this simple division, but for the casual traveler it is satisfactory. Add only one name for the Pacific traveler: Nimbus . . . the cloud which is derived from all three of the others but is tinted black with the certainty of rain. When on occasion it is also shot through with great jagged streaks of lightning there are few natural sights more impressive.

As one approaches islands in the trade winds they give a signal long before land is visible. These are the clouds formed by the trade winds pushing against solid land and deflecting currents of warm air into the sky. The result is enormous solid white clouds which for most of the year have exactly the same shape; a shape determined by the peculiarities of the hills and valleys of the land below. The formations are so distinctive and persistent that the old sea voyagers in their outriggers or double canoes regarded them as gigantic sign posts in the sky. These huge cumulonimbus clouds are, in fact, in a constant motion, a kind of cool moist roiling, but it is almost imperceptible. From a distance they seem like marble, each monster thunderhead holding its position, deep blue canyons in between them. At sunset they will catch the last of the light and long after the land below is dark the tops of the clouds will glow pink and then, in the last moments, a flaring purple.

In New Guinea there is a small upland village on the windward side which sits within such a permanent and prodigious cloud. The villagers, out of fear and tradition and conservatism, never wander far. In their language there is no word for cloud. The reason is that they have never seen one. They merely live in one. They are a dour group, very inhospitable and suspicious. Living within a cloud is a chill and wet existence.

For months these trade wind clouds will pile up over an island, casting a cool blue shadow on the island, dumping inches of rain on the windward side of the island and leaving the lee side hot and arid. Then as the weather breaks and the trades lose their force the great thunderheads begin to collapse. It is so spectacular a sight that it should be done to the sound of trumpets. But it happens in utter silence. The island people are only aware that suddenly the sun is out.

Occasionally typhoons will be seen across an empty sky. The clouds move like a massive circular cliff, whipped into long striations by the winds. They are a dull unnatural and somehow ominous gray. Beneath the clouds the ocean is whipped white. The typhoon clouds reach only into the lower atmosphere and at some altitude are usually beaten flat by the velocity of the higher winds. The typhoon itself travels rather slowly across the ocean but the clouds are moving in their tight locked circle at very high speeds.

At the other extreme are clouds which seem never to move. Above Mount Waialeale on Kauai in the Hawaiian Islands, for example, there is always a loose white fragment of cloud. That fragment is, however, one of the most astonishing pieces of cloud in the world. It replenishes itself endlessly by that peculiar process by which invisible water is formed into cloud . . . and rains almost steadily. That cloud drops 460 inches of rain a year on that tall sharp peak. Standing fifteen miles away in a water-hungry and almost arid piece of land (which gets no more than 20 inches of rain a year) one can see the long silvery ribbons of water start to rush down. Waialeale's side, cutting a straight path through the solid greenery. For fifteen minutes it will rain and then suddenly the ribbons will turn a dark glistening gray and the rain is over.

The island of Moorea juts out of the water seven miles from Tahiti and is said to be the most beautiful island in the Pacific. I would like to believe it, for I have a nipa house there and in a few months my children will start school there. What Moorea does have is two unbelievable steep peaks and an amazing cloud. The cloud stretches away from the tallest peak in a long tendril of mist that is blood-red in the morning, pure white during the day and a thin dazzling pink at evening. It seems almost always on the verge of detaching itself and scudding across the sky. But it remains locked to that sharp deep-green mountain by some physical law. The beauty of Moorea, I think, is somehow bound up in that strange affiliation ... the contrast between the raw young jagged mountain with its green so intense that it verges on black and the fragility of its cloud.

The Pacific is also witness to a strange and rare kind of cloud: the dense clouds of pure steam that rise when red-hot lava hits salt water. In the last century over one and one half billion tons of molten lava have flowed out of Mauna Loa. When this lava travels across country it seems to be merely a vast, black, very slow moving of earth. When it flows over a tree or house there is a brief puff of smoke, but it is quickly over. However, when it reaches the sea and the river of red-hot lava drops into the sea the scene is Dantesque. The sea boils and spits and a great confused mass of steam rises in the air. At night the cloud of steam is black and solid and rises from a heaving red base as if the earth itself were on fire.

In the Western world we have lost any sense of the sun, moon and stars. We live in air-conditioned houses which neutralize the heat of the sun and we forget its rawness, its capacity to burn and to nourish. In the Pacific, either afloat or on land, the sun regains its personality. In the Gilberts or the Moluccas, for example, the equatorial sun is so steady and blazing that it seems actually to be closer to the earth. Glance at the sky and the entire quadrant in which it rides will turn yellow, bring tears to your eyes. When it is obscured by thin clouds it can be seen as baleful and yellow, a great raging circle of fire.

I once saw a white man who had fallen asleep for three hours in the equatorial sun. When he awoke his chest had formed a single huge blister, the bottom of it sagging with the weight of lymph. The same kind of bags hung from his arms. His hat had fallen half across his face so that one side of it was a flat white color and the rest a puffy brick-red mask. For days he was close to death and for weeks he was in agony.

The night sky of the Pacific is clear and black when the moon is on the wane. We have gotten so used to seeing stars that have been dulled by smog or the loom of city lights that to see them in the Pacific is like viewing a new sky. It is, of course, a new sky in one sense. The North Star has vanished and the Southern Triangle and Magellanic Clouds come into view as does the dazzling brilliance of the Southern Cross. But the real difference is the pure quality of the air. The stars are not obscured by dust and haze. As a result they glitter rather than glow. The constellation of Argo Novis, for example, is a complex and intricate thing. But even stars of the second magnitude in this constellation stand out distinct and clear, sparkling coldly in the blackness.

Almost everyone in the Pacific has an interest in the sky. For navigators the stars yield a position. For farmers the sun and clouds will determine his crop. For fishermen and reef dwellers the phases of the moon are critical. On the nights of full moon the creatures of the reef remain deep and hidden, retreating from the light. On jet black nights they come swarming up ... worms, snails, crabs and the fish that feed on them.

It tells something of the Pacific dweller's mind when we learn that the natural objects from which they most often choose names for their children are stars and flowers.

The land dweller who journeys across the Pacific must readjust his sense of space and time. He must develop new nerves and perceptions, be able to resist boredom by seeing the small changes which constantly take place about him. The distant flight of a bird, the change in cloud formations, the speed and direction of the wind, the color of the sea are slight things by themselves, but when put together they can give a slow-pitched excitement which ends by being enormously attractive.

At night, with the stars glittering above, the Pacific is magnificent. No one has caught its eerie beauty better than that hard-eyed scientist Darwin. In his *Voyage of H.H.S. Beagle* he wrote:

> Every part of the surface which during the day is seen as foam, now glowed with a pale light. The vessel drove before her bows two billows of liquid phosphorus, and in her wake she was followed by a milky train. As far as the eye reached the crest of every wave was bright. It was impossible to behold this plain of matter, as it were melted and consuming by heat, without being reminded of Milton's description of the regions of Chaos and Anaerhy.

5. The Depths Below

It is an accident of the evolution of the human eye that the most agitated, exciting and restless part of the Pacific is invisible. Only in the last generation have we been able, by the simple device of a faceplate and a rubber mask, to see below the surface. Before that human eyes stung with the salt, saw with distortion and for only a short distance whenever they were below the skin of the sea. The faceplate opened up a new world. Other devices, more elaborate and expensive, have taken the human body to the black depths where tons of water pressure are resisted by steel spheres and thick glass windows. Into the deepest "deeps" grappling hooks and nets and thermometers and core-drills have recently descended.

They have discovered a great deal. Enough so that we know that most of the deep sea is still a mystery.

If the Pacific basin could be emptied and explorers turned loose the landscape they would cover would not be particularly startling. Only the proportions would be surprising. They would move through depressions which are, on the average, 14,000 feet below our present sea level. They would find a vast plateau, called the Albatross Plateau, reaching from South America westward and culminating in mountains called the Tuamotu Archipelago and northward to the soaring ice peaks of Antarctica. They would look upward at enormous mountains which culminate in tiny peaks we call Hawaii and Kauai and Oahu. They would look upward at one gigantic peak called Mauna Kea which would rise so high that it would dwarf Mount Everest by over 2000 feet. There would be long rolling foothills rising gradually towards the continental bulk of Asia and North America and South America and Australia. They would also encounter some canyons, jagged and sharp, that would be reminiscent of the Grand Canyon. One of these, the Mindanao Trench, would have a narrow pinpoint bottom which is close to 50,000 feet below the tip of Mauna Kea. The enormous expanse, bigger than any other named object in the world, would be pockmarked by over three hundred active volcanoes trying to build themselves into mountains. There would be scores of dormant volcanic giants resting between eruptions. There would also be other deeps: the Tuscarora, the Ramapo, the Nero, the Planet. But the deeps would be as exceptional as the Grand Canyon. Most of the floor of the Pacific would rise and fall slowly in an endless stretching away of foothills and plateaus and mountains. Only the volcanoes, Mauna Kea and the vast distances would be unique.

But, in hard fact, all that the actual traveler will see is an opaque skin. Flat on hot still days, ruffled on windy days, but inscrutable at all times and in all weather to the naked eye.

Below the surface, the reality which the unaided eye cannot perceive, is a frothing, a battling, a deadliness, a regularity, a madness, a preying, an averaging, a capriciousness, a chaos which is beyond our calculation. There are silent currents as massive as a hundred rivers. There are millions of tons of gold and silver and nitrogen and salt and nickel in suspension. There are fish and squid and plankton and vegetables which, in one year's cycle, could have fed all the humans that have ever lived. There are pressures and heat and cold more extreme than we have known or can imagine. The immense and the tiny are bound together in a balance so delicate that is, at this time, beyond our capacity to either measure or understand.

And the balance extends over the entire reach of salted water. Let an Eskimo be given a gift of a repeating Winchester and greased cartridges and the havoc he wreaks among seals will, months later, reduce a swarming reef in Bora Bora to nothing but fingerlings ... and an atoll will be abandoned, councils will be held, an evacuation will take place, the French government will have a problem. De Gaulle will not tumble, but there will be an abundance of human civic trouble. The guilt rests with the gift-giver who gave the Winchester. But he gave in innocence and the chain of events is too complex for any of us to unravel at this time. Later? Perhaps.

Let us start with what the traveler sees, the skin of the ocean, and work down. The greatest activity takes place where the cold waters rise towards the surface. They bring with them, like oceanic dust, a rich supply of minerals and salts. This primary food is carried in very cold water. One of the few creatures which can devour and grow on this nutriment is the plankton. The plankton are the first step, the primary converter, the inexpressibly simple animal that can convert vegetable and mineral into animal ... and in that instant becomes the prey of the animal-consuming animals.

There is, for example, a varying line off the South American coast where the warm and cold waters meet. Voyagers under sail, their hearing unimpaired by the sound of engines, have literally *heard* this line. It gives off a snapping, vicious, hair-raising sound. If I could label it I would call it "Darwin's Line." It is the

point where the plankton group to ingest the vast
swirls of food that come welling up from the cold
deeps. This is also the line where ths sea creatures
that can consume the plankton gather.

The result is a compressed, speeded-up and frantic
version of the cycle of underwater life. But such
places are exceptions. Generally the cycle plays itself
out in long stretches of water. In the South Pacific the
warm waters are not as rich in nutriment as the colder
waters of the far north and south. As a result there
are not the vast schools of salmon, halibut and pil-
chards which are found in the colder waters. In hard
fact the South Seas are relatively sparse in fish as
compared to Japan or Alaska. Prices for deep water
fish in the fish market at Papeete, Tahiti are as high
as San Francisco prices. Reef fish abound and anyone
with a faceplate, a spear and a little training can
usually catch enough fish to live on. However, the
reefs around the island of Oahu have been practically
"fished out." In some of the larger archipelagoes the
natives move from motu to motu to allow the fish life
to renew itself, much as a farmer allows a plot to lie
fallow.

All fish life hinges on the presence of plankton
which in turn depend upon minute algae which take
their nourishment directly from the sea. They are
present even in the clearest water of the most sparkling lagoon. Plankton occur in an unbelievable profusion and variety. Plankton is merely the term to
describe a shared characteristic: an incapacity for
voluntary movement. Some plankton are vegetables,
some are simple animals such as diatoms, some are
crustaceans and larval fish. But whatever their character, whether vegetable or animal or trembling on
the brink between the two, they are defenseless ...
almost. They cannot flee. They cannot fight back.

They can only submit. For all creatures with the appropriate mouths they are a cheap and helpless victim. But they do have a defense: a staggering capacity to reproduce. Their ability to multiply creates a kind of Malthusian chaos. There is no limit to their growth, for all they need for existence is sea water. Where the water is rich enough the plankton will become so thick that they form an edible cloud. It is set upon instantly by creatures as small as arrow worms and as large as whales. The slaughter is immense, but some always survive.

The smallest animals which prey upon the helpless protozoa have been beautifully described by Rachel Carson.

> There are fierce little dragons half an inch long, the sharp-jawed arrowworms. There are gooseberry-like comb jellies, armed with paralyzing tentacles, and there are the shrimp-like euphausiids that comb the water with their bristly appendages. Drifting where the currents carry them with no power or will to oppose that of the sea, this strange community of creatures and the marine plants that sustain them are called "plankton" a word derived from the Greek, meaning "wandering."

It is at this juncture that the plankton-eating fish such as the menhaden and herring enter the picture. They, in turn, are prey to fish-eating fish such as tuna and sharks. Next come pelagic squid, in all sizes and shapes, from the very small and tender which turn up in Italian restaurants around the world to huge Architeuthis which, for many years, were thought to be only a nightmare invention of Jules Verne. The squid, in turn, are set upon by the sperm whale which combs through dense layers of squid like a monstrous toothy harvesting machine. The most titanic of these encounters involve battles between the sperm whale and the Architeuthis squid and the backs of many a whale are lacerated with the sucker-like scars which the great squid inflicts. No one has seen one of these gigantic battles, for they take place at depths of 1500 feet or more and rage over great stretches of deep black water. But that they do occur we are reasonably sure.

There is not a visible Darwinian order to all of this, or if there is we are not yet informed enough to perceive it. Occasionally smaller savage fish will combine and attack larger individual fish. For unknown reasons some of the savage fish will live intimately with smaller and more peaceable species without bothering them. But, in a rough sense, the top 200 feet of the Pacific, the depth to which the sunlight reaches, is a kind of rich Darwinian jungle. It is thick with eggs and sperm and the debris of millions of encounters. It is rich in the minerals which sustain life. It is prowled by copepods, glassworms, pelagic shrimps and winged snails and countless other forms. Life is quick, crowded, intricate and always doomed. It is also filled with the constant swirl of escape and attack, of matching camouflage against speed, of thousands of tricks of evasion.

Only occasional signs of this intricate struggle show on the surface. One of the most dramatic examples of both the richness and profligacy of the Pacific can be seen when the palolo worm comes to the surface to breed. Normally this small worm remains deeply hidden in coral rock. Almost invisible it leads a timid and modest and unnoticed life. It is intensely fearful of light and shrinks back into its hole whenever the light increases. It sucks its food from the ocean, ingesting tons of water to extract ounces of plankton.

But at a certain time, triggered by the cycles of the moon, the worm begins to grow in size. One-half of the worm becomes distended with egg or sperm and, suddenly, the palolo worm no longer fears light. Simultaneously, over huge areas, the palolo worm tears itself in half. The reproductive half twists and writhes its way to the surface. Slowly the surface of the ocean begins to fill with coiling worm forms . . . by the billions. They form a layer which is several feet thick and miles square.

From above the sea seems to be crawling with phosphorescence, the light rising in a loom, exuding from the billions of excited worms. At dawn the frenzy reaches a climax. The sun, which had formerly repelled them, now is pure excitement. The worms twist so violently that they rupture their own bodies and in a short time the sea is dense with an outpouring of sperm and eggs. The carcasses of the half-worm continue to move feebly, but they are dying. They begin to settle to the bottom.

All of this has not gone unnoticed. The worms and their eggs and sperm turn the ocean into a vast defenseless feast. Fish of all kinds come slashing into the worms, wild with excitement, their jaws snapping. All during the cycle the fish are cutting through the cloud of worms until they swim away in dull satiation. But the quantity of eggs and sperm is so great that some palolo always survive. By late afternoon the fertilized eggs have turned into small mobile larvae which at once start to fight their way back to the security of the coral. They are followed by newly arrived and voracious fish, but now the battle is slowly equalizing, the rate of slaughter diminishes. The palolo larvae are not only agile, but once they reach the coral they are safe. The slightest crack, the smallest outcropping of the reef and they have disappeared. The carnage has been fantastic, the casualty rate staggering. But enough larvae will reach safety to fill the surface with teeming billions of worms the next year.

For centuries we believed that below the layer of light the ocean must be empty of life. We knew that it was black and cold and the pressures were enormous. Life in such circumstances seemed impossible. The mere notion outraged common sense, bordered on the impossible and, perhaps even on the frightening.

But the evidence grew that life was possible at these great depths and in these dread circumstances. The stomachs of deep-diving seals yielded the skeletons of fish which the human eye had never seen. A sounding line coming up from 1260 fathoms had thirteen starfish fixed to it. Cables that had rested in extremely deep water for years were found to have living forms attached to them when they were pulled to the surface. Then we reached a period where it was possible to actually photograph the ocean, layer by layer, and even the very deep bottom.

We now know that the black cold deep water manages to sustain life. At several hundred fathoms, for example, there is a layer of some form of life so dense that it returns a "false bottom" on sonar gear. This layer of sea life has not been identified and various theories argue that it is fish or planktonic shrimp or squid, but we do know that as the sun comes up the whole vast layer, reaching for thousands of miles in all directions, will slowly sink deeper in a massive shrinking away from light. Whales and seals dive deep for these rich layers of sea life, scything through the dark waters with mouths agape. But there are few intruders from above. Life in the deep waters is too specialized ... animals must not only be able to resist enormous pressures, but they must be able to move in total blackness.

Falling constantly through the Pacific waters is a rain of debris; the waste generated by the complex economy of sea life: excrement, bones, bits of shell, eggs, clouds of sperm, gobbets of flesh, decayed seaweed, particles of dirt and sand. Occasionally this endless rain of matter contains the bodies of men or the wreckage of a ship or the garbage thrown overboard by a luxury liner. Finer than dust, almost invisible, worked into the tiniest particles by the ocean this silt falls ceaselessly through the water. In many parts of the Pacific the silt has reached a depth of over 1000 feet.

Waiting at the bottom of even the deeps of the Pacific is another layer of life which lives on the shower of debris, moving carefully and slowly through the ageless ooze of the ocean bed. Worms, slugs, stringlike gorgonidae, sea squirts . . . everything is primitive, tiny and diminished. Over time they have adapted to the enormous pressures by a simple process. As they went deeper and deeper the cell pressure within their bodies became equal to that of the surrounding water. Eventually they were able to withstand pressures which would crumple man-made steel and iron structures. If man wanted to and went about it gradually there is no physiological reason why he could not acquire the same capacity. But it is most unlikely that any human or group of humans would voluntarily doom themselves to existence in that dread watery darkness. But they complete some sort of huge and delicately balanced cycle, some massive rhythm which is still too intricate and complex for our minds to grasp.

These strange animals seize upon everything that is

edible and ignore only things like the teeth of a shark or the hard earbone of the whale . . . these are allowed to sink into the ooze untouched. Everything else is ingested.

A THEORY

*Thousands of white men head for the South Seas
expecting to live there permanently. Some hundreds
actually stay. Spread over all of the islands they
become a thin white strand in a sea of black and
brown. On many islands there is only one white man.
On others there are none. In places like Papeete or
Vila there are solid clusters of white men.*

*The motives of the white man who stays in the
South Seas are mixed. It is easy for those who stay
home to say that such men are "escaping." This is
correct . . . in a crude and heartless way. Most of the
white men who live permanently in the South Seas*

are in flight. They are possessed by a sickness of the soul. They try to purge themselves by alcohol or promiscuity or the appearance of toughness or isolation. But then the sickness and the purge are common among those that stay at home. Those that flee to the South Seas have only changed their environment.

But it is an environment in which everything, including men, rots faster than in a cooler climate. The drunkard and the lecher and the anchorite reach their climax more quickly. In a sense their lives are more open simply because they are so compressed.

I do not know the motives of such men. As a group they possess only two characteristics that I can identify. They love to have their photographs taken, especially the anchorites. They look older than they are.

Occasionally, however, there is a man who comes to the South Seas in search of something. What such men seek is often so slight and fugitive, so unlikely by most standards, that it does not make for a dramatic story. It can only be told. It cannot be contrived. This is the story of one seeker, as close to the truth as I can make it.

6. Jack Nash

THIS STORY is eight tenths true. One tenth false because the hero's name is not really Jack Nash and one tenth false because I do not really know how he died, although I think I do.

I met Nash at a gunnery school outside of Honolulu

in the days right after Pearl Harbor. I disliked him at
first sight and so did every other man that met him.

We were assembled in a large room at the anti-
aircraft school. A chief petty officer laid out the
heavy gray-black 20-mm machine gun on the table. It
looked sleek, blocky and very complicated.

"Gentlemen, you might just as well get used to the
idea right now because there are no exceptions," he
said in that peculiar voice, suspended between
official respect and informal scorn, that chiefs reserve
for junior officers. "No one gets out of this school or
goes to sea until he can take the 20-mm apart and put
it back together ..." and he grinned and added,
"blindfolded."

He slowly disassembled the gun for us, naming each
part as he took it off, holding it up for examination.
When all the parts were laid out he looked up, boredom on his face, and began to reassemble the gun.

"The after locking bolt, which restrains the trigger
guard, which is tensed by the trigger spring," he said.
On and on, a curious litany, taken directly from a
manual, but said with pride. Finally he was done.
"All right, gentlemen, that's all there is to it. Let's
start."

The chief glanced over the room and saw Nash's
shoulder boards with their two gold stripes which
made him the senior officer in the class.

"All right, sir, let's start with you," he said pointing
at Nash.

Nash walked forward and stood behind the table.
He was a small man, well muscled and he was very
tan. He had something of the air of assurance that
most bantamweight fighters have when they are on
the way up, almost an aura of arrogance. He held his
hands over the gun for a moment, the fingers relaxed,
gazing down at the slabby oiled surfaces. He ran his

fingers over the breechblock and the barrel, in a gesture that was both searching and appreciative.

"Press the barrel lock to release the barrel," he said. He pressed the lock, twisted the barrel and it came out with a metallic click. The chief nodded unimpressed as Nash disassembled the major parts, identifying each part. But when Nash started to disassemble the small, intricate, lapidary parts of the firing mechanism without a break in his motions or voice, the chief flushed. When the gun was completely stripped there was a moment of silence in the room. Nash picked up the barrel and looked down it. He twisted his little finger into the breech end of the barrel and rotated it. It came out with a reddish-black smear on it.

"And a bit of rust," Nash said. He said it without irony and no one laughed, but the chief went tense.

"All right, sir, now reassemble it," he said.

Nash went through the reverse process without a mistake. When he was finished he ran his hands over the gun again, an odd gesture which I was later to know more about.

He stood looking at the chief. It was a look that could have been mistaken for arrogance and most of us took a hard dislike to Nash at that moment. Actually, I later learned, it was a look of the most absolute confidence; a certitude so great that it was flawless. It made him even less attractive.

"You can go now, sir," the chief said. "You've passed the 20-mm and there's no sense wasting your time."

When Nash left, one of the ensigns asked, "Chief, don't you think he boned up on that 20-mm? No man could learn it that fast."

The chief looked at the boy with a pitying smile.

"Some men can," he said. "He's one of them. A natural."

Later I heard that Nash had flown around the

entire Pacific as a Pan American pilot and had just been commissioned into the Naval Air Transport Service. We lived in the same BOQ and after dinner each night I would question him about the Pacific.

He neither invited conversation nor resisted it. He answered questions economically, briefly and without coloration. His language was grammatically awkward and I later learned that he had quit school when he was fourteen. He went to work for a master airplane mechanic who had a rambling shack of a workshop alongside the strip that was later to become the Oakland Terminal.

Talking with Nash, no one ever called him Jack, was like listening to a badly written *Encyclopaedia Britannica.* He would thumb through a back copy of *Popular Mechanics* or an aircraft maintenance manual as I talked, listening to what I said, but glancing quickly over the pages. I never saw him read a novel or any sort of book except books dealing with mechanics.

"What about Shanghai?" I would ask.

"Lousy maintenance facilities. Be sure and filter aviation gas through chamois to get out the water. About two good Chinese mechanics, but no tools," he would say.

"No, what about the girls, the restaurants? Stuff like that."

He would turn his head, squint his eyes in recollection.

"The same as everywhere else. All depends on how much money you want to spend," he would say. Then he would name, as if from a list, a few of the better whorehouses and restaurants. He would look down at the manuals, make a quick calculation on the margin, nod approval.

In these long evenings I learned about Nash. Nothing that I learned made me like him more, but it was the price I thought I ought to pay for the information he gave me on the Pacific. Actually he exacted no price, I imposed it myself. He would just as soon have sat quietly, turning over the leaves of his manuals and books. He had absolutely no desire to talk about himself. But I did not know that until much later.

Nash had taken most of his pay at the Oakland air strip in flight lessons. This was just about the time that Pan American was starting to open the flight routes across the Pacific. It was the time of excitement in flying. Nash was there when two collapsible villages and a construction crew and a quarter-million tons of fuel took off for Wake and hacked an air station out. People like Sikorsky and his immense ponderous S-42B seaplane were involved. Nash worked with Bill Mullahey, that big bearlike man who had been born in the Pacific and is possessed of one of the keenest minds and sweeping imaginations to be found anywhere. Nash had known Captain Ed Musick who had flown so long that he was an epic, but an epic that ended when his Samoan Clipper blew up like a fireball off Auckland with all hands lost. And none of this excited Nash. He admired Pan Am's maintenance record, the thoroughness with which they inspected their engines.

I discovered what Nash was really like by accident. We were talking on a lounge in the BOQ and my left hand was lying alongside the back of the sofa, my wrist a foot from his head. Suddenly he went rigid, cocked his head to one side. I went on talking. He held his hand up for silence.

"Your watch is not working right," he said. "It sounds off. Let me see it."

I gave it to him and right there in the lounge he went to work on it. His mouth opened with pleasure as the back of the watch came off. Again he made that gesture he had made over the 20-mm. Then he set to work to repair it. He did not even notice when I left.

Nash had only one thing inside him: a great admiration for machines. Something had happened so that spontaneity or people or books or ideas had been cut out of him as neatly as if by an emotional lobotomy. I would have regarded him as a monster, a freak, except that he was so gray and quiet and completely undangerous. All of his love and intelligence went into machines and keeping them perfect. I do not know how it started but by the time I met him he was as smooth and flawless and unreachable as his machines. Most of the officers in the BOQ actively disliked him. But there was nothing to dislike.

He was an excellent flier and had a reputation for efficient cool handling of a plane. They told me that in the air he always seemed to be listening to the engine sounds, his eyes darting over the controls. His fellow fliers did not care much for Nash either. They wanted to see flying as an adventure and he insisted that it was just a machine. He loved the airplane not because it was fast and went through the air: he loved it just because it was a machine.

Occasionally at the Officers' Club we would overhear carrier fighter pilots just back from the big battles to the south. As they got drunk their voices would get excited and they would begin to recreate the battles with their hands, describing just when they did a wing-over, an Immelmann, a power dive ... make a machine-gun sound with their tongue and close one hand and drop it as the Japanese plane "splashed." At another stage in their drunkenness they would begin to talk about the thrill of flying alone in a small plane, high above the ocean, everything resting on one's own skill. Invariably one of them would mutter thickly, at the very end of the evening, "Nothing like it since chivalry. One man against one man. Last kind of chivalry . . . very, very last."

Nash would listen to their conversation with a cool detached air.

"Do you ever feel any of that when you fly?" I asked him one night.

He turned to me with a puzzled look on his face, shook his head.

"No. At first I just thought these fighter boys drank too much," he said. "But they all go through the same routine when they get drunk . . . all this stuff about solitary splendor, glory of soaring above the clouds. I never feel a thing like that. Never did. I feel the same way about a Model-A Ford or a 20-mm as I do about a plane. It's just a machine. I like to have it working right."

One night we went into the Officers' Club and there was a peculiar quiet. Everyone was standing still listening to the radio which had been turned up loud. The announcer was describing the sinking of the British battle cruisers *Repulse* and *Prince of Wales* off the Malaya coast. The two ships had been considered invulnerable by the British and had been sent out to Singapore to keep the Japanese navy at bay. With a fearsome self-confidence, they sortied from Singapore with almost no accompanying ships, certain of their ability to resist submarine, air and surface attack.

As we listened to the detailed description of the sinking of the two ships we were not only fascinated, but for a special reason we were embarrassed. In one corner of the club, sitting where he sat every evening and drinking gin and orange soda, was Captain Watson (Retired) of the British Royal Navy. He had been recalled to active duty when England went to war and was something of an expert on repairing of damaged hulls. The British had loaned him to the U.S. Navy right after Pearl Harbor to help raise the ships which had been sunk on December 7. He was a jovial, very proud, country-squire sort of person. Almost every night his table was surrounded by a group of young American officers who listened to the endless stories he had to tell of the British Navy. He managed to tell his stories in such a manner that they never reflected on the U.S. Navy. He was an unending expert on every aspect of ship handling and maintenance and could run off from memory the precise way in which to drop two anchors simultaneously from a destroyer or cruiser and have the ship swing to only one chain. He was easily the most popular man in the Officers' Club.

Captain Watson listened carefully to the announcer's voice as he told of the swarming Japanese torpedo planes. When he spoke of the torpedo hits on the *Repulse* and the sharp list she took, Captain Watson's ruddy complexion went a bit pale, but he continued to smile. When the announcer was finished he still had the proper British smile, but his face had gone so pale that his eyes seemed enormous in his head, and very blue. *Childlike eyes*, I thought, *out of another age.*

"A double, if you please," he said and looked surprised at the hoarseness of his voice. As if to reassure himself he tried a remark. "Win some, lose some. That's the way battle at sea goes." The hoarseness stayed in his voice.

The officers around his table began to talk quickly of other matters. Their talk flowed around Captain Watson and for the first time he was unmoved by it. He sat rocklike, the smile growing crooked and stiff and finally vanishing. He drank a half dozen double gins and when it was closing time the officer-in-charge shook his head when the bartender started to close the bar. He nodded his head at Captain Watson and the bartender nodded back. Whenever Captain Watson lifted his glass the Filipino steward would take it and fill it. By 8:30 almost everyone had drifted out of the club. Captain Watson seemed unaware that he was sitting at an empty table, in an almost empty club.

As Nash and I left we walked past his table. Captain Watson swung his head up and his large blue eyes were not those of a drunk person. They seemed to be staring at a distant object. Suddenly they seemed to have discerned what they were seeking and went blurred. I realized that Captain Watson was weeping. He spoke and his voice was very clear.

"Sunk by those bloody little planes," he said in wonderment and grief. "Those beautiful clean ships. Clyde ships. Five centuries of skill in them. Best we had. And sunk by little buzzing planes."

"Ships can't be sent out against planes without air cover," Nash said crisply. "Six torpedo planes can carry as many torpedoes as a destroyer and travel ten times as fast. Send in enough planes and they'll sink any ship in the world."

"Any ship?" Captain Watson asked. His eyes, behind the tears, were pools of a confusion so deep that it was obscene. He was not the least bit drunk. He was, I realized, perfectly aware of what was being said.

"Oh, for Christ sake, Nash, knock it off," I said and took his arm and jerked him halfway to the door.

As we walked silently back to the BOQ I really hated Nash. His love of machinery, his exquisite skill with his hands suddenly were a mark of a narrow and single-minded person. It was a strange sort of narcissism; a worship of measured finished objects. For a moment I thought of some way to rip him apart with words, to hurt him. But I knew it was hopeless. At his center there would be nothing to hurt. I hoped never to see him again.

But I did, of course. A year later my ship was operating in the Solomons and I heard that Nash was flying one of the DC–4's that brought emergency supplies into Henderson Field and took casualties out. The air raids, the sinking of the four cruisers off Savo Island by the Japanese, the seesaw explosive battle on Guadalcanal, the PT boats dragging back into Tulagi each morning with their dead lined up on the fo'c'sle, the slinking for protective covering during the day and the black terror of movements at night, the rumors of great battles over the horizon induced a peculiar mood among us.

We were not only frightened, but we were beginning to live on the fear. It was like an itch that one knows is worsened when it is scratched, but gives a perverse pleasure, a double satisfaction.

We sucked up scuttlebutt of doom with an unwholesome relish ... there were six, twenty, maybe eighty destroyers and ten or maybe twelve Migamo-size battleships gathered at Rabaul for a surface strike at Guadalcanal. It was said that an Annapolis-trained engineering officer had inspected the sleek little Japanese destroyer grounded off Tulagi and reported that it was capable of 46 knots ... which meant that it was fifteen knots faster than our PT boats. There was a weird competition in passing on pessimistic news.

In the midst of all this the news that Nash was flying into Guadalcanal was oddly attractive. For some obscure reason I wanted to see him, to see how he reacted to all this. I took a day off and wandered over to Henderson Field. Henderson Field was a special kind of chaos and the tempo was higher than what we endured on the ships. Bulldozers roared around the field covering the holes which had been made by last night's bombs, crippled and lost fighters from aircraft carriers came careening down and made long flaming belly landings and were scraped up by the bulldozers as if they were planned operations. DC-4's tried to land and were held off until a fighter strike of F4-U's returning from an attack on Munda and out of gas could land. A heavy-set man with a cigar in his mouth and his clothes dark with sweat smears was identified as Pappy Boyington. Another was identified as Joe Foss, a leaner man, his tall body slightly bowed with strain. The control tower was a roaring tense place, but out of sheer urgency and pressure it maintained a kind of fierce efficiency.

I asked a harassed j.g. if Nash's plane was in. He looked down a list, grinned up at me.

"In good and solid," the j.g. said. "It got strafed by a Japanese fighter that tailed an SBD strike back and hit Nash's DC-4 just as it landed. Nash has been assigned as pilot to a Ventura which has been converted into a reconnaissance plane. He's out on patrol now. He's due back at 1600. His crew is down at the far end of the field working on the DC-4. If they ever get it fixed, and they'll get no god-damned help from us, and we can spare Nash from recon I guess he'll take it out of here."

It took me an hour to find Nash's DC-4. It was parked in a revetment which had been carved out of the coconut plantation. Three or four men were working on the body of the plane. From the open hatch of the plane a yellow syrup-thick mixture, streaked with red, was dripping slowly. I climbed the ladder and looked into the interior of the plane. A sailor was sweeping the yellowish mixture towards the hatch, his nose wrinkled with disgust. The substance was over an inch deep on the deck. It looked like raw scrambled eggs mixed with bits of glass and blood.

"What is all this?" I asked.

"We were carrying blood plasma, sulfa drugs and some other medical supplies when that Jap bastard stitched us," the boy said. "Must have been some kind of explosive bullets 'cause they tore hell out of the cargo. We only salvaged a few dozen bottles all told. Those red streaks are Tony Hoffman's blood. The stupid son of a bitch was stretched out on top of the cargo getting in some sack time and he took six slugs . . . from his head right down to his feet."

"When does Mr. Nash get back?" I asked. "I'm an old friend of his."

The boy was looking for an excuse to get out of the stinking interior of the plane. He came out and we walked over and sat under a coconut tree.

"Mr. Nash is supposed to get back sometime today," the boy said. "I hope to hell he does and that we can get out of here. The plane won't be perfect, but she'll be O.K. to fly back to Santo and we can fix her good there. These people here won't give you the time of day much less the loan of tools or a good motor mac. But Mr. Nash will fix it up enough to fly. You a good friend of his?"

"Yes, I guess so," I said.

"He's one hell of a skipper," the boy said. "The Jap hit us five hundred feet away from the runway and aside from killing Tony and smashing the cargo he shot away the brake controls. Damned how Mr. Nash knew, but he did. There is no instrument to indicate brake loss, but he just felt it. So instead of taking a long safe glide he slams her onto the deck so hard that she bounced back in the air with all the tires burst. We went hopping down that field like a

damned kangaroo, but the friction of the tires and the
bounces took the speed off. If he hadn't done that
we'd have hit the coconut trees at the end of the
runway and creamed ourselves and the plane." He
looked bitterly down at the control tower. "All they
would give us were extra tires and Mr. Nash had to
fight like a dog for those. Those silly bastards wanted
to bulldoze her right into the junk heap. I never saw
the skipper hot before, but he took the ass off a
full commander who was running the tower. Said
he'd have the commander court-martialed if he ruined a good plane and snowed the poor bastard with
so much talk that he finally gave us the tires and got
us towed down here. Big deal."

We talked about Santo and a promised leave the
boy had coming in Sydney. The tough talk, the hard
protective veneer which sailors develop so as to
maintain their sanity on a crowded ship and a huge
organization, slowly faded away.

"You know that Mr. Nash got married?" he asked
suddenly. I shook my head. "Yep, married and wid-
owed all in six months. She was one of those funny
little girls you find around Honolulu ... you know,
part Portagee, part Hawaiian, part some South Sea
tribe like Samoan or Tahitian. Some of the crew
thought she was part nigger, but I didn't." He looked
at me, suddenly appraising me and in a surprising
instant he was angry. "Even if she was I wouldn't
give a damn. God damn, mister, she was not pretty,
but she was sweet. A swab jockey who worked in the
O Club at Pearl said they wouldn't let her in there
... said she was colored or something. Mister, I
wouldn't be an officer in this god-damned navy if
they made me a rear admiral. Not if they'd keep
Terry out of their shitty little club."

I realized that the boy was close to tears. I changed

the subject, talked steadily for five minutes while he rubbed his hands against his pants, clenched them into fists, unclenched them. He did not listen to my words, but finally his hands opened and he laughed.

"I'll tell you something," he said. "It was Tony said Terry was part nigger. We had a fight over it. I'm littler than Tony, but I beat the shit out of him. Tony was all right though. Mr. Nash asked all of us to the wedding including the boozing afterwards. Tony said he still thought she was part nigger, but it didn't matter."

Later I put the story together. Her name was not really Terry it was Terita and she had come to Honolulu from the Austral Islands on a tramp steamer in 1938. She accompanied her father who had tuberculosis and who after a lucky year in copra and the discovery of a 12-cm perfect pink Oriental pearl and the sale of his land had enough money for passage to Honolulu. He had heard that there was a sure cure for TB in Honolulu. It turned out that he had run across the ad of a Chinese herbalist in one of the cheap magazines that circulate around the Pacific.

Later I saw the ad; Nash showed it to me. A grimy piece of paper with the face of a fat Chinese in the middle and below it the usual incredible claims which herbalists make and a Honolulu address. Terita's father could not read English, but a crewman from a schooner read it to him and had translated "respiratory afflictions" into tuberculosis. A thin little accident on which to build.

Terita and her father arrived in Honolulu, went to the herbalist shop, the Chinese took one look at the old man and knew he was dying from TB and said there was nothing he could do. He referred them to the hospital, but there were all sorts of delays because Terita's father was not a citizen, had not lived in the

Islands long enough to qualify as a charity case, and on and on. He died two weeks after they arrived. Six months later Terita knew she had caught TB from her father. She went to work in the Dole factory for a while, but they had to fire her after a medical. She worked as a cook's helper for awhile and then someone offered her a job in a cocktail lounge as a waitress. Her English was poor, but the place was frequented mostly by Filipinos, working class Chinese and sailors at the rag-tail end of a liberty. Everyone spoke pidgin English and the conversation was not very difficult.

Nash met Terita on a hot clear day when he was driving from Honolulu to Kaneohe, the Marine air base, on the windward side of Oahu. She was walking along the road with a coil of net in one hand and a pandanus bag in the other. During the war it was the custom to pick up hitchhikers even if they didn't have their thumbs out.

Later Nash told me that it was her strange shy giggle, so typical of Polynesian women, that first caught his attention. It is not precisely a giggle, it is a kind of low laugh that, depending on its inflection, can indicate curiosity, surprise, annoyance or just delight. Terita was sitting very straight in the seat and when she giggled it was pure delight. Nash looked over at her.

"First car," she said without looking at him. "Many trucks and buses, but this first car ride. Mai-tai, mai-tai. Veree good." She ran her hand over the plastic seat cover.

"How far are you going?" asked Nash.

She told him she was going net fishing and would get out at the first beach they came to. She explained, speaking carefully and slowly, that she had been in Honolulu only a short time and did not know the names of any of the beaches.

Nash also sensed something else: the girl was unutterably lonely. Loneliness must be one of the most fugitive of emotions and it must have been the only emotion still left in Nash.

Nash stopped at the first beach they passed, a quiet little crescent of sand with some green water on the shoreward side of a broken reef. She eyed it expertly and then turned to Nash, smiled and thanked him. Nash asked if he could watch her make a few casts. She nodded.

Terita had woven the net herself during off-hours at the bar. The whole thing took a few rolls of narrow line and a pound or two of lead weights. When it is finished it is a rather shapeless, drap-colored thing. Only in use is it beautiful.

"Stand back," Terita ordered Nash. "Fish not like the man's shadow."

Nash obediently stood under the shadow of a coconut tree. Terita put her bag down and began to fold the net over her shoulder, carefully folding the coils so that they did not overlap, her eyes glancing at the shoal water. Suddenly she tensed, bent low and quickly finished coiling the net.

Now throw-net fishing is a remarkable art. Everything about it is nicely proportioned, beautifully balanced, symmetrical. One mistake and the fish will escape. Terita was fishing for little reef fish that travel in shoals that form into a loose circle while they are eating and will mill quietly as they browse. At the slightest sound or shadow they freeze for the shortest slice of time and then dart off in a long darting flash of silver bodies. Throw-net fishing is an art because the fish must first be seen. Then the net must be thrown so that it makes a perfect parachute-shaped form in the air and all of the leads hit the water at the same time. The result is that the school of fish will be momentarily confused because the sounds come from all sides. They will race wildly in a circle for a few seconds and then make a slashing run ... but the net has sunk around them and they are caught. But let the thrower miscalculate the wind so that one lead hits first and the fish have vanished. Let his shadow show or his feet crunch too heavily in the sand and the fish veer off into instant invisibility. For people not born and raised close to a reef the first step, seeing the fish, is impossible ... the water merely glares back opaquely.

It was not the sort of thing that I would have thought Nash would find appealing. But later he told me about it in the greatest detail. She had walked in a bent-over position so that her shadow never quite touched the edge of the water, her toes feeling for a noiseless step, avoiding palm fronds and shells. Nash could see nothing in the water. It shimmered, but he could only see the coral heads and patches of green sand. Terita tensed, without rising she threw the net high into the air. The coils came flowing off her shoulder, slowly forming a perfect parachute shape, made up of thousands of tiny rectangles, each stretched to its full length. A single thick string ran from the thumb of her left hand to the center of the net. For a moment everything was still and motionless in the sun ... Terita with her arm outstretched and her body rigid, the line hard and black, the net open, but not yet falling. Then with a quick drop the net came down, all the leads hit simultaneously in a perfect circle, throwing up tiny explosions of water, Terita stood up with a scream of delight and rushed into the water. The net hissed down into the water.

Nash did not realize how involved he had become

until he rushed into the water after her with his shoes and khaki pants on. He stood beside her, softly cheering her on, staring down into the water. It took him a few seconds to see the fish. They were whirling in a small desperate circle, occasionally would turn and forming an intuitive wedge would rush at the net and form a black cluster against it for a moment. Then they would return to the free water in the center which grew constantly smaller as Terita, with little careful jerks, closed the net. Finally with a long scooping movement she drew the mouth of the net free and lifted it out of the water. There were perhaps sixty fish in the net, none of them more than six inches in length. They made a solid silver quivering mass. Terita walked up on the beach and carefully flipped the fish out of the net. They gasped wildly on the sand, spread out over a few yards ... always jerking in the direction of the water, flailing and twisting, inching instinctively towards the sea. Terita blocked them with her foot, carelessly tossed them back up the beach. In a few moments they were all still, although they still quivered.

"You like lunch here?" she asked. "I fix 'em raw. Very good that way."

"No, not raw," Nash laughed. He was breathing hard, excited in some odd manner.

"O.K. You like most white men. Beefsteak raw in the middle O.K. Fish raw, no eat," she said laughing. "O.K. I cook."

She quickly gathered a few palm fronds and coconut husks that littered the beach and put them in a little heap. She looked up at Nash questioningly and he dug some matches out of his pocket. When the little fire was going she put a few bits of coral on top of it. Then she picked up a handful of fish and went to the edge of the water, squatted down and started to clean them. It was strange, but Nash was fascinated with the gutting. Terita held the tail of a small fish against her palm with her little finger. Then with a quick gesture of her thumb she gutted in one motion. She washed it in the water. After gutting the first one she turned and held it out to Nash, her face drawn up puckishly. He shook his head. She ate it quickly, starting with the head and ending up with just the tail in her hand. She squatted there with the tail in her hand, deliberately antic, an exaggerated expression of delight on her face.

"Veree good," she said.

"Look, while you're cleaning the fish I'll get some beer at the Chinaman's just back down the road," Nash said. "We need anything else?"

"Lime. Two or three limes."

"How about some bread?"

"No bread. Ship biscuit better with fish. See if they have. You have money?" she asked raising her eyebrows. "Money in my bag. You take."

"I've got money," Nash laughed.

As he drove to the little Chinese store he laughed out loud. A girl so dumb she didn't know how much money a full lieutenant made. At the store he bought six cans of Budweiser and a sack of big round heavy crackers which are a distant descendant of the old ship's biscuit and are loved by Polynesians because of the fact that they contain fat and salt.

When he got back to the beach Terita was waiting. She had torn some leaves from a papaya tree and made a little circle of leaves on the sand. To one side the fish were neatly stacked on another leaf, waiting to be cooked. When she saw him coming she quickly laid a layer of fish over the hot coral stones.

"Ah, ship biscuit," she said. "That very good." She took the bag from his hand and opening it took one out and began to eat it. "Fish ready in two minute. Cook fast on stone."

She turned them over then ran to the water, gathered a double handful of salt water and trotted back. She dribbled it through her fingers, a few drops on the cooked side of each fish.

"For salt," she said. "Also taste of sea. That very good too. Now sit down. Drink beer."

Nash sat down by the circle of leaves and opened two cans of beer. He took a long drink from one and by then Terita had laid a leaf full of hot fish in front of him. He smiled at her and picked one up by its tail. He looked at the head for a moment and Terita giggled.

"No. You a strong man. You start with head," she said between giggles. "Close eyes and take a bite. Forget it fish head. Very good."

Nash took another long drag at the beer and bit off the fish head. It crunched between his teeth and for a moment he paused, but it was good. By the time he had eaten three fish he realized that the heads tasted better than the bodies of the fish. He also realized that the bones of the fish were so tender that the fish could be eaten whole. He ate the whole leaf of fish before he realized that Terita had not yet eaten.

"I'm sorry," he said. "I didn't leave any for you. I didn't even wait."

"O.K. More fish cooking," she said, chewing on a biscuit. "Anyway I eat three or four raw ones when you go Chinaman's." She took a sip of the beer. Over the can she was watching him intently, a sort of odd pride in her voice. "You like this way eating?" she asked and with a gesture took in the net and fire and fish.

"Sure. It's great," Nash said and then he hesitated,

aware that he wanted to say more, but not sure what it was. "It's nice and simple. Clean."

"Yip, clean," Terita said instantly. "No greasy dishes, no soap. Fish very fresh. Not like the restaurant downtown. Everything greasy. Fish old and dry. And all the food too hot."

"Don't you like hot food?" Nash asked in surprise.

"No. When we cook food in oven or pot we get it very hot, but don't eat it until it cools off. We like it about as warm as sea water," she said and laughed. "Haoles like everything hot or cold. We like it bellyheat. No more."

"Do the women always wait on the men in your island?" Nash asked.

"Oh, no," and she giggled and this time it was a condescending giggle, a sound of amusement. "Men always fix up food. Put it in earth oven, take it out, put on leaves. Men are the cooks. But women always clean fish."

She took more fish off the stones. Nash ate some and she put some aside to cool. He noticed that she drank very little of the beer. When the fish were cool she picked them up and ate them with an easy elegance, her white teeth showing as she bit into the fish.

For the first time Nash studied her face. By any standard he knew she was not beautiful. She wore no make-up and there were a few tiny pockmarks along her left jaw. But her face was symmetrical and pleasing. She smiled easily. And her eyes were huge and soft.

"I half Chinese, half Tahitian," she said candidly, aware that he was looking at her. "Mama Chinese, Papa Tahitian."

Nash decided not to go to Kaneohe that day. He asked Terita if he could drive her back to Honolulu.

He was not quite sure what was happening to him, but the girl amused him and something a little more than that. The way she had fished and prepared the fire and arranged the green leaves seemed so simple and yet so clever.

"I go work at five at bar," she said. "We get back by then?"

They drove back slowly and this time Terita sat far back in the seat. She fell asleep before they got back to Honolulu. Nash parked the car beside the Ala Wai Canal and let her sleep until four-thirty and then he woke her up. He woke her up by kissing her. For Nash it was a completely unexpected act, he had not anticipated it. It simply happened when he bent over and looked down at her.

It was an odd experience. Nash had gone with women before, but it was always a casual pickup ... a girl he would meet at the end of a long drinking party, one of the amateur prostitutes of San Francisco or Honolulu or New York or one of the hard professionals of Hong Kong or San Diego. When he bent over and kissed Terita she was instantly awake and her eyes went open with surprise, but she pressed her mouth back against his. Nash was aware of a sharp new knowledge: this was the first girl he had ever kissed whose breath did not smell of whiskey and cigarettes. It was a pure clean breath, slightly salted. Then he was aware that she did not kiss skillfully; had none of the expert grinding movements of the head, the flicks of the tongue which he had come to expect from kissing. Terita reached up, put her hands on his cheeks and pushed his head back.

"You should not kiss me," she said softly. "I like it, but I have a sickness that you can catch."

Nash's stomach went hard and his arms tensed.

"What kind of sickness?" he asked harshly. He was certain that she was venereal.

She tapped her fingers on her chest.

"It is the chest sickness," she said. "Here they call it TB. Very bad."

Nash felt an enormous relief. He laughed and hugged her. Then he kissed her very hard and very long.

"We can cure that," he said. "I'll take you to a doctor who can cure it. Don't worry."

"I not worry," she said smiling. "But it not easy to cure in my people."

Nash started the car. He had the sensation that the cans of beer he had drunk on the beach had, by some physiological miracle, saved their strength until this moment. He felt slightly high, terribly confident. He drove one-handed. With the other hand he covered both of Terita's hands. He whistled shrilly.

The bar where Terita worked was on Hotel Street, surrounded by tattoo parlors, saimin shops, shops loaded with the trinkets that sailors buy when they are drunk, barbershops with Japanese girl barbers. Terita told Nash she would meet him at ten that night outside the bar.

Nash got there a half hour early and went in for a drink. The place was not crowded. There were a dozen Filipinos and Chinese sitting on bare wooden tables drinking beer and the Hawaiian-made wartime bourbon which said on the label "Genuine Imitation Kentucky Bourbon Whiskey" and was made out of island sugar cane. Nash sat in a corner table. It took a few moments for his eyes to get used to the dark interior after the neon lights of Hotel Street.

He saw Terita standing at the end of the bar, filling a tray with glasses. For a moment he felt a despair which was precisely like a blurring of vision. She was wearing a cheap flashy dress which had several rows of sequins around the hips and a large bow on the left hip. There was a large white ivory comb stuck through her hair and she was wearing high-heeled shoes. Indoors is not the place for her, he told himself. He remembered how she had looked in the sun ... her face flat and not beautiful, but sensitive and responsive. Her figure was superb. She was small, but nicely proportioned and she walked with a motion that made her hips seem oiled.

The dress and the comb wiped all of this out. She could have been any one of a hundred mestizo bar girls he had seen in the Pacific. She saw him and after she had served the drinks she hurried over to his table. She teetered on the high heels and when she stood by the table he could see that she was wearing lipstick, a bright red lipstick which made her lips seem enormous in her face. She looked down at him quietly

"You like?" she said, touching the dress and the comb, running a finger over her lips.

"No," he said and was instantly relieved. He realized that he had expected her voice to have the brazen teasing quality which all bar girls adopt with their trade. But her voice was still soft and very gentle; he could barely hear it over the sing-song of Tagalog and Mandarin.

"Me no like," she said. "Me no like the shoes the worst. Island girls have big feet. The shoes hurt."

"Why do you wear them then?" Nash asked.

"The boss he order it," she said flatly. "I need job. For job he want girls dress like this. He buy the dress and I wear it."

"Not after tonight you don't wear it," Nash said. His voice had authority. "You're quitting this job."

"Tonight?" she asked. "After work I quit?"

"No. Right now," Nash said. "I'll tell the boss."

Terita looked at him without smiling, her lips slightly apart, watching his face closely.

"O.K., but boss throw me out of room upstairs," she said. "Then I live with you. That O.K. too, but think a minute. I got TB, you haole officer, we no have place to live. It will make trouble for you."

"If you're trouble I want more of it," Nash said.

Later he realized that this was the most endearing thing, the firmest commitment in words that he ever made to her. Neither of them were talkative people and their love was expressed almost completely in quick glances, smiles, physical contacts.

Terita smiled. With relief she took her bar towel and wiped the lipstick off her lips and slipped off her shoes.

"The boss is behind the bar," she said. "You tell him. I change upstairs."

It took Nash five minutes and ten dollars and a bit of toughness to placate the Filipino boss. He was still arguing, Nash's ten-dollar bill in his hand, when Terita came back into the dim bar. She was wearing her *pareau* again, her hair was combed out and gathered at the nape of her neck. She was carrying a small bundle of things wrapped in a pareau. The boss looked at her and his protest stopped in mid-sentence.

"O.K., Lieutenant," he said, his voice dropping from the hysterical pitch it had reached and becoming normal. His Malay face lost its quick surface anger. "Here, you take back the ten bucks. You don't have to buy the girl from me." He swung around, reached under the bar and brought out a bottle of genuine, bottled in bond, 100-proof Old Granddad. He poured two tumbler glasses half full and handed one to Nash. He raised his glass and they drank. They both looked over at Terita. Then the Filipino spoke, his voice was trembling with urgency. He spoke under his breath. "She is not a whore, Lieutenant. Lots of the other girls, but not her. You believe me, eh?"

"I believe you," Nash said. "Thanks. I'll invite you to the wedding."

They raised their glasses and finished off the whiskey.

That night Terita and Nash slept in his car. There were no hotel rooms available on Waikiki or even in the cheaper hotels along Canal and back up in the Japanese district.

The next day they found a house in the hills back of Pearl City. It was a small weather-beaten frame house, turned gray by the wind and rain and equipped with an iron frame bed, an icebox and a small coal stove, and a half dozen religious scenes that had been cut from Sunday supplements and put in frames. It had a veranda in front with a commanding view of Pearl Harbor, Ford Island and the Pacific.

Terita was delighted with the house. As soon as they had paid the Japanese landlord two months' rent, Nash had to leave for duty at the Naval Air Base. She only smiled when he apologized.

"You be back what time?" she asked.

"Around twenty hours," he said and then seeing the confusion in her eyes he translated the military time. "Around eight this evening."

"Good," she said.

When Nash returned that night the house was transformed. He was never quite sure how she had managed it. There were two rocking chairs on the veranda and a small table with a huge bunch of bougainvillaea in a jar, the living room-dining room had a big old mahogany table that was covered with pareau material, there were several pieces of bamboo

furniture around the room. The kitchen was equipped
with what seemed to Nash to be a very scanty supply
of pots, pans and utensils, but Terita assured him that
it was sufficient. The bed was covered with a brilliant
piece of yellow calico. And everywhere there were
flowers and bunches of greenery.

"You like?" Terita asked.

"I like it," Nash said. "But how did you get all this
stuff hauled up here? What did you use for money?"

"I make the furniture man bring it in truck," she
said. "I use the money I save from working in bar.
Flowers I just pick from around the house. You like?"

He made love to her for the first time that afternoon. It was a gentle low-pitched love-making of a
kind that Nash had never imagined. It was sensual,
but in an unhurried manner, utterly lacking in desperation. When it was over, Terita fell asleep almost
instantly and Nash looked down at her brown body
on the bright yellow calico. He realized that the TB
probably accounted for the quick bursts of fatigue
that overtook her.

Tomorrow we start on the TB, he told himself, just
as he fell asleep beside her.

Nash asked for a three-day leave the next morning.
It was then that he discovered that tuberculosis was
not simple. Somehow in his reading of popular magazines on the wonder drugs and the progress of medicine Nash had concluded that tuberculosis was one of
the diseases that had practically been eliminated. But
the first doctor that he and Terita saw ended that
notion. The doctor was a young Japanese who had
done his work at the University of California and had
a prosperous practice out in Kahala.

At Nash's insistence the doctor took X-rays immediately and had them developed at once. He then gave
Terita a thorough physical examination with Nash in

the room. He assumed that they were married. When the nurse handed him the prints he put them in front of a ground-glass plate, switched on a powerful light and studied them for a few moments.

"There is no way to be subtle about this, Lieutenant," the doctor said. "Mrs. Nash's situation is very serious. She has a well-developed case of tuberculosis and I would say the chances of her full recovery are very slight."

"But what about all those wonder drugs?" Nash asked.

"None of them are specifics for tuberculosis," the doctor said. "They have been ballyhooed up in the popular press until you think they can cure everything, but sulfa or penicillin won't touch TB."

"It's just crazy," Nash said. "Occasionally you hear of an American getting tuberculosis but no one takes it very seriously. They always recover."

"You don't hear, Lieutenant, about the Negroes in the South," the doctor said. "When they get TB it is deadly. They have been malnourished for years and also there seems to be a racial weakness against some of these diseases. Take a Polynesian like your wife. For reasons that we do not fully understand, once Polynesians get TB it takes them over like wildfire. I have heard of Samoans who have an absolutely clear X-ray one month and four months later their lungs are riddled with TB shadows, they have lost half their normal weight, they cough a little blood and in five months they are dead."

He looked at Terita. She was listening to the doctor, but she did not seem to be disturbed. She smiled at Nash. Nash felt a dull sense of anger towards the Japanese doctor, a sense of betrayal.

"You mean there's not a damn thing that we can do about it?" Nash asked.

"I didn't say that," the doctor said crisply. "You could put her in a TB sanitarium, give her complete rest, a beefed up diet and she might recover."

"What do you think her chances would be?" Nash asked.

"Her chances of survival, in my opinion, would be one in ten," the doctor said.

Nash's mind kept flicking to other alternatives. In his entire life the difficult problems had always been soluble. Up to now the difficult things and the important things had always involved machinery. He had always been able to nurse an engine back into peak efficiency, make the sensitive little adjustments which allowed an airplane to fly properly, find ways of draining airfields in tropical climates. He thought suddenly of the Navy and its vast and efficient medical system.

"Thank you very much, Doctor," Nash said. "You have been very helpful."

The next day Nash called on Captain Lanson. Lanson was a reservist who had a reputation for being informal and also very good. He explained his relationship to Terita, said that he intended to marry her in the near future, but would like to have her treated by the Navy doctors immediately.

"It's a little bit irregular, Nash," the doctor said "But I think we can just skip the formalities. I'll get whatever lung and TB specialists we have on staff together and you have her in here tomorrow at 0800."

As Nash and Terita walked down the corridor of the Naval Hospital, high above Pearl Harbor, the next morning, Nash felt a surge of relief. The place was so enormous, the nurses so white and aseptic, the equipment so new and glistening that he felt anything was within his power.

The procedure was different from the Japanese

doctor's office. Terita was told to undress and given a white smock to wear. Nash saw only the first few steps of her examination. She was placed under an X-ray machine, then wheeled into a room where technicians took blood samples. They told Nash that the rest of the examination would be done under aseptic conditions and he could not observe. He was told to report to the captain's office at 1000 hours.

Then he went into the office, Captain Lanson was talking cheerfully to Terita. Two other doctors, both lieutenant commanders, were seated beside him. All three of the doctors were smiling at something Terita had said. The captain motioned for Nash to sit down. He then swung his chair around and looked directly at Nash.

"Nash, it doesn't look very good," he said brusquely. "Dr. Gardner here is a lung specialist and he believes that if we deflated one of the lungs, put the young lady under complete rest, that there is a small chance that the deflated lung might repair itself by the time the other lung was ruined. We would then reinflate the cured lung and remove the second one. Dr. Richards believes that the case is too far advanced. Given the Polynesian inability to resist TB he thinks you would only postpone the inevitable by a few months."

Nash licked his lips. He looked at Terita. For a moment she had not understood the doctor, for she smiled quietly back at him.

"What if we flew her back to the States?" Nash asked. "Is there anything that they can do there that you can't do here?"

"Absolutely nothing," the captain said. "There is no magic they have back there that we lack out here. Now, remember that we could always be wrong. Occasionally, even the most hopeless cases will, for reasons we do not understand, make a complete reversal and stage a successful comeback. None of the three of us believe it is possible in this case."

Nash listened and was beyond believing. He looked at Terita and then at the doctors.

"Gentlemen, thank you very much," Nash said, standing up. "I very much appreciate what you have done."

The three doctors shrugged. The captain said, "Sorry, Nash. But to be optimistic when there are no grounds for it is the ultimate disservice."

As Nash and Terita were walking to the door, Terita stopped and turned to the captain.

"Can this fella catch TB from me?" she asked.

"The chances are overwhelmingly against it," the captain said. "Don't worry about that."

Instantly Terita was radiant. She smiled at the three doctors, nodded and then she and Nash were walking down the corridor.

When they were in the car, Terita asked if they could go to the beach where they had had their first picnic. Nash, without a word, drove out to the beach. They stopped at the same Chinese store and bought beer and ship's biscuits. It was sunset when they got to the beach and it was dark by the time they had caught the fish and cleaned them. There was no moon and the only things that were visible were the stars, bright and near, the slight phosphorescent line of the reef, and the red glow of their fire. Nash felt disembodied, as if the sand were holding him in some sort of suspension. Terita was lying with her head on his lap and when she began to speak, the strangeness of the night and the gentleness of her voice made her persuasive.

"This girl not afraid dying," she said into his ear, her breath fragrant as she uttered the deadly words.

"I know white folk they different. They scared dying. Island people not afraid. Some time we find old man in bed and he gone. Just gone. Smiling. No sickness. I no believe in hell and heaven. I believe I go and some day you go and maybe then we meet. But maybe not."

He felt as if he were going to vomit, his body went racked and tensed and then, to his surprise, he felt a moisture in his eyes. He was crying. It was a relief and the tears fell from his chin onto the brown flat face on his lap. He cried without sobbing and Terita's hand reached up and caressed his neck, her fingers ran over his wet cheek. Her hand was firm and comforting. She muttered some Tahitian words to him. At some point he stopped crying and she began to talk to him in pidgin English.

She talked for hours, until the sky lightened and began to catch the long low familiar shape of Molokai. She talked of growing up on her island, of the colors of the reef, of learning to fish, of going through the excitement of a typhoon when the waves began to cream higher and higher on the reef and finally washed across the atoll, of her endless aunts and uncles and cousins, of grating coconut meat to get coconut milk. And mixed in with all of this was the gossip of a village girl. Occasionally she would laugh, a low laugh and without scorn, as she told of Teti, the oldest grandmother on the island, who loved to cheat in trading deals for she had learned it from the Chinaman ... but when she won she would always dig the rocks out of her sacks of copra and show them, unwrap a bunch of first-class vanilla pods and show that the middle was stuffed with culls. She never made a franc on her cheating, but it was the passion of her life. Terita told Nash of the love-making she had done with island boys and she told it so gently that he felt no resentment. She told him of dancing, how to tell when a boat was approaching unseen land, how to cook a fish in lime juice, why pandanus made a better roof than coconut frond.

All this she murmured into his ears, her hands still firm on his back, rubbing his neck. Occasionally she would reach up and kiss his ear or the side of his face. Then she would return to the story of her islands. She went on with a persistence he had not seen in her before.

Gradually he felt drawn into that indistinct, vague, warm, formless and artless life which she described. He laughed once when she described the thrill of tasting a mango and he had an odd tingling taste in the back of his mouth. In a misty and screened way, the flow of pidgin English drew Nash deep into Terita's life. Half mesmerized, the only reality the stars above him and the grit of sand against his elbow, he drifted with her words.

Then, quite suddenly, although the sun was not visible, daylight arrived on their beach. The light was refracted down from the towering cumulus over Molokai. Nash looked down at the plain, flat-nosed face, possessed of only two beautiful features: the great brown eyes and the black hair. She smiled up at him and for the first time that night she kissed him on the lips.

"Do you want to go back to the island, Terita?" he asked. "Maybe we could arrange it."

"Oh, no," she said in panic. "I stay here with you. No time to return to the islands. But some day you go to the islands. They be good for you. Jack, you a good man, but inside of you too tight." She paused, seeking for a word, and then she laughed. She picked up his arm and pointed at the heavy aviator's wrist watch he wore. "You like this clock. Tick, tick, tick, all the time perfect. But the clock have no skin, no eyes, no tongue, no heart. In the islands you find all those things again."

They were married in the Navy chapel and Nash invited the crew of his plane, the three Navy doctors and the Filipino barkeeper from Hotel Street. Afterwards the wedding party went to the Filipino's bar which had been emptied of its regular clientele, had been swept clean and was full of flowers. Somewhere the Filipino had found enough Tahitians to make up a Tahitian band. He had also found a way to circumvent the strict regulations of the OPA: the bar was converted into a great array of crisp roasted pig, a huge roast of beef, long thin loaves of french bread, roasted chickens, plates of butter, a great bowl of fa-fa. On each table was a bottle of real bourbon whiskey and real scotch whiskey and a wine cooler with champagne.

The party was a great success. Terita danced the tamure with one of the Tahitians from the band, then she danced Western style with Nash. The guests ate and drank enormously. There were a profusion of toasts, some of them in English, but more often in Tagalog or Tahitian or the peculiar old Anglo-Saxon of Navy men.

After they were married their life fell into a pattern. Sometimes Nash would be gone for four or five days with his plane, flying to Guadalcanal or Samoa or Johnson or Midway or Fiji. When Nash returned, Terita would have the house full of flowers and the ingredients of a Tahitian feast. The first day he was home they would spend almost entirely on the big sagging bed with the bright yellow calico bedspread. Their love-making would be urgent and questing at first and then more leisurely.

The second day Nash was home they would go to

one of the little beaches on the windward side of Oahu. There they would swim, catch fish, sleep in the sun and talk. Often they would spend the night on the beach. Occasionally someone from Nash's crew would see them clambering over the reef, searching for their dinner.

Six months after they were married Nash had flown to Sydney with a cargo of radar parts. Then there had been an emergency trip to Nouméa with a group of Navy corpsmen. Then a quick series of emergency flights over most of the South Pacific. Nash was gone for a total of three weeks.

When he stepped out of his plane at Oahu, Captain Lanson was there to meet him. As always, the captain stood straight, his face unworried. But Nash knew why he was there. He walked over and saluted and then shook hands with the captain.

"Terita is dead," he said.

"Terita is dead," the captain said. "She went very quickly and with no pain. She called me to say that she knew it was her time. I went up to your house and tried to get her to come into the hospital. She refused, said she wanted to spend her time in your house. The Filipino bartender's wife took care of her, but there was not much to do. She was capable of movement and conversation until the very last and then she went very quickly."

"Did she leave me a note?" Nash asked.

The captain looked at him oddly.

"She could not write," he said. "Didn't you know that?"

"No. I did not know that," Nash said.

"She left a message, however," the captain said. "She spoke it to me. She asked that you not go back to your house. It would only hurt. She said she loved you. And then she said something about a clock."

"What exactly?" Nash asked quickly.

"She said you not a clock any longer," the captain said apologetically. "I wasn't sure I understood her correctly or maybe it's a pidgin English phrase. Do you understand it?"

"I understand it," Nash said.

"She was a curious girl," the captain said and he looked down at his feet. "We doctors cannot afford to become interested in patients. But she was different. I have seen a lot of people die, Nash, but I tell you that this girl died happy. It was not an act. She was not happy to die, do you understand, but she was happy. Maybe with you. A remarkable girl."

Nash did none of the conventional things. He did not get drunk. He did not carry flowers to Terita's grave. He did not volunteer for extra-hazardous duty. He did not go to see the Navy chaplain.

He did go to see the Filipino barkeep and his wife, however. He thanked them and then in that bar, again dirty and disreputable, the Filipino filled three glasses with bourbon and without a word he lifted his. They were clear-eyed when they drank and no one mentioned Terita's name.

I knew little of this when I talked to the sailor from Nash's plane on Guadalcanal. I put it together much later. Talking to the young sailor, my only reaction was that Nash had been had by one of the island girls that drift in and out of Honolulu . . . half prostitutes, half preying for husbands.

Late that afternoon, just at dusk, Nash's Ventura returned to Guadalcanal.

"Here's a Ventura," one of the sailors on top of the DC-4 shouted. Instantly the entire crew stood up, gazed out at the plane which was rapidly growing as it swept in for a landing.

Something about their rapt attention surprised me. Nash was not the kind of person whom a crew grew to like. Not the Nash I knew.

The Ventura came in fast, pulled up and touched down lightly. "That's the skipper," one of the crewmen said with satisfaction. "That's the way he brings them in."

"Nash is quite a mechanic, isn't he?" I asked the young sailor. "A real bug on maintenance."

The sailor looked away from the Ventura in surprise.

"The old man?" he asked. "Christ, no. He flies by the seat of his pants. Never even looks at the engines. Just asks Judkins, he's the chief motor mac, if they are O.K. and starts flying. And anything on the surface and he'll go down and have a look. I'll bet we've used ten thousand gallons of gas this last year circling outrigger canoes and atolls and little old islands with not a damn soul on them just 'cause the skipper likes to have a look-see."

The words jarred. For a moment I was sure that we were not talking about the same man. Then the Ventura taxied up to the hardtop, wheeled sharply around in a smoking skid and the engines were abruptly cut. The crew came out the hatch first, looked at Nash's crew with the strange appraising look which people in the same trade save for one another, and walked off in a group. Then Nash came out of the hatch.

From twenty yards away he looked as if he had aged. When he was five yards away he looked younger. When he recognized me and yelled, I felt only that he had changed. He waved to the crew and ran over to shake my hand. There was, for one thing, real pleasure in his voice. For another thing, he walked now with a peculiar sort of grace, a kind of animal quickness. His face had not softened, but it had new lines, was less rigid, his mouth less a straight line. He smiled more often.

"Damn, it's good to see you," he said shaking my hand. His left hand caught me above the elbow and squeezed very hard. "Someone told me your ship got sunk, but no one knew whether you survived or not. I guess you did."

"All scuttlebutt," I said. "We haven't had anything except near misses."

"I'm glad," he said.

He dropped my hand, but his left hand still squeezed my elbow, tightening and then loosening the grip. Now men are very sensitive about being touched by other men and it probably has something to do with homosexuality and our fear of it. But Nash's grip was not the caress of a homosexual, it was the grip of a man who likes to touch someone he likes, wants to be reassured of existence. I felt myself suddenly understanding why the crew had been tense all afternoon: they liked Nash. And so did I.

"You look all right, kid," he said. "A bit haggard, but shit, everybody is haggard out here. Give us all twelve hours sleep at the same time and we'd kick the Japs off this island in ten minutes after we woke up."

He dropped his left hand and turned towards the crew. They had drifted down from the plane and were standing in a semicircle around us.

"How did it go, skipper?" Judkins asked.

"You mean were the Ventura's engines in as good shape as Judkins' engines," Nash said. The crew laughed and Judkins laughed with them. "Well, they weren't. A bit ragged, but it didn't make any difference. Even ragged, that Ventura is a fast plane. We flew just over the water to Viru Harbor and then went

up to angels ten and started taking photographs.
Went right up the back of the island until we hit
Munda and then we could see the flak. First time I'd
seen it. Little black clouds. I almost crapped. Our
flight was coordinated with an F4–U strike and the
flak was going at them. No one paid attention to us.
We finished the Brownie work, swung right and came
on home. That's all there was to it."

"You visit any islands, skipper?" the young sailor
asked.

The crew all grinned.

"Sure. I went in low when we got back to Viru and
had a look at the plantation that Kennedy, the coast
watcher, runs," Nash said. "Nice setup. A big frame
house, a couple thousand coconut trees, a little native
village down by the water. The second time I circled
they knew I was friendly and I could see Kennedy,
or a white man anyway, with a bunch of natives.
They waved and I gave them a 'hello' on the Aldis
lamp. Kennedy could read it because when I asked
them if there was anything they needed he flashed
back 'gin.'" The crew roared. All of them were
crouched down on their heels now, listening intently
to Nash. "I flashed him we were sorry, no gin, only
medicinal alcohol. He said it was his favorite drink
after gin and to send it down. I had one of the
crewmen dig the six three-ounce bottles I had in my
own medicinal kit, wrap it in two life jackets and on
the third pass we dropped it in the water just off the
plantation. It was still falling when an outrigger put
out from the beach. That man must be thirsty."

"You going to fly that patrol plane out again?"
Judkins asked anxiously.

"Not after that Ventura crew talks to their intelligence officer," Nash said. "They thought I was nuts
flying around Kennedy's plantation. If our crate is in

good shape my guess is we'll fly out of here tomorrow. How is it?"

The crew chief, a fat, middle-aged CPO, told Nash that everything was in shape except that they wouldn't be able to pressurize the cabin and would have to fly low.

"Is Smitty back from his scrounging trip yet?" Nash asked. He turned to me and explained. "Smitty took a spare parachute and cut it up into Japanese flags. Whenever we hit a port he goes out to the merchant marine ships and trades them for whiskey. One flag, four fifths of whiskey."

"He isn't back yet," the CPO said. "No news is good news."

"You're probably right," Nash said. "I'm taking this character here," he gestured at me, "and see if the officers' club still operates. If Smitty gets back with the booze you can crack it tonight unless they scheduled us to take off before 1200. Otherwise save it for Santo."

As we started to walk away, Nash called to the young sailor whom I had been talking to. The boy walked along with us and Nash talked in a matter-of-fact voice.

"Billy, you're thinking that you're responsible for Tony getting killed," he said. "If he'd been at the radio where he belonged instead of having you spell him while he got sack time you'd have gotten it. That's what you're thinking, isn't it?"

"I don't know. Something like that, I guess," the boy said miserably.

"It's nobody's fault. It just happened," Nash said softly. "Tony was your buddy and it's too bad he got it, but do you think he's blaming you?"

Billy looked over at Nash, startled. Nash went on talking.

"He's not blaming you," Nash said. "Tony knew it was just the odds. You don't help Tony by dragging your ass around."

It was a queer conversation. I could not tell if Nash was telling Billy that there was a life after death or merely consoling him. It was also clear that the words were not quite clear to Billy. But he walked along with us quietly for another quarter of a mile and then stopped.

"Thanks, skipper," he said. His voice was normal. Whatever the meaning of Nash's words, they lifted a burden from the boy. "See you later." He faded away into the coconut grove.

By this time there were a number of officers' clubs on Guadalcanal in addition to the famous Hotel De-gink. Most of them were tents or quonset huts with a bar made of upended oil drums with a plank between them. They were open for only two hours a day. Nash led me to one that was on a slight hill and overlooked Iron Bottom Bay with Florida Island and Tulagi rising up twenty miles away. To the left was the perfect round cone of Savo Island. The club was full of men, marines, soldiers, fliers, sailors who had only two things in common. They were sweaty and they were tired. Nash and I, by comparison, looked as if we had just come from a rest camp. We arrived just as the bar opened.

"They serve two things here, beer and whiskey," Nash said. "What will you have?"

"Both," I said.

"Me too," Nash replied.

He pushed up to the bar and came out of the scramble with two white U.S. Navy coffee mugs full of whiskey and four cans of ice-cold beer. We took it outside and sat on a coconut log.

"They're pretty quiet in there," I said, nodding at

the tent, probing for a way to make conversation. The only sounds from the tent were the orders to the bartender, the sucking of beer out of cans, the gulping of whiskey and occasionally, hanging in the air and senseless, a four-letter word uttered without anger or emphasis.

"In an hour they'll be roaring and arguing and singing," Nash said. "It takes a while for the booze to wash the day off."

Nash took half of his mug of whiskey down in one gulp, followed it with a few swallows of beer. He turned and grinned at me.

"I drink more than I used to," he said.

"You didn't drink anything before," I said. "Just sipped at a whiskey sour."

"It worried old Captain Lanson when I started to drink," Nash said. He laughed. "He thought I was going to start lushing it up, go into alcoholic mourning." He looked sideways at me. "You knew I got married and she died? Willy probably told you."

"He told me," I said.

"Lanson was wrong about the sauce. I like to drink now. Not a lot, but enough to take the glaze off," he said.

"That's what every drunkard in the world said at one point," I said. "But you don't strike me as the drunkard type."

"I'm not. Oh, boy, am I not. My curse was the opposite. I wanted myself under control like an addict wants drugs. Didn't waste a word, a motion. I was a natural-born efficiency expert, it was built in. And proud of myself, oh Jesus, was I proud," Nash said. He looked down in the mug, finished it off and drank the rest of the beer in his can. "It was the kind of pride a contractor must get when he watches the iron skeleton of a skyscrapper go up ... rigid, precise, mathematical. He doesn't give doodley what goes into the building or how it looks ... he just has a terrible pride about that wonderful firm unyielding skeleton. That was me until I met Terita."

He went back in the bar and got another round. He started to talk easily and it is important that I convey the quality of his talk. He was not a boor, not anxious to persuade, not intense. He talked like a man who has let down some final barrier, was willing to expose himself, but not promiscuously. I suppose that the word is dignity. It was then that he told me about Terita. The rest of the story I filled in later from talking to Bill Mullahey and Willy and the Filipino bartender.

It was almost dawn when he finished. A few drunk officers were sleeping on benches in the bar. The mosquitoes began to go to wherever they go during the day. The morning mists on Savo slid down the little valleys and disappeared as they hit the water.

"And you didn't mourn after she died?" I asked. "Didn't miss her?"

"Miss her? Oh, I missed her. It was like a wound that you know is critical, but not mortal," Nash said. "I knew it would heal. Terita would want it to hurt for a while, but she would also want it to heal. I knew that. But I could not mourn. Terita taught me, without using any words, that mourning is artificial, a cooked-up emotion. Why should we put on black and cry and drive in long lines of cars to a cemetery and put pitiful obituaries in a newspaper over what we know is inevitable? I read the obituaries and if you believe them, the deceased is always a dearly beloved, fulfilled, adequate human. Why don't they celebrate, instead of mourning, the simple fact that he is dead? For Terita, death was an ending, but it was not tragic."

We got up and walked back towards the air strip. The coconut groves were filled with tents and exhausted men sleeping under mosquito nets. The cooks were stirring about, poking at field kitchens, opening cans and pouring them into huge pots. We went by a field hospital and it was the only place fully awake and active. It gave off the odor of ether and alcohol and under a dazzling light, two young surgeons were at work on an operating table. They must have been working on a seriously injured Negro, for one black leg hung over the edge of the operating table. Outside the tent there were three marines tightly strapped onto stretchers, so closely wrapped that they could only move their heads. Two of them strained at their bonds, heaved restlessly, their eyes rolling in their heads. The third one stared straight up at the sky with wide open eyes in a catatonic rodlike stiffness and his eyelids did not flick even when flies crawled over them.

"Battle fatigue they call it," Nash said wonderingly. "Good Christ, what men can do to one another." He paused a moment, waited until we came out onto the strip. "You know I read the Bible after Terita died. Not for comfort, because I didn't need comfort, but to try and understand myself and others. There was one line that I remember. It was in Genesis when the families of the sons of Noah wander onto the plain of Shinar and began to build a tower which they hoped would reach to heaven. The lines goes 'And they had brick for stone, and slime had they for mortar.' That line I understood. I realized I had been trying to build a monument to myself with my own life ... Nash the infallible mechanic, Nash the meticulous flier, Nash the man with control. And slime had I for mortar." He paused and grinned at me. "This is pretty heavy stuff for early in the morning, isn't it? Let's get something to eat."

We stopped at one of the kitchens and got a tray of dried scrambled eggs, thick slices of greasy bacon, oatmeal with reconstituted powdered milk and sugar, two big sweet doughnuts and a mug of coffee. We ate standing up. We were both ravenous and the food tasted good. It was the first time in months I had been hungry.

"What are you going to do now?" I asked.

"Fly the crate back to Santo and get it patched up and then fly wherever they tell me to," Nash said.

"No. I mean after the war," I said. "Back to Pan Am or some other airline, or what?"

"I'm not sure," he said. "I don't want to fly any more or to take care of planes any more. I think I'll go to the South Seas and look around for a while. I'd like to learn to sail a boat. Maybe buy a schooner and cruise around and look at the islands." He looked over at me shrewdly. "Don't worry. I'm not going on a pilgrimage to Terita's island. I just want to look around and see if there is something else I can put my life together with besides slime. When I used to fly for Pan Am I never really noticed the islands or even the sea. I just concentrated on the instrument panel. Now I look down and see a little white triangle of a sail and I wonder where the hell that outrigger is going. Or I see an island, even a little atoll, and I wonder what the people are doing there. Maybe I'll go have a look at all that. Not from a bird's-eye view, but from eye level, sea level."

His plane was ready when we got to it and they had been cleared for Santo. They took off a half hour later.

It was the last time I saw Nash.

I did not hear anything of him until six years after

the war. Then I received a thick packet from a French official in Papeete, Tahiti. The covering letter was written in very correct English.

> Dear Sir:
>
> As you can see from the enclosed letter this material was intended for delivery to you.
>
> This packet was discovered on February 21 of this year by a group of natives who were diving for shell on the abandoned motu of Tiri. The entire atoll has been abandoned for 22 years.
>
> The packet was found on the chest of a skeleton which was resting on a small raised mound of rocks. The packet was bound in several layers of thick plastic, three layers of oilskin, and finally by a leather pouch. All of the leather pouch had been eaten by red ants except the metal fixtures.
>
> The natives left the skeleton undisturbed, but brought the packet to Papeete. On the next tour of the government ship a landing party, including a doctor and chaplain, visited Tiri and examined the skeleton. It is the belief of the doctor that it is the remains of a Caucasian of about forty years of age. Cause of death could not be determined, but there was no injury to the skeleton. The remains were given a Christian burial in Papeete.
>
> If this party has left an estate I am obliged to inform you that this government would like to lay claims against the estate in the amount of $125 (payable in French Polynesian Francs or British Sterling or U.S. dollars). This is the cost of diverting the government boat from its usual routing and transporting and burying the remains in Papeete.
>
> > Most respectfully,
> > FRANÇOIS FEROT

The packet was a small, thick looseleaf notebook in which Nash had kept a diary. Inside the first page was a statement that in case of accident or death the diary should be mailed to me. On the next page was a letter to me from Nash.

Old friend [the letter began], this will come to you only if I have had a serious accident or am dead. Read it and then destroy it. I send it to you because I have read some of your stories about the war and the South Pacific and found them interesting. Also I remember the long night on Guadalcanal when you listened to me talk and for your time and ear I am grateful. Perhaps in this diary you may find something of interest.

To any casual reader the diary was most profoundly uninteresting. It was a laconic, flat, one-dimensional diary, almost like reading the log of a ship. Its first entry reported the purchase of the schooner *Blossom* for $2500 in Sydney. Other entries indicated that Nash had sailed from Sydney to New Caledonia and spent some time in the hills back of Nouméa living with natives. "Learned to eat sago today. Very flat. Helped set six snares for mountain deer. Caught one small one, 75 pounds," a typical entry would read. Then there would be a long series of entries describing the amount of water and stores he had taken on at islands all over the Pacific. Occasionally he would carry passengers for hire, three times he chartered the *Blossom* to Chinese traders. The last three years of the diary indicated he had been in French Polynesia . . . the Tuamotus, the Marquesas, the Australs. Always he went to the most remote of the motus and always he lived on the beach in the native villages, renting a hut if that were possible, living with a family if necessary. One entry leapt out of the pages. "Today finally mastered net fishing. Made three perfect throws. Caught twenty pounds of fish." Another time he wrote, "Gave *tamaraa* tonight for Vita who says she is pregnant with my child. Five demijohns Algerian red, ten cases Hainho beer, three pigs ... total: $35. Everyone very happy, including me." Months later and from another island Nash wrote "Have heard Vita had baby boy and it has blond hair and is named John. Have sent present of mosquito net, one gross fishhooks, picture of myself, quart of gin for Vita's father, calico for six pareaus ... which is what Vita said she wanted. Also enclosed alarm clock which Vita's mother wanted, but was afraid to ask for."

Then there were the last entries. They were written in the same firm hand as the rest of the diary.

"Two days ago I wrecked the *Blossom*," he wrote on December 10. "It was unavoidable. Caught in this particular kind of a typhoon, there was nothing I could do but run before it and hope that I would slide through one of the gaps in the archipelago towards which I was being driven. It was a wonderful storm and the sea was beyond belief. But, in the end, I lost the gamble. There was suddenly in the windy blackness a line of reef and it was so close that I did not even alter course. The *Blossom* crunched into the reef, I went over the bows in a life jacket and walked ashore without a scratch. But the *Blossom* went down in bits and splinters as the waves tore her apart against the coral. I think I am on the Tiri motu, but I cannot be sure. I have been sleeping for two days. There is no water on the motu and only two coconut trees."

Then a week later, "I have drunk the last of the coconuts and scraped out the flesh. I have tried to fish, but with no success. It is the water which is decisive."

Four days later was the last entry, still in a firm hand, "This must be the last day. I have tried everything and can neither devise an escape nor live longer on a waterless motu. I feel neither despair nor joy. I do feel a kind of contentment. It is the end and before it came I saw what I wanted to of the seas and the islands. I am thankful that I was able to come down from the skies."

7. The Coral Atoll

THERE ARE two types of islands in the Pacific. The "low" island or coral atoll and the "high" island. They could not be more different in appearance or in origin. One is the result of a minute cosmic patience; the other of a natural catastrophe.

An atoll is a misery to describe and stupendous to behold. There are a number of theories as to how an atoll starts, but Darwin's is as interesting and as well supported as any. He theorized that around a tropical high island a coral reef began to grow. The reef is formed by the action of a tiny polyp which has a brief busy life and uses it doing one major job: he extracts lime from the water and builds a tiny calcified prison within himself. A coral reef is made up of endless generations of these minute lime cells, each tightly bound to its neighbors. Only a fringe of the reef is actually alive. Everything else is made up of past generations.

At some point, Darwin argued, the high island

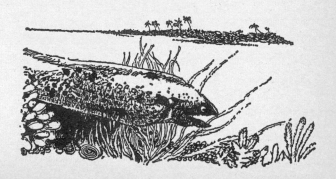

began to sink into the ocean. Eventually it disappeared altogether, leaving only the circle of durable and tough coral around a lagoon. Blindly and with furious energy the coral polyps begin to grow in the direction of the lagoon. Eventually they convert it into a very shallow lagoon or in some cases almost fill in the lagoon. Some lagoons, in relatively young atolls, are still deep and blue. In any case the living fringe of coral continues at work around the periphery of the atoll. It pushes out a fringing reef which may reach out hundreds of yards from shore. At the edge of this is the barrier reef, so cunningly contrived that it allows water to flow over the reef, but takes the huge ocean waves and reduces them, in the distance of a few yards, to low harmless humps of water.

Because the coral polyp can live only in salt water the atolls seldom rise high above sea level. Occasionally a deep convulsion of the sea will jerk a coral atoll high out of the water and this "uplifted coral" produces such places as Tongatabu.

Most atolls, however, are very low. The older ones have developed sand by the constant motion of sea and wind against the coral. Few things can grow in such a place, but, fortunately, the coconut palm is one. It flourishes with its roots dug deep into brackish and even salty water. The raised parts of the atoll are called *motus*.

Few atolls are symmetrical and generally the lagoon is much larger than the surface of the motus. Eniwetok is probably as close as one comes to a neat circle and it has a lagoon diameter of about twenty miles. Kwajalein, also in the Marshalls, is about ninety miles long and twenty miles wide and lies in a long curve. Generally each motu on an atoll is given a name and the largest motu becomes the name for the atoll.

The atoll seems a slight thing for the enormous amount of work and material involved. A drillhole on Bikini went 2500 feet deep and was still in coral. Experts estimate that it may rest on a vast formation of over 8000 feet of coral. And all that shows for this is a few acres of sand, a few coconut trees, a reef formation. Unless it enjoys a catastrophic "uplift" the atoll is doomed to remain always low and slight.

But *seeing* an atoll is something else. Most Westerners when they see a place of beauty experience a "shock of recognition"; they have been prepared for it. We behold Chartres, the Grand Canyon, the skyline of Manhattan, Notre Dame, the Valley of the Laire, the Rhine River, the Matterhorn—and we know what each is like before we see it. Postcards and motion pictures and parents have told us what to expect. We see each sight and it is beautiful as we expected it to be. We get out our cameras with a slight sense of duty, not with a surprised thrill.

But let the traveler see the atolls of the Tuamotus or the Societies or the Australs for the first time and he is stunned. The atoll is foreign to our eyes, to our notions of aesthetic balance, to our standards of color and balance and symmetry. Say, for example, that you first see an atoll from the air. Swooping down on it from a great distance, you will note the sharp classic stems of the coco palms. This is a wonderfully simple tree, it rises in a curve and then breaks into a burst of fronds. By some prescience the coco palms arrange themselves nicely along an atoll. Abruptly the deep bottomless blue of the open sea ends and the reef begins. It is only when the sea blue ends that you realize how deep, pure, almost black a hue it is; it absorbs the sun like a vast sponge, it sends back no softened colors. As the water shoals rapidly, new shades of blue appear—unfamiliar, unnamed primitive colors. And then, in a flashing second, the entire expanse of the atoll is visible, the new colors claw their way into the sky, make a physical assault on the eyeball and brain and past training. The colors are astonishing. The mind fights to tone them down, to moderate the chromatic attack, to re-establish some sort of control.

The eye picks out the familiar and fastens on it with a kind of desperation—the tin roof of a trader's hut, the neat rectangular shape of a pier, the nipa huts of a village, an occasional path, a parade ground, the whitewashed school with children playing in the yard, dogs running in yapping circles. All of this is pedestrian, sometimes even dingy.

The colors, however, transform everything. The sea beach is generally made up of many blues, owing to the splintering and irregularities in the coral: azure, lapis lazuli, pure cobalt, occasionally a smoky-blue twist that runs like a river through the deep hues. Each color, however, seems to be primary, to have an integrity and intensity of its own. There is no admixture of the blues, no running together of colors. Each patch will have distinct limits as if aware of itself and proud.

The raised part of the atoll is tawny and green and lined with an edging of white sand. The lagoon is shallow, often with knobs of coral that rear themselves above the water. Here is a green and white world. But again the greens have an almost weird clarity; a fierce, pure intensity. The white is sand and it ranges from a dead white when the sun is directly overhead to a dazzling crystal-like brightness when the sun is lower. During the day the whole lagoon is made up of these shimmering combinations of green and white, which intertwine with one another, take on different shapes, but are always distinct and pure. There are long slits of creamy green, banks of jade which tremble when the wind moves over the water, circles of bitter green, a tongue of striking emerald. The greens are liquid and they move, but they are all strange. There are no familiar greens, none of the weaker and more civilized colors. Everything shimmers and is deliquescent, but it is also primitive and raw.

As the sun goes down, the greens in the lagoon go out abruptly, one at a time, and the great flat stretch of water takes on an even, deep and flawless green that looks as solid as a vast thin sheet of crystal. When a fish jumps, you suck in your breath, expecting a high crackling noise as the brittle surface is shattered. But nothing happens, and soon the lagoon turns black and the white rim of sand comes up luminous as old bone. The coconut trees merge into a solid line and bend over the water in a short luscious curve.

I once flew over an atoll with a distinguished French painter who is also extremely articulate. We took off from Papeete, where he had arrived only two days before. Papeete and Moorea he found attractive, not wildly exciting but different. We flew for two hours and then the amphibian plane began to circle a group of atolls which happened to be deserted. We circled for five minutes before I noted that his eyes were closed and his face was pale. I asked what he thought of the view.

His words came back bleached, diminished, tiny. "No more. Let's go back. Something like this is bad for me. It burns out the fine artistic nerve endings which civilization develops." He wet his lips. "Some things are too primary, too violent, too raw."

"But it's gorgeous," I said energetically, reaching for the only word which came to mind.

"Exactly. Gorgeous, fantastic, spectacular," he replied, his eyes still squeezed shut. "Even wonderful and savage. But it is not art." Then he added wistfully, in a whisper, "I think."

He left two weeks later from Papeete without leaving the inside of Quinn's bar and his hotel. He was a man with courage, but he also wanted to preserve his training and his balance, and he was sure, with an iron certitude, that the Pacific would bleed him white.

The beauties of the underwater coral reef have been told so often, the magnificent colors and strange fish so often photographed that it would be feckless to repeat those experiences here. Only recently with the invention of the faceplate and waterproof goggles have men been able to see these things with their own eyes. But the marvelously simple discovery of the face mask changed all that. Now every person can, and should, peer into the hauntingly beautiful world of the coral reef. It is more than just an aesthetic experience, more than just the seductiveness of exotic colors and shapes. Peering into the life of the coral reef one has the knowledge, felt more in the bones than in the brain, that this is the beginning of everything. Here in the warm salty water teeming with primitive animals and gorgeous color one senses that life began. It is really a kind of primordial sense of kinship, of looking backwards into the common origins and, oddly enough, it is not an experience that is depressing or degrading. It is exhilarating.

In one sense, however, the look of a coral reef is deceptive. The coral seems hard and ageless, as strong as stone. It rips open the bottom of iron ships as easily as it lacerates the human foot. The coral reef withstands the constant battering of storm waves. Indeed, the reef seems monumental, eternal, powerful. Actually this is deceptive for the reef is being attacked, and eaten away and consumed almost as rapidly as it is being built up.

Robert Louis Stevenson, that fey and sensitive visitor to the South Seas, once reported tearing a piece of coral from a seemingly solid wall of the reef. Dangling from the chunk of coral were the spaghettilike bodies of dozens of coral worms; pasty white and disgusting, utterly blind, these soft worms have a diamond-hard mouth that can chew through coral. When they infest coral they can reduce a solid-looking reef to a riddled structure which will wash away in huge chunks.

In fact the coral reef, which seems so firm and monumental, is the scene of a constant struggle between forces that build up and forces that gnaw away.

The building is done primarily by coral polyps of many varieties. By some unknowable instinct each colony arranges its thousands of cells into characteristic patterns ... great gray brainlike masses, structures which look like black leafless trees, great boulders with holes at perfectly symmetrical points, long green stalactites that seem to wave in the water, but are as hard as basalt. In among these bigger structures crawl thousands of tube-building worms which leave a hard limestone tunnel behind them. There are also curious algae which deposit lime on the reef. Moving cautiously in among the tortured passages of the coral are sea animals with the capacity to extract the lime from sea water and add it to the bulk of the reef. Gorgonians, algae, starfish, sea urchins, crabs of all kinds, clams and mussels live in an incredibly intricate balance. As one glides past a reef it seems to be still and stonelike ... actually it is waving millions of tiny antennae in the water and sucking in lime and food. Water circulates through the tiny passages of living coral in an intricate and perfectly functioning pattern.

There is a living and dying, a struggle, a mechani-

cal fight for food, an elaborate mating, the place
swarms with sperm and eggs hoping to come together, a quiet preying and being preyed upon. And,
somehow, life is almost non-animal here . . . it is something between a palpable vegetable and a mechanical
animal . . . limited in movement, locked into tiny and
minute relationships. Here animals die without a
struggle for struggle is impossible.

Minute, wormlike, sightless animals build formations of the most staggering size and the most gorgeous color. Countless reef animals spend their entire
life within a world no bigger than a thimble. They
can feel the passage of more adept creatures, the
scraping of a crab's claw, the slick passage of a sea
snake, the scuttling of ghost shrimp, the gelatinous
sensations of a sea nettle settling on the reef. But the
builders of the reef have no notion of all of this. They
are sightless drones. Their function is simplicity itself:
to build a limestone cell. When they die their fate is,
again, simplicity itself: they become a dead layer of
the reef. And above them the endless building goes
on.

There are also the destroyers and the parasites.
There are long spaghetti-shaped worms. There are
also other animals which bore savagely into the coral,
breaking down its structure and weakening it. Some
kinds of crabs actually encyst themselves in the coral
and allow it to build up around them until they are
in a prison which they dumbly occupy. Usually these
are the female of the species and they keep open a
tiny hole to the surface through which their males,
much smaller than the female, can dart in to fertilize
the eggs. The newborn crabs, by one of those in-
choate and marvelous mechanisms of nature, are
small enough to escape from the opening . . . which
the female then allows the polyps to seal off forever.

Life within the reef is soundless, sightless, indeed

almost purposeless. But life *around* the reef abounds
with activity. The waters are almost unbelievably
busy and hectic. Part of this is due to the fact that
there is so much food around a coral reef. It is rich
with seaweeds; the tides bring in water heavy with
minerals and miniscule particles of debris. The water
is also dense with floating eggs and sperm for the
mating cycle is so casual and formless that enormous
numbers of eggs are laid so that a few may survive.
Life about the reef is more vivid, sharp, quick ...
there is an extravagant almost drunken voraciousness.
There are parasites of all sorts, even one type that
specializes in living in the gonads of other animals
and slowly gnaws out the reproductive organs.

The means of defense and offense are weird. Fish
depend on speed and camouflage ... and camouflage
of the most eerie sort, so that they can seem like a
weed or a dangerous stinging type. Slugs move about
that are covered with a slime so caustic that no creature can touch them. Other crawling things can eject
a milky acid at enemies. One strange creature has the
most novel of defenses: it deliberately ruptures its
skin when it is attacked, explodes its intestines out-
wards in the hope that the invader will settle for
them rather than for the barely living husk that is left
... and sometimes the husk itself dies.

One of the most deadly of the animals that lives
close to the reefs is the moray eel. It is an animal
from a nightmare. Its body is like that of a long
flattened snake, one long muscle designed simply to
launch the huge gaping mouth of the eel. Poised on
top of the head are two small eyes well located to see
in every direction. It is an infinitely patient stalker,
skulking in the coral until precisely the fish it desires
passes. When it does strike the rows of thin white
teeth sink deep, the whole musculature of that purposeful body snaps in behind the jaws.

Once in the Tuamotus I saw a pearl diver deliberately hunt a moray. It was not for sport. A moray in a pearling area is so dangerious that it must either be eliminated or the pearl fishing abandoned until the eel moves. The diver surrounded his arm with thick splints of coconut wood and bound them securely with clean white cloth.

I floated on top of the water with a faceplate and snorkel. The diver wore old-fashioned glasses, wooden eyepieces handcarved to fit his eyes and fitted with bits of glass from a broken gin bottle. He did, however, wear modern rubber fins made in Paris. He went straight down and then, at the last moment, curved in towards a black hole in the reef about the size of a basketball. He held his body utterly still, but his arm he waved slowly in front of the black hole. Nothing happened. He stayed down so long that my lungs began to ache in sympathy. Then he backed cautiously away, his arm still in front of him, still waving hypnotically. He surfaced and grinned. He took several great breaths, winked at me.

"The old man is being very very careful," he said. Then his lips closed and with an easy movement he rolled over and started down, his rubber fins fluttering.

Again he curled in towards the black hole and began to wave the bandaged arm up and down. Then the eel moved. Its huge ugly head came clear of the hole, suspended in the water. The eyes looked grotesquely small when compared to its great underhanging jaw, but they glittered like illuminated jewels, seemed somehow to have enormous power. I was instantly certain that the eel, with eyes like that, was too knowing to be trapped. Its head waved back and forth, peering at the bound arm, looking around and beyond the bait. Slowly the head went back in the hole. The diver backed away and ballooned up to the surface.

"He's too smart today," he said in Tahitian. "But we are smarter." He reached in the outrigger canoe and rubbed his bandaged arm in the bottom of the boat. It was lined with the slime of thousands of fish, long dead. When he lifted the arm it was stinking of dead fish.

This time when he got to the hole the eel's head came out. The movements were more terse and sharp, the eyes more concentrated ... they never left the bandage. It seemed almost to be sniffing the water. Then the head sunk back into the hole. Then, so quick that I could not see it, the eel struck. It was really an uncoiling of muscle: a single brutal lash of the entire body. There was a magnificent simplicity about the shape of the animal, his ferocity, his deadly single-mindedness. Once its jaws are locked into a victim it will not separate them until the victim is dead.

The diver put his feet on the bottom of the sea and pushed off. The eel whipped its body in long desperate black twists that, by pure instinct, were designed to push both eel and diver towards the bottom. The diver came up slowly against this resistance. When he hit the surface the eel, who had probably never been free of the water before in his life, thrashed violently. The water about the outrigger was whipped into foam. The diver held his arm high, grinning wickedly. Like some strange and frantic whip the eel's black shiny body snapped in the air, curled in a huge circle. For a second it curled around the diver's arm, squeezed powerfully and realized instantly that this was a hopeless tactic. It unleashed itself and began to whip again through the air.

By this time, however, the boys in the outrigger had laid hands on the eel. Roaring with laughter they pinned the body, its teeth still sunk in the arm bandage, to the bottom of the boat. The diver leaned over the boat, wild with excitement and pride. With four pairs of hands holding it down the eel was brought under control . . . a trembling, vibrating, uneasy control. Tiny muscles flecked and rolled along its body, occasionally the eel tried to coil itself and the arms of the boys were raised inches from the bottom.

"That is enough," the diver said finally. "The old man is done. Cut him at the neck."

One of the boys lifted a machete. Waiting for the right moment he suddenly slashed at the eel. The knife parted the head from the body. The body, now released, continued to thrash for ten minutes. At the moment of the dismemberment I was looking at the eel's eyes. For several seconds they remained the same . . . yellow, ferocious, glittering, frantic. The head seemed to have a life of its own and to cling, by some miraculous means, to what was left of life.

Then quite quickly the eyes glazed. They did not close, but the glittering jewel-like sharpness, the exquisite edge of life, went out of them. The eyes stopped rotating and stared straight ahead.

The diver undid the bandage, slipped his arm out, collapsed the bandage and shook it loose from the needle-like teeth of the eel. The mouth, now separated from its massive musculature, remained open.

The diver picked up the severed head . . . held it with respect.

"He was a good old man," he said. "A good, strong, black old man. Plenty of mana."

Suddenly he reached forward and sank his teeth into the neck of the eel and tore off a piece. Laughingly he chewed at it and swallowed it. But I noticed that he carefully wrapped the head in the remains of the bandage. He never told me what he did with it.

Little of this savagery, this inhuman and intense dronelike life, this immense, intricate and vegetable-animal existence is visible unless a person gets below the membrane of the sea-surface. From the surface all that the human eye sees is a vast sweep of coral which is barely awash. Once the coral has reached the surface it must stop. The atoll lagoon begins to fill in, to give off splendid colors, to slowly build up sand beaches which are made, grain by grain, by a multitude of tiny gnawings and the endless friction of sea and wind.

There is, below the startling chromatic beauty of an atoll, a rather grim and relentless cycle. Great chunks of coral are torn loose during storms and go crashing soundlessly down the great sea wall into the bottomless depths. The breaches are patiently repaired by the automatic organization of the coral and their legions of helpers. And all of this for what? For the human the reward is chiefly aesthetic. The atoll, once its bottom has been stripped of pearl oysters and *bêche-de-mer* has almost no economic value. Indeed were it not for a fantastic accident, the ability of the coconut palm to live with its roots in salt water, the atolls would be unable to support human life. But with the addition of coconut palms a kind of low-level and very pleasant life is possible.

It is not quite as pleasant as many novels have made it. One must be prepared to put up with mosquitoes and dozens of other insects. The pure white beaches occasionally are blanketed with varieties of sand flies . . . each sting of which is almost unnoticed but when set upon by thousands they can reduce a human to agony. Fresh water is a rarity and the natives of atolls have gotten used to the brackish water.

For the white man who would live on the atolls two qualities are necessary. First, he must become used to living with a natural beauty which is not only spectacular, but which, if it thrills one every day, would soon burn out one's brain. Most white men, quite unconsciously, soon come to blank out the natural beauty in which they live or to remark it only occasionally. I have traveled with old Pacific hands who for weeks will not have a word to say about the glorious atolls that swim up out of the horizon, take shape against the hump of the sea. Then they will open, by accident, an old copy of the *National Geographic* and pointing at a picture of an English meadow or a French château exclaim, "Beautiful, eh? Now that is what I call beautiful."

Secondly, the white man must become used to the sameness of the days. The first twenty or thirty days which dawn cloudless, darken up in the afternoon and give off a quick dense shower, then clear up for a quick colorful sunset will be exciting. After a few months the strange absence of seasons, the even rhythm of the days, the predictable appearance of the trade winds, the regularity of the showers will become oppressive ... unless one can manage to simply overlook them. Which is what most men do.

The atolls are there ... by the thousands in places like the Tuamotus, the Cooks, the Tongas and the Gambiers and the Societys. Tiny specks of places. Unlikely places. Held a few feet above water by the frantic activity of billions of polyps, so small that a hundred of them would not fill your palm. Beautiful beyond the Western capacity to absorb. Uneconomic, but capable of supporting a few souls. For the patient man it is still possible to find one that has the right combination of wind and sand and coconut trees and an absence of nagging insects. They are probably as close to a paradisical place as we will find on this earth. But, alas, it is also a shock to discover that not many mortals are prepared to live long in paradise.

8. The High Island

THE HIGH islands of the Pacific are there by the
thousands. Some are a tiny knob of rock no bigger
than a tract house. They support perhaps, a single
magnificently isolated Malay family. Other high islands are almost the size of continents and maintain
huge populations, deserts, perpetually snowcapped
mountains, and a great deal of unexplored land.

Thousands of these islands are unoccupied, but do
not believe thereby that they could be had for nothing. Even the simplest primitive of Melanesia learned
the basic lesson of World War II: it was a strange and
violent conflict over land. The native is often not sure
why the land is so precious, but if men will shed
blood, kill men, expend food and sink ships for land it
must be precious. Aborigines living high in the wet
mountains of the Philippines have cheerfully been
burning off forest and planting crude crops for centuries. The notion of ownership was as novel as a

guided missile and as unlikely. But they watched the fighting silently and learned the lesson. Since 1945, they have been drifting into the offices of cheap small-town lawyers and begun to lay claim to their land.

In the Tongas, there is a small island, completely deserted, which has a small sign stuck in the sand at the high tide mark. It reads "For Sale" in four different languages, gives the name of a local chief as the owner and concludes with a sentence in English, "Pound Sterling and U.S. Dollars only. No damn Chinee or French money."

The high islands are made in two ways. Either they are fragments of former continents which have been isolated from the mainland by glaciers or erosion or they are formed by volcanic action. Whatever the method the moment the land thrusts itself above the surface the Pacific and its elements begin to work on it. One has to see it to believe the corrosive quality of salt water. Moved by only the tides and winds salt water can cut a continent in two, can undercut an island so that it takes the form of a giant mushroom and then the stem is worn thin and breaks. As the waves patiently work they often form great undercut plateaus which reach hundreds of feet back of a perfectly normal looking beach. The only sign will be an occasional blow-hole. But the water that surges through these blow-holes is ejected at such a velocity that they will send salt spray far inland. On Kauai one such blow-hole was depositing so much salt on valuable pineapple land that the workers dampered it with a great cement plug.

Seen from the sea or air, most of the high islands are more reassuring or familiar and much less shattering than the atolls. Savo Island in the Solomons, for example, is a small, soft, round, green puff of an island. The only word for it is cute. There are islands in the New Hebrides which have valleys, slowly rising foothills and mountain ranges. In the morning, and from the sea, a slight white mist forms in the valleys and blurs the soft green. Were it not for the fringe of coral reef, the islands would look, for all the world, like an island off the coast of Scotland or of Maine.

Some of the high islands can look ominous and dangerous, from whatever angle they are viewed. The sea approach to islands like Pitcairn, which have been undercut by the pounding of waves, have produced enormously high sea cliffs which drop in a straight line from a gretn knife edge at the top to a boiling green and white tumult of water at the bottom. These cliffs are often hundreds of feet high. Storm waves crash against such cliffs with a deep fundamental boom that carries through air and water for miles. The white spray claws its way up the cliffs, some-times for hundreds of feet, clings with a hard caress, then instantly turns green and slides in reluctant cor-rosive rivulets back to the ocean. Geologists with imagination can almost hear the sounds of the tiny crystals and irritants of the ocean wearing away the cliffs. It is a battle which the ocean always wins. These cliffs, both in color and quality, have none of the pleasant softness of the White Cliffs of Dover. In the sunlight they glitter with an unnatural blinding whiteness because of the accumulation of salt crys-tals. Occasionally, as the cliff is undercut and the cliff weakens, the whole face will split away and crash thunderously. For a few months the fresh face will be gray and basaltic. Then it also becomes coated with dried sparkling salt.

Bougainville, for no reason which can be justified, has an ominous feel to it. Perhaps it is the deep unnatural green of the rain forest or the trail of vol-canic smoke that blows away from Mount Bagana.

One has the impression that it will be dangerous and unpleasant and one is correct.

But these are the exceptions. At first glance, most of the high islands are reassuring. There are stretches on the island of Mindanoa in the Philippines, for example, which for on-rolling miles look precisely like a Texas cattle range: a slight cover of grazing grass, scrub trees. There are empty river beds which are dry for so long that the mountain aborigines will build huts in them and be drowned when rain falls miles away and produces a quick snap flood which fills the river bed from bank to bank with red water. On the big ranches there are even herds of St. Gertrudis cattle from the King Ranch in Texas and Filipino children wearing Levis and authentic cowboy boots.

On the vast island of New Guinea there are long stretches of savanna grass. In the mountains above the grass there are pure stands of pine and other softwood trees. Along the coast are long stretches of white sand which look as tamed as Jones Beach.

As one's eye gets closer to land, however, there are some notes that jar. One is warned that these are tropical islands, less tamed than the islands of America. The mangrove tree is one thing that disturbs. It grows most abundantly at the points where rivers disgorge into the ocean and reduce the solidity of the water. The tree walks out into the water on thick spidery roots which come together several feet above the water to form the bole of a tree. The roots go deep looking for brackish water and the trees stop their dense growth only when they reach the strongly-salted waters of the ocean. Travel through a mangrove forest is a perfect torture. The roots are slick and smooth and curve at such an angle that the foot can never get a firm purchase. When one stumbles it is always into mud so ancient and rotten that its odor will linger under a fingernail for two months. You can stumble in a mangrove swamp of New Britain and two months later scratch your nose in a New York bar and get a faint sickening whiff of the mangroves.

On some islands there are vast swamps of sour water. No one, not even the natives, tries to penetrate or live close to such swamps. But with binoculars, one can see the strange, sometimes beautiful and sometimes dangerous, life of the swamps. An iguana will raise itself on its front legs and twist its pre-historic body in a searching gesture, crocodiles lie motionless and discolored and invisible until they open their great slablike jaws. Perched above these antique animals will be the beautiful bird of paradise, most of them rust-red, but occasionally an azure blue, with feathers the rarest and most expensive in the world. The voice of the bird of paradise is unbelievable. It has a raucous, sharp, sandpaper voice which is like a strangled shriek. It is precisely like hearing a cool and aristocratic woman talk with a whore's accent.

Travelers will see such approaches, however, only if they search for them or if they reach an island by trade schooner which must, of necessity, call at the villages which lie close to such outlandish places. More often the traveler, whether foreign or native, will approach settlements which are located in the most attractive and comfortable parts of the island. At the right time of the year, for example, one can live along the beaches of New Caledonia and Tahiti and imagine that he is on the French Riviera; even to the nicety of excellent French bread and *vin rouge* for lunch.

There are only a few generalizations which can be made of the high islands. They occur over such a vast sweep of the Pacific, in such different latitudes, are swept by such various currents, have developed so bizarre and exotic a form of plant and animal life that almost no rule holds good for every island. A famous contemporary of Darwin's, Alfred Russel Wallace, once attempted to draw a line through the islands of Indonesia to indicate the limits to which Asian forms of fauna and flora had made their way. The line cuts squarely between Borneo and Celebes, two huge islands, and then dropping in a straight line for hundreds of miles cuts through the Java Sea and runs between the tiny islands of Bali and Lombok. To the west of that line, Wallace's theory ran, were the familiar Asian mammals such as tigers and squirrels. The birds were Asian birds. To the east were the strange marsupials; the cuscus, a gentle but oddly shaped animal somewhere between a squirrel and a monkey, the tarsier with the body of a rat, the hands and feet of a monkey, and the great melting eyes of a Hollywood screen star, and dozens of others even more bizarre. Along the Wallace line the advance of Asian trees and flowers and shrubs was also stopped. The line makes a rough common sense. The straits which separate Borneo and Celebes do seem to separate two entirely different worlds. Borneo is Asian, pure and simple. But in Celebes one can find whole landscapes which look precisely like Australia and which are inhabited by the same type of animals, covered by the same kinds of trees and bushes.

On the greater Sunda Islands, west of the Wallace line, one finds continental animals: the orangutan, sun deer, the sambar deer, the rhinoceros, tree and ground squirrels, brushtailed and true porcupines. Across the Wallace line, into the lesser Sunda Islands, and the rhinoceros are replaced by buffalo, the squirrels by the weird flying fox, and the air swarms with exotic birds, each one of a different color and shape.

If a high island is small, life tends to be homogenous and uniform. In many ways it is like life on the coral atoll. There will be no mountains, many coconut trees, no rivers, the boom of the surf can be heard everywhere and the people will be expert fishermen.

On the larger high islands, life, in all forms, becomes compartmentalized, is divided into zones. The different environments are determined largely by altitude and by configuration of the land. Small natural accidents may produce fantastic disparities. On some of the big islands, for example, the almost perpetual shape of a trade wind cloud may throw a shadow, of irregular shape, over part of an island. Within the shadow, lacking the sunshine, all vegetation is paler green and stunted. In the single footstep, that takes one out of the cloud, grass will amost double in height and the green will be several shades darker.

Once past the beaches and swamps of a high island, the land starts to rise and the character of everything changes. Plant life breaks away from the primitive simplicity of the atoll; the coconut palms and the pandanus and mangrove trees disappear. On these low, warm, wet rolling hills the plant life becomes more sophisticated and then erupts into a kind of floral madness. It is almost impossible for the botanist to describe this richness. It is the province of the poet. For example, on New Guinea alone there are more than 2500 different kinds of orchids and much of the land still has to be explored. In the Philippines, not far removed, are 900 different species of orchids, practically none of them duplicates of those which occur on New Guinea. The so-called "higher plants," trees and shrubs and ferns, grow with a mutational craziness. Over 50,000 varieties have already been reported. By comparison, all of the northeast part of the United States has only 6000 different kinds of higher plants.

Botanists are staggered and delighted by the problems of collection and classification, but the traveler's reaction will be more visceral and visual. The hot low areas are so rich in life, so abundant in strange mutations, that the eye becomes jaded. Eventually one can stare at a huge tree drenched in a hundred types of orchids and not feel surprised, only numbed.

This area is probably the only place in the world where it is literally true that fruit falls from the trees and man does not have to work. Wild bananas, for example, grow in such profusion that man, monkeys and birds, make only slight inroads. The fallen fruit makes a rotten layer several feet deep beneath the trees.

At the higher altitudes the air begins to cool and the plants become more familiar to the western eye. Here there are buttercups, rhododendrons, raspberries, huckleberries, violets and even huge oak trees. As the altitude rises the ferns and mosses and orchids grow thicker and thicker on the trees. Finally there is a line at which the trees stop. Beyond that, the tall mountain tops are covered with a weird, thick growth of mossy shrubs and flowers. Moving through the moss forests is like moving through a landscape made out of green gelatin. Nothing is solid or substantial. A machete can, in a single stroke, cut through a stubby tree trunk that is twenty-four inches thick and looks like ironwood. This mossy growth ends only when the mountains are high enough to support perpetual snow. Some of the perpetual glistening snow and ice pinnacles are found only five hundred miles from the equator.

The rain jungle lies between the low hot hills and the perpetual snows. It is the precise opposite of the atoll. On the atoll, everything is clean, distinct, unmixed. It is strange but it arouses no fear. But the moment that one steps into the rain jungle one has the instant crushing sensation that something is strange and evil about the lushness; that it is a doomed kind of richness. It is a luxuriance that can support everything except human life.

Whether it occurs in the Solomons, the Philippines, New Guinea, or Borneo the rain jungle is the same. The details will vary but the mood, the sense of oppressiveness will be identical.

The only humans that can endure the rain jungle do so under duress. These are the pygmy tribes, which have been forced out of more desirable lands by their stronger competitors. Finally they have, with a resiliency which is almost frightening, learned to live in the rain jungle. Eventually they have even come to prefer the rain jungle life. The pygmy comes into the sunlight with blinking eyes and a look of fear. There is no such thing as a fat pygmy nor is there a pygmy that smiles. The life is too spare.

The rain jungle starts with distinct layers of trees. First, there are the immense trees that rise over a hundred feet into the air, straight as a flagpole, and then branch out into a great protective growth. Until they explode with leaves and foliage at the top they have a bare shaven look. Beneath the giants there is a second level of trees, big in themselves, which reach to the first branches of the giants. Below this there are smaller trees which can exist without sunshine. Below these is a mass of foliage which is indescribable, but which is often literally so thick that one cannot cut his way through it.

I once saw an experienced planter walk to a huge, perfectly straight tree that reached almost two hundred feet towards the top of the jungle. He gave the tree a single powerful hack at its base and stood back. The tree shivered along its entire height, hesitated a moment and then collapsed slowly downward in a shower of white dust that rose almost to our shoulders. Parts of the tree, like flesh clawed from an animal, were held in the air by vines and wood, and presumably, were consumed by them. The tree itself had been eaten hollow by termites or some other insects of the jungle.

The lower trees are clotted together by a vast tangle of tough vines and soft parasites. Some of these vines, like the wakurikuri, are as tough as Manila hemp. Others will remain strong and pliable as long as they are alive and connected to roots but will turn to jelly minutes after they have been cut. Others, paradoxically, can be torn loose very easily when they are alive, tied to rafters while they are still green, and when they harden they tighten up with a grip as strong as that of the best commercial glue.

From everything hang great parasitic growths. Some of these are as magnificent as the orchid. Other growths hang like great bags of white suet. Strange-colored fungi will settle on normal plants and use them to breed a great spongy colony that grows to enormous size. In one case I have seen a huge multicolored mass of material, the size of a large American automobile, that weighed no more than twenty or thirty pounds. The base of this huge growth, the object which nourished the whole thing, was a tiny ordinary bit of lime tree with a few miniature roots.

In this strange environment ferns grow to prodigious size. Some ferns actually become small trees and have a bole so big that one can cut a soccer ball from the pith. It will maintain its elasticity for weeks. Natives with a sense of humor will cut a tiki twice the size of a man out of the spongy fern and place it in the sun. A month later it has shrunk to the size of a doll and in a year it is a tough little precise replica which can be used as a watch charm.

Nothing is quite as it seems or as it should be in the rain jungle. I once saw a Marine, clearing a path through jungle, yank at a thin strand of vine. He winced and then showed his fingers. The fingers were cut almost to the bone by thousands of crystal-like barbs in the vines; it was a natural kind of barbed wire.

There are trees with magnificent and intensely red flowers which shed tiny capsules containing their seeds. The capsules are surrounded by vicious sharp hairs, so tiny they are almost invisible, which easily pierce the skin of humans and produce an instant pain that is staggering and provide a protection for the seeds. Vines which appear perfectly normal can exude a juice which will raise painful welts a half inch thick on humans. Oldtimers have reported moving through clouds of pollen which left them blind for days afterwards. There are strange little fruits; objects as big as a thumb, which taste exactly like an orange, but are pale white and have a skin as tough as a nut; roots which are as hard as spikes, but when cooked, soften into an asparagus-like food. There are plants that apparently live on nothing but air. They will attach themselves to a high-reaching tree but are not parasitic. Like some enormously resourceful parasite they suck their nourishment from the air.

The passage from flora to fauna in the rain jungle is almost invisible. Degener reports seeing an air plant on a fallen kauri tree. It was a turgid mass of matter, which gave rise to several thick rounded twigs and yellowish tiny flowers. When he cut it open it contained complicated galleries of larvae and ants which lived in a delicate balance with the air plant. Other plant explorers have reported finding colonies of extremely vicious ants living in such growth. When disturbed they will charge out and attack and persist until the last one has been killed or the intruder flees.

In the rain jungle leeches have moved out of the water and are capable of living both on land and on leaves. They reach out, a liver-colored swaying piece of raw flesh, waiting for something to pass on which they might feed. If one moves his hand in front of such a leech it will respond by moving also. They will sway if one's hand sways, but let the hand get too close and they lunge. They attach themselves without noise or sensation to the human body. Moving through the jungle one might not be aware of them for hours, although dozens will have crawled under his clothing. Invariably they gather by one's belt where their motion is stopped. At the touch of a burning cigarette or a bit of salt or bourbon whiskey they will instantly drop away from the body. They leave tiny wounds which quickly grow into impressive sores and take weeks to heal.

The rain jungle will also contain other almost invisible but hard-working assailants. There are ticks in infinite variety. Most of them dig their heads deeply into human flesh and if jerked the body will come free leaving the head buried. They can be removed by the same things that cause leeches to loosen their grip. The air is also dense with strange stinging flies, centipedes, scorpions and mosquitoes. There are cockroaches so huge and beautiful that one can only admire them. They can pick up a wrapped cube of sugar and scurry away with it. There are "walking sticks" which grow to be inches long and are mobile but scarcely ever move. Butterflies fly through the air in outrageous shapes and sizes. Butterflies are not my favorite creatures because their flight is so awkward. But in the dim gray light of the rain jungle the brilliance of the butterfly, its familiarity, makes it a welcome diversion.

Most of the rain jungles have snakes which, regardless of the species, are usually spending most of their time trying to avoid being offensive. The fearsome king cobra, for example, is the most docile of beasts until any animal comes close to its mate or nest. Then it will attack anything. There is an Indonesian snake which is rumored to spit venom into its victim's eyes. I have never seen it, but I do not doubt it. Given the fantastic mutation of animals in the Pacific this would not strike me as remarkable. The boa and the python both live in the West Pacific. They are sluggish in their actions and there is many a Filipino boy who will grease his body and tackle a twenty-foot python for less than it costs you to go to the motion pictures.

The floor of the rain jungle is always wet. Hours after rain has stopped, hot drops of water will still be falling from the trees. When there is no rain the leaves give off slow drops of sap or resin which form a sticky thin layer on the ground. The silence is smothering. All sounds are absorbed by the soft wetness. The shriek of a parakeet, for example, will come to your ears once: hard, sharp, clear and then gone forever. There are no echoes. There are endless stories about the weird powers of the rain jungle to envelope, smother and absorb.

One such experience involves Captain Hugh Birch of Qantas Airlines. In 1950 while making a flight from Guadalcanal to Rabaul, he received a radio message that Rabaul was socked in and he was instructed to land on an old abandoned military air strip built on Bougainville during World War II and wait for the weather to clear. The strip was very visible in the jungle, a narrow trail of metal strip and coral.

That night no one on the plane slept because of an odd metallic screeching that started with a single sound and then was joined by other identical sounds. It was a skin-crawling, unnatural sound.

In the morning Captain Birch found the source of the sound. Fifty yards from the single usable runway was another runway which the jungle had now covered. Parked on it, in perfect order, were twenty P-38's buried in four years of jungle growth, but the

ailerons of the planes swung in the wind and gave off
the creaking noise.

"Everything edible on the planes was gone," Captain Birch reported. "Straps, leather, rubber tires, anything that animals or insects could devour. Even the
stronger pieces, the wings and the body of the planes
will eventually, and not too far in the future, disappear. Already trees have grown to massive height,
toppled in the wind and broken off a wing or a tail.
Half of the planes were already on their bellies and in
a few more years will disappear into the mulch of the
jungle."

Travel through the rain jungle is like travel on a
strange planet. It is green, hot, wet and tortured. The
air takes on the palpable qualities of the earth, it is
heavy and laden with moisture and the scent of rottenness. The earth is soft and yielding. Officers of the
Australian Trust Territory have described patrols in
which each night is "like sleeping at the bottom of a
very deep grave which has not yet been filled in."
Occasionally they would stumble upon tiny tribes of
natives occupying several knobs of high dry land, for
all the world like dwellers on isolated islands, with
absolutely no contact with the outside world.

The destiny, the sheer impenetrability, the green
hot obstinancy of the rain forest is almost unbelievable.

During World War II our United States Marines
sent out patrols into the rain jungles of various islands. These people were superbly trained, wonderfully equipped and possessed compasses and portable
radios. Almost inevitably they became lost. Contact
disappeared, they seemed to vanish into the green
spongy wetness as the rat vanishes into the thicket
which is occupied by mongooses.

Rescue platoons were sent out to find the lost patrols. Both sides had radio equipment and the advan-

tage of slow flying reconnaissance planes above them. Almost never did the lost and the rescuing patrol meet one another.

Later, when they came to compare their charts, they discovered that they had been within a few hundred yards of one another. With every advantage known to modern man, with planes soaring overhead, with radio contact, with flares that could be projected three thousand feet into the night air, with concentrated rations, with compasses, and the assurance of an endless supply line behind them the rescue patrols almost always missed those they were supposed to rescue.

The ability of the rain jungles to absorb both sound and life is unending. Even the Australians, who have developed an uncanny ability to live on scarce resources in physical surroundings, are balked by the rain jungle. They have sent out beautifully equipped patrols, both in peace and wartime, and never heard from them again. One would like to believe that the "hateful savages" have stalked and devoured the patrols. Alas, it is not quite true.

The rain jungle is such a phantasmagoria, such a bewildering effect of color, sweat, surprise, contradiction, and simple strangeness that it is an unnerving experience for anyone that was not raised in the environment. Here Westerners need have no sense of guilt. Take a Fijian from around Suva and put him in the rain jungle and he will be as helpless, as forlorn and miserable as any white person.

Blackness of skin and a tolerance of heat are not the only qualifications for living in the rain jungle. It calls for much more than that. Plants and animals live there in a queer and exotic existence. But humans are the rarest species in this environment.

The Negritos, the pygmies, live here with an ease that is almost delicate. They have learned what can be eaten and what is poison, when to run and when to relax. They navigate by means which no white man has ever learned. Some whites believe that the pygmies have memorized pathways through the rain jungle; have literally committed saplings, vines and trees to memory.

It is their domain. I give it to them willingly. But, I also have a lingering regret that there is much that we have missed in not being able to do what they have been able to do.

Westerners that fall into a cheap and quick envy of primitive ways of life gain no sympathy from me. Those, however, that are able to understand the incredibly subtle life of humans that live in the rain jungles command my most elemental respect. I would not want to be with them, indeed, I could not be with them. There is something about a Western upbringing that makes rain jungle life even more fearful than life aboard a submarine.

There is much about the rain jungle that I do not understand. There is much about the rain jungle that I admire. Any person, black, white or tan, that has been able to make his peace with this awesome environment instills a kind of respect in me. I am also grateful that the rain jungle makes up only a part of the high island. Many a white man has spent a lifetime on a high island and never been within the rain jungle. More often they stick to the uplands, the plateaus or the long reaches of magnificent shoreline.

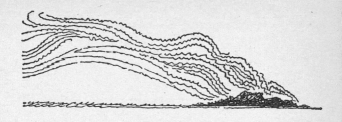

9. The Smell of the Pacific

THERE IS another aspect of the Pacific which, for reasons I do not fully understand, is almost never remarked in writing. That is the smell of the Pacific. In America we have deodorized our culture and our land. Fertilizers are nonorganic and hence farmlands odorless; factories such as breweries and bakeries, which used to give out a great redolence, now have their smells snatched up by blowers and either absorbed chemically or shot high into the sky. And so it goes with almost every smell of America. It is tamped down, obliterated, extinguished.

Smells, even good ones, become not only unpopular, but indelicate. The only smells Americans will discuss socially are perfumes.

In the Pacific all of this changes. Things smell. Some of the smells are fundamental, vast, seductive and exciting. Others are shocking and almost beyond the capacity to endure, though one does endure them and finally even ignores them.

There is, first of all, the great emanation that comes from the Pacific itself, for the sea has an odor It is made up of iodine, algae, dried salt water and, occasionally, the sharp smell of fresh water on hot flat salty water when a rain squall passes. Coolness itself, you discover in the Pacific, also has an odor: slight, elusive, pleasant. Let a passing cloud or puff of wind drop the temperature a few degrees, and the difference makes itself felt first of all as an undefinable odor.

Then there is the smell of land. This is the smell of ancient vegetation, tropical plants, and the rind of the sea—mollusks, crabs, mussels, seaweed, tidewater flats, mud. It is a fume that reaches far out from land. In the old sailing days, when sailors traveled on ships which themselves were rank with too many men in jammed quarters and with no water for bathing, the first smell of land was invariably pleasant. Today, for different reasons, it remains so.

As you get closer to shore the thin general odor is replaced by the more solid individual odor of the land you are approaching. This is a more heavy, acid, and sometimes tantalizing smell It is as if the land projected its personality far out to sea.

There are dozens of places in the Pacific that a blindfolded old-timer could identify merely by sniffing. Let me try and describe a few.

Take Suva, the capital city of Fiji You approach it with the trades at your back, swing into the channel—and suddenly you smell the town There is, as everywhere in the Pacific, the sweet scent of copra, which from a distance reminds you of a freshly opened jar of dried coconut but which grows more unpleasant as you come closer. Then there are the smells of curry, of unwashed bodies, of garlic—and that is the Indian section of Suva. There is also the smell of fresh-cut grass, tiny and persistent, wafted off the lawns of the Grand Pacific Hotel and Government House. There is the smell of beer from the dock-front pubs and restaurants. There is also the smell, low and soft and muted, of rotted sugar cane, coming from the husks of crushed stalks. The last smell is that from the fish markets, and then you are in Suva itself.

Or take the odor of Pago Pago. You come upon the harbor suddenly, entering through tricky channel. You swing left, and abruptly the ship is in a harbor which is like a pool at the bottom of very steep mountains. What you smell is the meeting of jungle and sea, first the smell of coolness because of the shadowing mountains, then seaweed with its rich iodine overtone, then a smaller fume of tidewater life which comes from wind over exposed live coral and the rotting of crab shells and the gas from a stranded Portuguese man-of-war. Only lastly, and very faintly, do you smell humans: smoke, cooking coconut oil, sweat on pandanus mats. It is the smell of nature modified only slightly. The smell is wonderfully honest; the Polynesians of Samoa live very close to nature, coiled in its smells.

Take Macao. It is the oldest European colony in Asia and stands at the tip of a peninsula and is brooded over by Communist China. It has been under Portuguese rule for centuries. The colony is dying and it smells accordingly. It has the odor of an old maiden aunt whose skin has gone waxy, whose energies have slowed, but who still keeps "the big old house" going. Macao smells of dust and the faint aroma of grapes; no vineyards grow there, but they do store hogsheads of fine port and claret in the warehouses. It smells like an uncongested, emptied and resigned place. There is none of the smell of vitality or energy or waste about it, only the odor of well-tended lawns, the smell of paper from the ancient government offices where Dickensian clerks work over huge ledgers, the smell that comes from whitewashed buildings during a rain squall.

Some smells have a splendid individuality. They occur in only one place and are not blended with other smells. The smell of vanilla, rich and sweet, over salt water and one can be sure he is in the channel between Moorea and Tahiti where the heavy wet breezes from the valleys slid over acres of beans and slid out to sea with the vanilla odor twisted through it. The heartwood of sandalwood has an aromatic odor which, apparently, lives as long as the wood does. There was a time when the odor was heavy in the Hawaiian Islands as the sandalwood was cut for export to Chinese cabinet makers. The stands were virtually eliminated. Today the only place where the sea and sandalwood smells meet, that I know of, is the island of Eromanga in the New Hebrides.

Honolulu is, of course, an almost completely westernized city. Its smells reflect its prosperity and respectability. But it still has one unique smell: the smell of pineapples. The smell comes from the Dole packing house near Waikiki. Close to the packing house the smell is a bit too rich, too thick, too heavy, but over the ocean or diluted with the trades the smell is delightful. Indeed, it is the only tropical smell in Honolulu. The wonderful aroma of Hawaiian flowers is buried in neat cellophane bags, locked behind glass windows, closed up in refrigerators.

Some smells found in many places in the Pacific are really the odor of the entire area. Copra is one such smell—the scooped-out meats of coconuts which are dried out, then pressed for oil. There is the appalling stench of *bêche-de-mer*, which is a sea slug dried in the sun and eventually sold to the Chinese, who value it highly as an aphrodisiac. There is the slightly acrid, low-pitched smell of buring coconut husks and the tough persistence of decaying fish scales. Often there will be the pure sweet odor of fruit, separate and discrete in the air—limes, mangoes, durian, papaya. In Indonesia and parts of the Philippines there is a

strange nose-puckering smell that floats far out to sea
and comes from rubber being processed. There are
also the storybook smells of cinnamon, raw black
pepper, saffron, sandalwood, drying fish, litchi nuts.

There is one smell for which the American should
be prepared. He seldom enjoys it, but he usually gets
used to it. This is the smell that comes from the great
congested cities of the Pacific: Nouméa, Suva, Manila, Port Moresby, Rabaul, Jakarta. It is simply and
brutally the smell of people living where sanitary
facilities are only slightly developed. I have known
Americans who were stunned by this great raging
giant of an odor and who thought that somehow the
smell itself, the great cloud of odor, could infect
them.

Once I met a chipper, bright and energetic American woman, the wife of a diplomat, who had adapted
to everything Africa and the Near East could offer
but was simply defeated by the smell of the Pacific. "I
know it's silly," she said, holding a handkerchief
drenched with #4711, "but I can't help it. The place
smells unnatural, unhealthy. I'm afraid to expose the
children to it. We're going back."

She did go back. And so do many Americans who
find the Pacific unnerving, corrosive in a subtle way.
Almost always their restlessness stems from the disturbing knowledge that in the Pacific man has not yet
dominated nature. The raw smells of the Pacific are
only a physical proof of this. There is always the sensation of living in a fragile, awed, waiting world,
sometimes the expectancy is for something certain,
like the monsoon rains, sometimes it culminates in the
shattering impact of a typhoon or an earthquake. But
the raw colors, the great foreign smells, the sweep of
wind and sea always underline a simple understanding: man is not fully in control.

For any American this is a startling realization;

some part of him fights against acknowledging it. To a great extent the world of America is controlled; bound down by steel rails and black-top highways and storm-proof fences; the rain is gathered by culverts and canals and dams; the land is tamed by factories and sweeping subdivisions and green lawns and tennis courts.

"Nature" for most Americans is a primordial memory, something lost in time, no longer taken seriously. For the American traveling in the Pacific, the constant awareness of natural force is no problem, he is scarcely aware of it. But the American who lives in the Pacific must come to share the view of the Pacific dweller or leave. This does not mean that he must fear nature, but only that he should realize that outside of man there is a vast balancing power to be reckoned with.

10. The Black and the White

His NAME was Zola, Zola Martin. That incredible name signed to an innocent letter was what first called him to my attention. That plus the fact that the letter was postmarked Tahiti and that beneath the politeness of the letter there was a rasplike indication of toughness.

He had written to criticize a sea story which I had published two years before. In that story I had described the fate of a group of survivors adrift in a sailless lifeboat. The story was based on an old incident that had turned up in British Admiralty files.

> My dear sir,
>
> In your otherwise excellent story you state that your survivors in a lifeboat without sails drifted northeast at the rate of three knots an hour until it was thrown up on an atoll of the Society Islands. It appears to me that this is a very unlikely circumstance.

He backed this assertion with a dazzling knowledge of the wind, currents and waves of the Pacific. He made an intricate calculation which demonstrated

that the drifting boat would have missed the most
southerly of the Societies by at least one hundred
miles and went on to suggest that either the Admiralty report was written by sailors who did not know
their true location or, in fact, the lifeboat had been
able to put on a bit of sail.

I wrote him and thanked him for his criticism. Also
because I was working on a number of other sea
stories I asked him some detailed questions about
ocean and island life in Polynesia. He responded and
we began an exchange of letters that lasted several
years. His letters, in English, but written in an elegant
copperplate French handwriting were, at first, very
distant and factual. Over the years, however, I came
to know the following facts about him: Zola was
fifty-five years old, he had a steady small income from
vineyards in Burgundy, was properly married in
church to a Polynesian woman, had five children by
her and had sent all of them to European schools.

In one of my letters to Zola I asked him, quite
casually, why he had left Paris to live in Polynesia.
When his reply arrived two months later, even before
I opened the envelope I could tell it had been written
in a different mood. The handwriting was still elegant, but somewhat more sprawling; there was a
brown smudge on the envelope as if a cigarette ash
had burned out on it. When I opened the letter the
top half of the first page was smudged and I sensed
at once that it had been blurred by spilled alcohol.

Proust has described life in Paris and its rottenness
very accurately [Zola wrote]. There is no need for
me to try and improve upon him. The forced masculinity of the *bon vivant* made them seem like dandies
with the minds of roosters. The simpering of the
women, their endless efforts to strike a balance between seductiveness and purity, came to nauseate
me. The constant grubbing for money, whether it

was done by elegant men at the Bourse for millions of francs or by peddlers for a mean percentage, pervaded everything. But the basic flaw, the most awful consistency in Paris, was the true inability of anyone to love. It is no accident that Proust was a tortured homosexual. He was well aware that love in Europe is a kind of organized and shrewd torture, a device for skewering people on the twin spikes of eroticism and propriety.

I came to Polynesia, to a tiny island, to escape all this. Do not conclude, my dear sir, that I am one of your Rousseau romantics. I am not. But love in these islands does have a simplicity, a spontaneity, a kindness that we Europeans have lost. Here a man can sometimes feel some of the bull-like assurance which a man should feel without being bound up in the awful artificial skeins of Western notions of marital love. Nor does he have to become involved in a slippery smart evilness of adultery. Here a man can live the life he is supposed to live: the life of the body, the life of the mind, the life of the heart. Some terrible by-path which we Europeans and you Americans have taken has been avoided here in Polynesia.

And then, quite surprisingly, he invited me to visit him. Something about the burnt paper, the alcoholic sprawl, the urgency of his words made Zola more than an unknown person. I wanted to see him.

Almost by accident I did. A movie company operating at Papeete had chartered a flying boat to search for shooting locations and were going to make a sweep through the Tuamotus and Marquesas. They offered to drop me off at the Frenchman's isolated atoll and pick me up within five days. We made the flight in a World War II PBY, flown by two English pilots with mustaches, lean handsome faces marred only by slightly bloodshot eyes caused partly by Hinano beer and partly by flying over the glare of open ocean. They both had hard Manchester accents. The plane badly needed paint and inside it was dirty, but the two engines were in magnificent shape.

The two pilots tried to give the impression of flying by the seat of the pants, but actually they could both pilot and navigate beautifully. They hit the Frenchman's atoll on the nose and made a long languid sweep of a descent which was both artistic and safe.

The atoll was the shape of a teardrop. At the heavy rounded end the land rose fifteen or twenty feet above the surface and was covered with cultivated coconut palms. The thin point of the tear also was slightly elevated and there were signs of an inhabited native village there. The atoll was four miles long and two miles wide at the widest point. Like most atolls only five or ten percent of the outer ring rose high enough above the water to be livable. The pilots needed only the one pass to detect a long streak of green-white water which indicated enough depth to land.

They brought the plane down exquisitely, the first contact with the water so subtle that it felt as if oil had been splashed along the keel. As we came to a standstill they cut one motor, the power of the other propeller turned us in the water and we had stopped precisely in front of the Frenchman's house. One of the pilots came back, tossed a yellow rubber life raft over and handed me a paddle. He tossed my gear down to me without saying a word, but as he pulled the hatch shut I could see that beneath his mustache he was smiling. I was only ten yards from the plane when the prop-wash caught me and pushed me halfway to shore. I knew they had done it deliberately, a final signature of their skill.

As I rowed the rest of the way in I looked at the Frenchman's house. It was the largest Tahitian-type house I had ever seen outside of Papeete. On three sides it had a long overhang of roof which formed a veranda railing which was barbed with dozens of small intricately carved *tikis*.

Every form of building has its marks of perfection. Thatch roof comes in two qualities: Pandanus or coconut thatch. Pandanus is infinitely superior. Another mark of quality is how close the spine of the thatch mats are laid together. The closer together, the more that are used, the thicker the roof, the longer it will resist the attack of wind, rain and rats. On Zola's roof the spines of the mats were no more than a quarter inch apart. From the house down to the beach there was a lawn that was neatly clipped. Separating the house from the coconut grove was an artful arrangement of fruit trees very carefully blended for shape and color. A papaya tree by itself can have a slightly obscene look, but here the papaya trees were scattered among mangoes and *frangipani* trees so that they looked tall and elegant.

Zola was on the beach to meet me. He walked out into the water up to his thighs and steadied the yellow boat as I climbed out.

"Ah, ah. The literary friend from California," he said, although he must have been guessing for I hadn't any way to tell him of my arrival.

He was a surprise. Somehow I had expected a tall, lean somewhat withdrawn man. Zola looked much more like a rounded bourgeois shopkeeper. His face was rubicund. His manner was cheerful and friendly. He talked very fast. And he gave off the slightest odor of gin. His eyes, however, were those of the man who had written the brilliant letters. They were large, almost beautiful, a deep black. He had a birdlike energy, quick small gestures which seemed ineffectual, but were remarkably efficient. He hustled my gear out of the rubber boat and onto the veranda in a flurry of jerks, steps, tugs and pulls before I could give him a hand.

"I would have written, but the chance to come was so sudden that I did not have time," I explained.

"And I do not have a radio," Zola said with delight. "It is a pleasure to have you. What difference would it have made if you had written? Everything would be the same. Here there is no need to prepare for a pleasure."

His curious eyes glanced over me, his mouth pulled up into a laugh. Together we pulled the boat up onto the beach.

"You have a beautiful place here," I said, waving my hand to take in the entire atoll.

"Yes, it is beautiful," Zola said quietly. "And all of this with no politics." He burst out laughing.

In our correspondence we had had a long debate on whether or not politics figured large in the life of Polynesia. He insisted that there was no such thing. He was wrong, but that is another matter. He paused and for the first time the smile vanished from his face. "I shall also demonstrate to you that my description of love and the South Pacific is precisely as I said in my letters."

His wife was waiting for us on the veranda. I knew from his letters that her named was Toma and that she was in her early forties. Uniformly when Polynesian women have reached this age they have started to take on weight. The breasts and the thighs begin to thicken. But Toma was different. I guessed from her face that one of her parents must have been Chinese, because her cheekbones were higher and her face was thinner than those of most Polynesian women. She was also quite slim. She wore a pareau that had been washed often enough so that the glossy cheapness that it had when it came off the looms in France or England had disappeared. Her hair was thick and very black and was drawn up into a large loose bun on her neck.

Zola paused for a moment at the bottom of the stairs, his arm around my shoulders, and restrained me. He bounded up the stairs, put his arm around Toma and stood smiling down triumphantly at me.

"A pretty picture, eh?" he shouted. "A picture of the East and the West and a proof that the twain shall meet. Where is your camera? It would tell you more than a thousand words of conversation or a hundred books."

I explained that I had no camera and he roared. Toma came down the steps and shook my hand. She spoke a few words of English, just enough to say hello and to welcome me. After she had shaken hands she went up the steps ahead of me, went over to a large fresh sprig of *tiare* that was in a jar of water, plucked one of the flowers and put it behind my right ear. Zola and I sat down in the rattan chairs to talk. Toma drew off to one side and then did a thing which is very disturbing to Occidentals, but is typically Polynesian. She studied me from head to foot, without any attempt to disguise her interest. She stared at my tennis shoes, my bare legs, my khaki shorts and shirt, my arms, my neck and my face. Her attention was direct and obvious and was punctuated every few seconds by a nod of approval. She shook her head, however, when she came to my colored glasses as if they were somehow out of character. I knew that within a few hours she would have described my physical appearance in the greatest detail to everyone else that she met on the atoll. I have sometimes heard these descriptions of others by Polynesian woman and they are uncanny in their ability to reproduce verbally the physical looks of a person. Every small spot, the length of the hair, the shape of the ears is remembered perfectly.

When Toma had finished her scrutiny she came over and asked us in French if we would like something to drink. She offered us coconut water, lime juice or fresh pineapple juice. I settled for pineapple juice and she turned and walked down the steps towards the cookshack. At the bottom of the steps she turned and said, "With gin?" I nodded and she smiled broadly.

Later Toma served us an excellent Tahitian lunch; raw shrimp in lime juice, small red fish buttered and then broiled whole on hot coals, a plate of fa-fa and a plate of freshly cut pineapple. There was also a large carafe of Algerian red wine. When we had finished this, Toma brought over a large tin coffeepot of very strong coffee and we sat on the veranda sipping.

Zola and I began to talk in English about the matters we had discussed in our letters. Like everyone else in the South Pacific we also exchanged gossip. That incredible gossip about people and events which stretch over an area much faster than in the United States but in which land and people are so few that events on islands thousands of miles away have a great interest for everyone. We discussed the mystery of the large Japanese tuna boat. It had arrived in the South Seas, spanking new and gleaming, from a shipbuilding yard in Japan and was to be the first effort by the Japanese to fish the tuna-rich water. It had left port on its first cruise, disappeared and was never heard of again. We gossiped about a Chinese gentleman in Nouméa who was reputed to be running opium in the South Pacific by an ingenious device. In Laos his agents mixed raw opium with paper pulp, pressed into ordinary pages, printed up into books and then mailed to him. The eventual consumer merely had to dissolve the book pages in vinegar and the pulp floated to the top and could be skimmed off. Left in the sun for a few days the mixture became almost pure opium. No one knew if it were true, but it is a good story. Our conversation droned on and eventually Zola said that he wanted to take a nap.

He asked me if I would like to look through his library and led me into a large airy room which had a view of the lagoon. He apologized for the condition of the books and pointed out that the salt air, humidity and tiny bugs of an atoll were all highly destructive of anything as soft as paper.

"But what is here is yours," Zola said. "Treat it as your own." Those words were a mistake. If he had not uttered them I would not have discovered his secret life.

Zola was right. The books were in very bad shape. Although he had shelved them carefully with blocks of wood between each book to allow circulation of air, the edges of the pages were brittle and came away in tiny crisp fragments as I turned the pages. By the time I had gone through a half dozen books there was a semicircle of broken powdered paper on the table.

Even so the library was exciting. It contained not only works on Polynesia and all the languages of the world, but it contained typewritten manuscripts of old songs, genealogical tables of Polynesian families; beautiful little sketches, as fragile as the tracery in a butterfly's wings of long-vanished and old-fashioned huts; long verbatim records of stories that were passed on from generation to generation orally; a meticulous file of the signs that appeared on various tikis and *maraes* along with shrewd guesses as to what they meant. It was a magnificent example of practical scholarship done by a single man.

On a small table in the corner of the room there was a box, built very much like a cigar humidor. On the top it had a small brass plate which said "Memoirs." I opened it without a moment's hesitation. It might have been the memoirs of anyone, and, after all, Zola told me that I could look at everything. The humidor was two thirds full of handwritten

manuscripts. I recognized the handwriting as that of
Zola. But oddly enough most of the memoirs were
written in English instead of French. Later I sensed
that he did this so that the manuscript could not be
read by the natives, many of whom can read French
fluently.

The first entry in the memoirs was twenty-five
years old. It was written aboard the ship that carried
Zola from Marseilles to Tahiti. It was only ten pages
long, but it was remarkable. It was one of the most
bitter, lucid, incisive, tragic instructive commentaries
on the European situation I had ever read.

With the strange clarity that is possessed by the
very young or the very angry, Zola caught, in acid
detail, every affectation, every depravity, every hypocrisy, every flaw of European life. In his letters to me
his criticism of Europe had been abstract, here they
were personalized. He described the manipulations by
which his mother and sister entrapped a wealthy
young Parisian who wanted to be an artist into becoming the daughter's groom and a merchant in silk.
It is a commonplace occurrence, but in Zola's spare
prose, it looked suddenly obscene. There was a description of a business deal in which Zola's father had
outmaneuvered his best friend. It was an ordinary
business deal, quite legal, but put down without the
usual soft words it almost stank of rottenness; devoid
of heart or even of meaning. There was a description
of a family Christmas reunion, no more than seventy-
five words in length that revealed the avarice and
jealousy that hung, like invisible fog, around the
Christmas tree, the roasted goose, the presents, the
incantations of love. There was a description of the
private schools Zola attended and it was depicted as
an expensive institution for squeezing the life out of
children. Instilling a feral competition among them,

giving them a civilized veneer to hide an inculcated meanness.

It was a remarkable piece of writing and with a bony economy it destroyed individuals, a family, a city, a culture.

Zola had also put down what he had expected to find in the South Seas. He had read the romantic novels of the South Seas, but he had also read the grim anthropological journals and reports of French administrators. He was no romantic. He was prepared for elephantiasis, the neat line of feces along the white sand at low tide, the fact that natural beauty could become boring, the sure knowledge that there would be long periods of loneliness. Zola came to Tahiti as a bitter young man with hard perceptive eyes, a fugitive from the intolerable, expecting no moments of grace, a searcher for himself.

When he arrived in Tahiti he spent only a few days in Papeete and then moved to the tiny village of Tautira on Tahiti. Here his eyes was still sharp, his comments clear and unsentimental, but he was entranced. There was almost a mood of delirium, of enravishment, of illumination, in the early pages he wrote on Tautira. The gentleness of the Tahitians, their complete lack of duplicity, the apparent absence of status were precisely what he needed to wipe out the bitter memories of life in Paris. Two entries that he made in his memoirs during this period I quickly scribbled down in my notebook:

> I return to my hut to find Kaoko rifling my sea-chest. He had ignored the bundle of franc notes, but held in his hand an American box camera, and a large Swiss pocket-knife with a variety of screwdrivers, blades and other gadgets sunk in its thick handle. "I was borrowing these," Kaoko said without the slightest embarrassment.
> "Would you have brought them back?" I said in

anger. "No, probably not," Kaoko replied. "I intended
to borrow them permanently."

Kaoko had not the slightest sense of guilt. I
realized suddenly that he had absolutely no notion
of theft . . . just as the children in Europe must be
carefully indoctrinated with a notion of property
before they can be made to feel guilt about theft.
This man had been brought up in an environment in
which there was no notion of theft. I told him that
I would need both the camera and the knife and he
handed them to me without even the hint of a roguish
smile. He simply handed them back.

A few days later he wrote in his diary:

Last night I slept like a deadman on the beach. I
had gotten drunk on beer and wine and the dancing.
I fell asleep with the stars in my eyes . . . big, explosive, pure white stars lost in the purest blackness.
When I closed my eyes, the stars still seemed to
glint somewhere in my eyeballs, tiny pleasant dots
of light.

During the night I awoke slowly and there was a
hand in my lava-lava. It was the hand of a girl who
was crouched down beside me, staring into my face
and smiling. She was perhaps thirteen years old.
She was very slim and her breasts were barely large
enough to hold up her pareau.

She bent her head close to my ear and whispered
into my ear in French. She told me that the dancing
had excited her especially because she had never
seen a white man dancing. As she spoke her hand
wandered over my legs and between them.

For a moment on that warm beach my European
conscience rebelled. I felt I could not do what the
child wanted. What she wanted me to do was
technically a crime in every civilized country of the
world. She sensed my reluctance and laughed. It
was not a nervous or hysterical laugh, it was the
curious laughter of an inquisitive child. I took her
and it was sheer pleasure. She made love in the style
that the natives call *maori*: quick, savage, silent. At
the climax her tiny body arched up, she moaned,

and then her fingernails scratched down my face. It was over quickly, but it was a very skillful performance and the girl was deeply satisfied. I am not quite sure how I feel today except that I am excited.

I knew then that Zola had not intended for me to read these memoirs. It was the kind of document that is kept only for the eyes of the author. I had always been curious as to why authors would specify that certain of their letters or notes or unpublished writings be destroyed upon their death. It had always struck me as a wanton waste of talent, a reckless and selfish pouring away of creative energy. Now I understood.

I should have stopped reading but I could not. The memoirs went on to describe his meeting with Toma.

Toma came to Tautira from the atoll on which Zola was now living. She had relatives in the village and had been living with them for a year. At Zola's invitation she had moved from her relatives' house into his. They lived together for six months and then Toma told Zola that she was pregnant. Zola insisted upon being married, and being married in a church. Toma was puzzled, but she consented. After the first child was born they went to Toma's native atoll and at once Zola decided that they would live there. After this the entries in the book became very scanty. For five years he wrote no more than a line or two a month, recording the planting of coconut palms, the amount of copra harvested, the birth of children, the arrival of books on the trading schooner. It was as if his days were so satisfying that he no longer needed the solace of the memoirs.

Six years after his arrival on the atoll, however, the entries in the memoirs began to lengthen. One of them said:

Toma is still as attractive as when I married her. Still as kind. Still as generous. At one point she began to take on weight and I did something for which I am ashamed. I insisted that she diet and stay slim. She argued that weight is a sign of prosperity and of dignity. But she has gone along with me.

A few days later there was another entry:

There is a blankness about Toma that disturbs me. I have been trying to teach her to read and write French, but she simply does not have the interest. She will spend ten or twelve hours a day gossiping with members of her family on some petty thing such as the name of a new child. But she will not give attention enough to learn to read or write. I am puzzled.

A month later there was a long entry:

I think I understand Toma and through her, the Polynesian personality. She lives literally in the moment. She loves tiare and her eyes will light up when she sees them, but she will not plant them. She has started vegetable gardens five times at my insistence, but each time has allowed the gardens to wither. She loves radishes, but not enough to grow and fertilize and water them. Three times she has agreed to hire workers to build an outdoor privy next to the bathhouse. But each time the money has gone for calico or tobacco. Flowers, radishes, a privy . . . all of these are things of the future and Toma does not think of the future. Polynesians do not know how to calculate future pleasures. I do not know why this should exasperate me but it does.

The entry after this was the last one: "I am bored, bored, bored, bored."

Later that afternoon Zola and I went for a long walk around the island. He was cheerful and talkative and his knowledge about everything about the South

Seas was monumental. The habits of fish, the diseases of coconut palms, the old histories of great Polynesian kings, where infanticide was practiced and where it was not, were only a few of the things he discussed in the greatest detail. Now, however, I listened with a new ear. Zola's encyclopedic knowledge of Polynesia no longer seemed to me to be based on a simple fascination with the people, rather I had the impression that he was trying desperately to use the facts and information to fill a great yawning chasm of despair. He threw facts into it as his Polynesian chiefs threw victims over cliffs to satisfy a dimly seen, but terribly feared deity.

We had almost finished our walk when we met a young boy and girl walking in the opposite direction. They said hello to us and then vanished on the path. Zola turned and looked at me.

"They have just finished making love in the bushes," he said. His voice was expressionless.

"How could you tell?" I asked.

"Really it is an exercise in probability," he said. "Quite literally every time a Tahitian girl or boy meet casually it leads to sexual intercourse. The only exceptions are if they are sister and brother, or if one of them is malformed. Then also the boy's face had a few scratches on it. As you probably know Polynesian women at the climax scratch the man's face. The men often do the same thing."

"I knew that, but it still surprises me," I said. "They are so gentle in everything else that you would think when they are making love that it would carry over there too. I have never been able to understand their use of violence in sex."

Zola turned and looked out toward the sea. The tide was just starting to flood, crabs scurried about gradually moving toward the sand like a disorganized army in retreat. The waves boomed solidly against the reef, but aside from the sound, there was only a flat layer of foam to show their force.

"For them sex is not really an act of love," Zola said. "It is a way to break tedium, a way of breaking the monotony of endless beautiful days. It is like a game, but no more than a game."

That night after dinner a strange thing happened. We ate on the veranda overlooking the lagoon, watching the water gradually change into an even flawless green. In the center of the table was a flower and shell arrangement which Toma had made. It had a startling miniature beauty to it. Tiny shells, stamens of some sort of flowers, the green from the throat of wild orchids and an edging of blue petals which had been picked from flowers.

"That is a beautiful arrangement, Toma," I said.

Toma was pleased. Zola looked down at the arrangement and smiled.

"It is a beautiful arrangement," Zola said. He watched it intently for a few moments and the smile went from his face. He bent forward and with his hand gently pushed the tiny arrangement apart. He looked at me as he spoke to Toma.

"Put it back together, Toma," he said.

Without a word Toma leaned forward and her fingers flicked over the diminutive shells and flowers and petals. Almost at once it was back in order. Then I realized that it was back in *exactly* the same order, it was an exact duplication of the first arrangement.

I looked up from the arrangement and Zola was watching me. His lips were turned up in a smile but there was something like a pleading in his eyes.

"Can you do any other arrangements," Zola asked Toma without looking at her.

"No, this is the only arrangement I make," she said. She smiled. "They taught us this when we were children. Mai-tai, eh."

"Mai-tai," I replied.

"Mai-tai and every girl on the island can do this single arrangement and the girls of the island have been making this arrangement for over four hundred years," Zola said. His voice was empty.

Zola's face was held in a tight little smile, but his eyes were suddenly deep and black with a strange expression. I sensed that he had looked over the edge of the chasm. Between us hung the knowledge that Toma could make only one flower arrangement, could cook poa only one way, cook fish only one way, make love in only one way, sing in only one pattern of songs, dance one kind of dance. Anything outside of the simple patterns did not interest her. And years ago Zola had come to know all of them.

Zola and I did not discuss this during the remaining days I was on his atoll. We walked and talked constantly, but he never referred to himself. When the PBY returned I rowed the old rubber boat out to it after saying goodbye to Zola and Toma. The sweat was pouring into my eyes by the time I reached the plane. I was tired. Just as I shipped my oars and looked again at Zola's house the salty drops of sweat fogged my vision. Zola seemed shrunken, small, hunched, almost bleached. He had stopped waving. Toma seemed lifesized and natural.

He was a prisoner not of a dream, but of those faded years in France which had instilled into his nerves and brain and soul an interest in questions beyond himself and beyond the day in which he existed. He had escaped only the real presence of European life; twisted through his mind like a maze of black jets were a set of conditionings and experiences which had burned into his youthful mind. From these he could never escape.

Zola is typical of a whole breed of men, of white men that live in the South Seas. Sensitive to the rawness of their native society, they flee to the apparent tranquillity of the South Pacific. But by then the damage has been done.

To every white man in the South Seas this dread knowledge of thinness, sameness, an endless unrolling of identical acts, the haunting absence of distinct personality, must some day be faced. For many it is too much to face. This is one reason why so many of the white men of the Pacific are the most quietly desperate alcoholics in the world. They have burnt all their bridges; there is no path back to Paris or Dubuque or London. They must, because of pride and sometimes sloth and sometimes poverty, stay in the South Seas. But the original vision has been cauterized over with the scars of experience. So they must be sustained by alcohol or gambling or opium or driving economic activity or, as in the case of Zola, by a frantic search for the fullest knowledge of a culture which he did not really value.

There is a lesson. If you want to live in the South Seas start early. Early, very early, our nerves become civilized. It is not easy to then slough off the coatings of civilization; they are more durable and tough than the softer stuff of primitive life.

11. The Melanesians

THE ONLY thing easy to understand about Melanesia is its limits. Draw a rectangle on a map which is just big enough to include the Fijis, New Caledonia, the New Hebrides, the Solomons, the Bismark Archipelago and the huge land mass of New Guinea and you have enclosed Melanesia. Only one other thing is certain. Melanesia is derived from *melanin* which is the name for the pigment in animals, any kind, which makes their skin black. Hence: the black islands.

Even the blackness is sometimes inappropriate, for at the fringes of the rectangle there will be a blend of Polynesian and Melanesian which gives a *café au lait* skin. In the middle of Melanesia, for no reason that anyone can offer, is the island of Rennell which is occupied by tall lean Polynesians.

If any area in the world is a mystery it is the islands of Melanesia. We know only the barest facts about the land or the people. There is much land and many people in the area that no white eye has even seen. There

are places where villages within five miles of one another speak entirely different tongues and see one another only in the murderous mood of a raid. There are islands where in a single footstep you can move from the humid wet heat of the rain forest directly onto a red-dirt desert which is without water or people. There are tribes which even today watch white men with a sullen hatred and ambush them whenever possible. There are other tribes that are fawning in their greetings to any stranger and rhapsodic in their hospitality to whites. There are tribes which have vicious, dark phantasmagoric dreams of blood and phallus and death. There are other tribes that are lamblike in their docility. Some Melanesians give gifts with a fierce intention to obligate and humiliate. There are other tribes which share what they have in what seems to be a primitive communism. And in all of this there is no rhyme or reason, no pattern, no logic. It is a hard place to know and no white man knows it all.

This is a place where anecdote is not only admissible as knowledge, it is really all we know. One can only hope that one's anecdotes are representative. He cannot be sure.

Take the swamp areas off New Guinea. There are great reaches of brackish water through which freshwater rivers sweep unnoticed and which occasionally are washed over by salt-water tides. The mangrove tree grows like a great curtain over the swamps, but is thinned out by the salinity so that there is a passage for canoes. Occasionally there are clumps of mud, held loosely together, where the sago palm grows. The light which comes through is a dull mottled gray even when the sun is glaring hot above the topmost leaves. It is a nightmare, but it is a nightmare in which thousands of people live, neatly divided into villages, never crossing their boundaries, never stepping on solid land, never running down a stretch of white beach. In a two-day canoe ride the language will change ten times. There will be a memory, even today, of a "Gov'ment man, he walkalong long long time past. We eat 'em." The mud and mangroves are too dense and thin to invite Government. Some of the Melanesians here have heard an airplane, but there is seldom enough clear sky to actually see one for any length of time. They believe that a plane is a large excited silvery bird. They have not the slightest idea that they are under the sovereignty of the Australians or the Dutch or anyone. A native who can speak pidgin is accomplished beyond belief.

Here the Melanesians are the picture of sloth. They hang from their elevated houses and gossip and watch by-passers and calmly move their bowels into the mud below as they talk to an interpreter. And then the surprise. In the middle of this, rising high into the air and possessing elegant proportions, is a huge men's tabu house. The sweep is Grecian, staggering, unbelievable. The roof is neatly woven together, the floor is uneven, but solid . . . and the whole thing is sometimes 400 feet long. The impression of sloth is somehow shaken. This is too finished a structure, too architectonic, too meticulous in detail. Yet the few white men that have seen one built say that it is done without orders, planning, discussion. One day the old tabu hut is done and wordlessly they start on a new one. Bamboo, sennit, thatch, fronds flow in precisely when they are needed. The tabu building, it is too large to be called a hut, goes up quickly. Perhaps there is order in all of this; almost surely someone must have planned it, someone must be sovereign. But the eye and skill of the white man cannot detect it.

The dance they do in this building is haunting. At night they gather, the men only, until the place is jammed with quiet men, their numbers suggested only by the glint of hundreds of pairs of eyes. Some-

where a hand hits a drum, there is a long measured
pause and from a hundred throats comes a grunt.
Nothing more. Not even a chant. Merely an ejacula-
tion of air. But then it comes again and more quickly
and a hundred knuckles rap on the wooden floor and
the hair on the back of a white man's neck rises. The
grunts flow together, become a song ... of what I do
not know. An eerie song of raps and grunts and gasps,
but a song and moving. And it ends with a sharpness
like sudden instant death. Not an eye blinks, the
glitters reach away into the ends of the hut without a
motion. Then the song starts again.

It is sung again and again and again. Nothing
changes. Living a thin life these people have learned
the immense drama of simple repetition. The pace
becomes faster and the tension in the air becomes
palpable. It is a magnificent success for by the most
elemental means an unbearable sense of expectancy
is created.

Finally, just as nerve and patience are about to
give out, a figure looms up in the darkness. It is tall,
taller than five men, it casts a primary shadow a
hundred feet long and dozens of splintered and
truncated shadows against each wall. The Melanesians shiver and gasp and you shiver with them. The
figure comes closer, sways and dips, pecks sharply.
The chant has become soft and fast. It is a man inside
a huge mask, literally wearing it about his body. But
you can believe only in the humanness of the feet
below the mask ... the rest, the swaying shivering
mask is alive and inhuman. On the menacing body of
the mask there are paintings, but of nothing one has
seen before ... and somehow familiar and fearsome.
They are abstractions of the most absolute universali-
ty. They would terrify any man on earth. Wombs,
jaws, phallus, blood, bones, fire, food, water, hunger
are there, but not in symbols which I can describe.

There is also hope and affirmation and, like a streak of lightning at the edge of visibility, love.

The mask totters into view, the chorus grows softer. The mask goes to the edge of darkness and then just as it disappears the chant dies. There is a moment of silence. A long moment. Then someone stirs. The show is over. You put out your hand and touch the shoulder of a Melanesian and you realize because of the trembling of his shoulder muscles that you also are trembling.

The next morning the grayness lightens and it is day. The mass of men have disappeared. In nearby huts a few men lounge, gaping at the mud and water. Their women stir in the mud looking for food. Last night was impossible, you suddenly realize, an extravagance of your own imagination. But weeks later back in the bright sun and the open sea you know that it was true. The night happened and it happened precisely as you remembered it and those slothful black men evoked it.

Take another scene. The place is on the lowlands behind a coral beach. It is the making of sago; an endless process which is done every day in the same way. A band of black men and women start off across a white beach and disappear into a jungle path. They find a good-sized sago palm and the men begin to chop. Most of them have axes. A few still have stone axes. Eventually the tree falls, is clawed into submission and crashes lengthwise. It is split open and the men are now through with their work. The women take over. Each women hacks out a basket of pulp from the palm. It is now kneaded and pounded and rinsed endlessly with the brackish water of the jungle and finally strained. The result is a mass that looks like dirty gelatin. It is wrapped in a large leaf and taken back to camp. There it is aged if times are good and it is eaten at once if times are bad.

Why describe this? Because it is the chief thing that these Melanesians do. They do tell stories and build houses and trade and make weapons but these are minor activities. Chiefly they gather sago and they eat it. The evenness of their life is broken by only one excitement. Occasionally a wild pig will stumble upon an opened sago palm and start to eat and will gorge until he is stupefied. The natives will fall upon such a beast with stones and axes and gleefully beat it to death. Sometimes they will make a fire, but only if the conditions are right and the rubbing woods are dry. Otherwise the pig is torn to pieces and eaten raw. But however it is eaten one thing happens. Under the richness of the diet, the sudden excess of protein, their erotic life is sparked alive. That night the whole clot of men and women will be locked in a frenzy of love-making. Nine months later there will be a new generation of children. These particular Melanesians have not yet made the connection between the pig and the love-making and the arrival of babies.

Another scene. This time it is one of the pleasant plains that slopes away from the *massif* that runs down the spine of New Caledonia. The approach is by launch. Set far back from the shore is a large white frame house. A carefully tended lawn rolls down to the coral beach and the small quay. The house is surrounded by coffee trees, coconut palms, grazing lands. A few goats are like black dots in the high pasture. Long before the launch touches the quay there is a neat line of ten native boys drawn up in a straight line. They wear neat lavalavas that are identical and are trimmed with a narrow band of red felt.

As we approach one of the boys blows on a whistle and the master of all this walks out dressed in white linen and marches across the lawn to greet us He is

our host. He is half French. As we walk by the boys
one notes that they are sweating; they have just
trotted in from their work on the plantation. After
they have handled the luggage there is another whistle and they return to work.

We shower with warm water, a bar of scented Paris
soap. Our clothes are laid out neatly and the black
valet has selected trousers and a shirt ... and a tie,
the only one I possessed. I put it on and went out to
cocktails.

The host did not remark it, but I saw that the
martinis were made of Beefeater gin. They were
served in small very cold glasses. The host was an
amateur scholar of French naval history and, curiously, a fierce egalitarian and defender of the working
class ... the white working class. I do not know how
he came by the first interest, but the second sprang
from the fact that his father had been one of the
Communards that arose in Paris during the revolt of
1870. For a few dazzling days the workers of Paris,
supported by intellectuals, held off trained armies,
proclaimed a republic of the world, administered
themselves brilliantly. A flame ran through the workers of the world; and a cold shiver down the back of
bourgeois everywhere. The revolt was finally shattered. Hundreds of the Communards were shipped to
the prisons of New Caledonia and found out about
bastinados and chains and blistering exposure to the
sun.

Our host's father had hungered to get back to
France. In their isolation the Communards worked
out a discipline and intellectual solidarity that would
have made them a dangerous force to reckon with if
they had ever secured their return. Most of them did
not. His father lived out his days as a *libre*; free, but
only free in New Caledonia. Our host did not know

his mother. He was only slightly darker than a Mediterranean Frenchman.

We had another martini which was served in a fresh cold glass. Then lunch was announced.

"Nothing is from France," our host said pointedly. "Nothing. Not even the clothes on my back. The saddest day of the year for me is when I write a check for taxes."

The lunch was served by four uniformed boys. It started with a few dozen oysters drenched with lime juice and served on the half shell, a plate of crabmeat, and a very hot venison sausage made from the tiny deer of the island. This was followed by a poached salmon, caught locally, and covered with mayonnaise and dotted with small green olives. There was also a plate of the choicest bits of grilled flying fox, the strange batlike creature that can soar seventy feet without losing an inch of altitude, but is not a bird. There was also a vast platter of roasted pigeons, each tiny body glazed and surrounded by a bed of small peas.

We went back to the veranda and had fresh fruit and goat milk cheese. There were liqueurs, but they were not the great liqueurs of France. The host had made them himself and they were excellent.

"See that boy, the old one," our host said. He pointed to a wizened old man. "Note that on his lava-lava he has a special felt insignia." It looked somewhat like the insignia which some tennis club members wear on their shirts. It was the shape of a phallus. "The boys insisted that his uniform be somewhat different as a special honor. When he was a boy he ate part of a human. He tells it very elegantly. They cut the man's gonads into tiny slivers and our friend ate one of the slivers. It has given him a great distinction ever since. He enjoys, even now, a great reputation as a lover." The host shrugged. "From what I can tell it is deserved. He still has young women, even a Tonkinese occasionally. They seem satisfied."

Later he pointed to another boy. This one was around twenty-five, very muscular and he had fierce brilliant eyes.

"That one is a Marxist," he said wryly. "Can you believe it? He reads Marx and Lenin and dreams of the day when barricades will go up in the streets of Nouméa and the black men will pour out of the hills and conduct a perfect revolution. He hopes to be the leader. He is really something of an expert on insurrections."

I watched the two men. It was a startling compression of history. From cannibalism to the "state that will wither away" in one generation. Meanwhile both are very good waiters.

Another scene. This time in the Solomons and over a decade ago. A Melanesian is bound to a stretcher by forty feet of rope. His eyes roll in his head and for long moments he strains against the ropes, bringing them taut and thin, almost to the bursting point. His pupils have disappeared, his eyeballs are white shot through with a web of bloodshot veins. Out of his mouth comes a stream of obscenity in English and Melanesian. It is obscene in only the way that the truly mad man can be obscene: a scatological linking of the Virgin Mary and various disciples, a flow of four letter words in a context of associations that are so bizarre that only the deranged could invent them. He spits them out like weapons, with projectile force. In his eagerness he sometimes bites his tongue and blood froths in the corners of his mouth.

The stretcher rests on a rickety pier on one of the smaller islands. He is due to be transported to Guadalcanal for treatment. A white missionary explains.

"He was a coast watcher during the war," the white man says. "He was decorated by both the Americans and the British. He was courageous beyond belief. An American Marine officer toasted him at the officers' club in Purvis Bay. He associated with Americans and British on the few leaves he had from Bougainville. When the British returned and took over the islands he made only one request: he asked not to be called 'boy' any more. He asked to be called by his last name. He quit a good job on Guadalcanal to escape the word 'boy.' He must have brooded over it. Last week a British policeman called here and yelled 'boy' at him. He stood for a few minutes, shivering as if he had the fever, and then he started for the policeman his hands stretched out to choke him and tears coming down his cheeks. He has been like this ever since."

The other Melanesians watched indifferently. Occasionally one of them would pour water into the madman's mouth and it would come gushing out, pink with blood, followed by a flow of obscenity. The other natives laughed. They looked at the horizon expectantly. The boat was overdue. Tied to the end of the stretcher was an old Bull Durham bag. In it were the madman's two medals.

I do not know what all of this means. The vignettes and anecdotes do not fall into any pattern for me. There are Australians who are certain that they have the answer: firmness coupled with justice, for the Melanesians are children who will never learn. But one is not quite certain that the Melanesians are so docile or so childlike. One remembers the abstract paintings on the walking masks and the agonies of a mad Melanesian and wonders if there are not currents which administrators cannot sense ... or cannot allow themselves to detect.

The Pacific Island Monthly is a rugged conservative pukka magazine which circulates widely in the Pacific. It has a consistent editorial policy towards blacks: keep them in their place. It is a mixture of

nineteenth century pure laissez-faire economics and
18th century Blimpish colonialism. But a few Melanesians are already in the twentieth century . . . one
has the awful feeling that they may be enough to
doom what the P.I.M. stands for.

The British Solomon Islands Protectorate is one of
the most efficient and enlightened administrations
that I know. Its officers are well trained, they put up
with great hardship, they spend interminable years in
a hard environment. Many of them speak native dialects. All of them have an understanding of what
they face . . . and also of what they do not understand. In all probability the Solomons cost the British
more than they earn. But I have never met a British
Solomon's official who had the faintest notion of
where it would all end. They are doing a good job,
but do not know if it is enough.

"What do I know of the Solomons?" an official in
Honiara, the center of government, on Guadalcanal
asks. "We've got seven big islands, maybe thirty smaller ones and hundreds of islets. After that go a little
slow. We have a native population of one hundred
thousand . . . maybe. No one has seen some of the
mountain villages. Maybe there are ten thousand people we've never counted. But that's not important.
What is is that we don't know what they think. We
don't know what goes over the bush telegraph.
Maybe they hate us. Maybe they have a revolution
well organized. Maybe they love us. Maybe they are
lazy."

He looks out his window at the well-ordered layout
of Honiara; the tennis courts, the offices, the hotels,
the warehouses.

"It's like living in a room which is always just a
little too dark to really see things clearly," he says
wistfully. "You know where the big things are. The
chairs and tables and buffets. You don't knock things

over. But nothing is very clear. You wish you could find a lamp that would brighten everything so that the detail would come out. Maybe it never will."

What we know for sure about the Melanesian are usually the surface physical things. We know, for example, that in his "pure" condition he tends to be the color of black that is so deep that it has a sheen of purple to it. We also know that he sometimes allows his fuzzy hair to grow into great masses. His body tends to be stocky and very muscular and when he works he is the most durable and powerful worker in the Pacific. He has a broad nose and thick lips. He is, in short, Negroid. On the fringes of Melanesia he has mixed blood with Polynesians and Malays and Caucasians and has lost the classical Negroid look. But everywhere there are exceptions. There are Melanesians with long lean bodies; others with proud, thin hooked noses; some with skins as light as gold. A few would be beautiful by Hollywood standards.

But it is the psychical life of the Melanesians which has escaped us, which flows away like quicksilver whenever we seek to understand and organize it. Maybe the gulf between the very black skin and the very white skin is beyond bridging. Or, perhaps, we have not gone about it in the right way. Certain it is that the white men that live among Melanesians exist in a great black pool of ambiguity and uncertainty. No one is quite certain what goes on behind those soft eyes, sunk deep in a hard skull. On occasion Melanesians have acted with great tenderness towards their own kind and towards whites. On occasions they have acted with a spasm of savagery towards everyone. Sometimes a Melanesian will follow an intricate idea with the keenest understanding and every evidence of high intelligence. Sometimes he will sit in a brutish sullenness and gaze at one with an implacable will not to comprehend. Sometimes these qualities are found in the same Melanesian.

There is one white man who claims to have a complete understanding of the Melanesian mind. He is a slight man, very intense, an Englishman and had a record of great heroism as a coast watcher during World War II. He has a hundred stories to indicate depth of understanding, but one is typical of all of them. During the Japanese occupation of his island two American fliers, survivors of a plane crash, stumbled into a distant village. After a few days the village turned the Americans over to the Japanese. The Englishman heard about it and at once set out for the village. He called the entire population of the village together. He asked the headman to step forward. An old man stepped out and faced the Englishman. The Englishman took out a pistol and shot the headman squarely between the eyes. He then asked for the successor to the headman to step forward. This man he also shot between the eyes. He asked for the third in succession to power to step forward. When a much younger man stepped forward the Englishman already had his pistol back in its holster. He gave a gentle lecture to the new headman on the necessity for delivering all military personnel, Allied or Japanese, to the Englishman. He left and the village obeyed him. To this day he lives in apparent harmony with the natives.

On the other hand there is an Anglican priest who lives on Ugi Island in the Solomons where he runs a school for native boys. He treats the natives gently and with sympathy. He speaks their language. He also lives in harmony with the natives.

What is strange is the fact that both men are treated, as far as the eye can tell, in precisely the same manner by the Melanesians.

The traveler will not worry about the insides of the

heads of Melanesians and, perhaps, there is no reason why he should. He is there to see things. Allowing for geographic and landscape differences most Melanesian villages will seem the same. Entering a Melanesian village is like entering a familiar, but vaguely disturbing dream. There will generally be two rows of huts with smoke oozing from the breaks in the coconut thatch. Close by will be a tabu hut occupied exclusively by males. There will be people in motion, but the moment they detect the presence of a stranger they go into a slow collective freeze. Women stare down at the mats they are weaving, men fall silent. The miscellaneous dogs and children move in slow motion. There is a preternatural quiet.

Eventually a headman will appear, his betel-blackened teeth and blood-red gums crooked into a smile as automatic as that of a hotel greeter in Atlantic City. The headman can usually speak pidgin English, but the conversation has an unreal brittleness, and this is not abated by the fact that these people are using U.S. Army helmets as cooking pots and a substantial number of them are wearing crucifixes. Presently the headman will start to make the expert hand motion of a P–38 dogfighting with a Zero. The Zero comes spinning down with a long, expiring hiss from the betel-black lips, explodes in a fist-hitting the ground, a pebble rolls out of the hand and looks like the burned body of a Japanese pilot. The headman looks up in triumph, and then his face glazes again.

The headman knows precisely what is expected of him in his many roles. If the visitor arrives accompanied by a government official, the headman will listen patiently while he is scolded because his village is delinquent in paying its head tax; or he will be reminded that three of the village's brightest boys were supposed to have been sent to the distant government school and he will promise again that it will be done. One senses that none of these things will be done.

If the visitor is alone and unaccompanied he will be invited to buy a pre-Misi carved figure. The genitals will be enormously exaggerated, and no one is sure if this reflects the Old Way or American G.I. humor. In any case it is too late to discover now. But the price will be high and the bargaining will be shrewd.

If you come accompanied by a missionary, the reception is somewhat more enthusiastic, less frozen. This is specially true if the missionary has brought a portable organ for hymn singing; the Melanesian loves to sing. Again the carved figure will be offered, the price will still be high, but the figure will be wearing decorous shorts and a tiny crucifix will be carved around its neck.

When the missionary leaves, he usually takes the headman aside and cautions him not to practice the rituals of *neoho* and "pointing of the bone." The first time a missionary explained neoho to me I refused to believe it; not in the second half of the twentieth century. The ritual is simple. When a calamity such as drought, famine or pestilence strikes a village, someone must be blamed and this person is called the *mookua*. There is endless argument and counterargument, but finally a scapegoat is selected. The mookua may deny and resist and rant, but the village is monolithic in its conviction. It may take days before the mookua concedes. When he does he picks up the neoho necklace and puts it around his neck. At once he starts to sweat, his skin turns clammy and gray, his eyes roll, and soon he is dead.

The ritual struck me as story-book rumor. However, when we returned to Rabaul my missionary friend gave me a recent issue of a scientific journal on the South Pacific. It contained an article by a doctor reporting on a number of neoho deaths and asking other doctors in the area to send along corroborating cases when they occurred. The doctor concluded that the mookua goes into a state of deep shock and then dies.

"Pointing the bone" is a more spiteful and individual form of witchery. In this ritual almost anyone can gather a rooster's eye, some bat's blood, a few odd feathers and, after a few incantations and burning some twigs, point a bone at a clay model of his victim. All that remains is that the victim be told that this was done. If he is sufficiently impressed by the *mana* or power of the pointer of the bone, he simply lies down and dies. If he is not he goes gaily on his way and is not harmed. Missionaries assure me sadly that natives who profess a Christian faith have no special immunity from such sorcery.

Indeed in this vast area of dense parasitic rain jungle, of sudden strands of pure white beach, of tiny villages tottering on spindly pilings, of surprising stretches of orderly coconut groves with cows grazing beneath them and a tin-roofed planter's house on a hill, of Burns, Philp copra steamers, of incredibly beautiful and tiny islands which come up green and sharp and are utterly empty of people, in all of this one has the sense that the area is more "black" than Melanesian. It seems a place out of time and place, an attractive limbo which has only the lightest relevance to the modern world.

These lovers of the primitive who want to see the noble savage kept savage may well have their way in Melanesia. This is no rich frontier. With the exception of the nickel mines of New Caledonia and some gold mining in New Guinea and a bit of lumbering all over, the area is relentlessly unproductive. It is true that the whir of turbojets and the sewing-machine sound of small planes is heard more frequently in the area, but the planes carry government officials, missionaries and tourists, not businessmen looking for deals. Africa, by comparison, is a bustling bourgeois continent.

All of this makes Melanesia a marvelously seductive place to visit. There is a haunting wildness to the place, a weird balance of green and black and lead-like hotness, a sense of the fey and the by-passed. It is still the slightly ominous place which Jack London visited in *The Snark*. Not for a long time will the glittering towers of Hilton poke up above the parasitic jungle and the glistening coral. Until that time the hardy visitor will be able to view one of the rawest and most beautiful areas of the world.

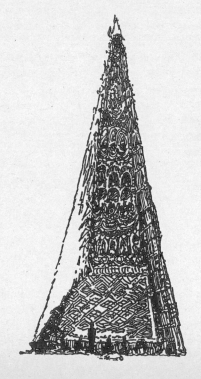

12. Lincoln Carver Bonaparte

THIS STORY is at the most only one tenth the truth. Maybe less. But it is based on two facts. First, the report of an Army company of Negroes of a single man missing and unaccounted for. Secondly, it is a persistent rumor throughout Melanesia, the kind of rumor that one hears in bars in Rabaul. The rest is all imagination.

Lincoln Carver Bonaparte had only two disadvantages. For an American Negro, however, they were considerable: first, he was bright. Bright not only in the raw intellectual sense, in that technically his brain was superior, but bright in his intuition about people and situations. As a boy of three he could remember watching an argument start between his father and mother in their slummy St. Louis apartment. Both of them were red-eyed from drinking cheap bourbon. With an awful prescience, with a prediction as perfectly formed as a red dot of blood on a laboratory plate, he knew how it would end. He sensed murder and that was how it ended. With his mother slumped back in a kitchen chair, a fistful of greasy spareribs in her hand, a wide grin on her face and a butcher knife through her heart. From his very first days, although he tried to push it beneath his consciousness, to lose it as a talent, he always retained this eerie ability to predict how an argument would end, who would come to dominate whom, how a situation would climax. The other parts of intelligence he enjoyed. The advantage it gave him in prediction he hated. But he also knew that he could not have one without the other.

Bony (he had been called that from the first time his teacher in grade school read out the full name of every student and it had stuck because he was in fact bony and angular) had a second colossal disadvantage: he was so black that there was a purplish sheen to his skin. He was the color of old Africa, raw Africa, Africa before the slightest drop of white blood had arrived. It was a color which could resist sun, mosquitoes, heat, the blast of sand. It was also a color that everyone, especially other Negroes, associated with a primitive mind. Even when he was young Bony was aware of the paradox. His smoothly working, logical and oiled mind could look down at his skin and understand, even better than his critics, why they regarded him as primordial.

Bony had once taken a high school course in biology which led him to read Mendel and his laws of heredity and he discovered one afternoon in a sunny St. Louis high school library that he was a biological impossibility. It was impossible for a child to be darker than either of his parents. But Bony was. He was darker than any Negro in St. Louis; dark with an underglow of deep purple that occasionally one sees on a finely wrought rifle.

When World War II started Bony was eighteen, two years out of high school, working as a steel puddler to save money to go to college, and an isolated man. Isolated, but not lonely, for loneliness requires a sense of deprivation, a sense of one's having no association. Bony's purple-black skin had neatly kept him friendless his entire life.

Bony chose the Army, for he sensed very quickly that as a Negro in the Navy he could only wind up as a steward's mate. In the Army there was little to be optimistic about, but the laws of probability would be working for him. He might turn up an interesting job.

He did not. One pudgy sergeant after another looked at Bony's fantastic I.Q. and aptitude record, glanced up with a look of expectation on their faces, slowly slid their eyes over Bony's skin and features and assigned Bony to straight work details. To a man they were convinced that no one with those features or that skin could be anything but a hand worker.

Bony became used to being assigned to crews of Negroes who waited patiently while white privates and corporals sorted the mail, and then hauled the mailbags. He stood behind cooks with rolls of fat on their necks and sweat on their faces and antagonism in their eyes when they saw him and learned never to correct them . . . just haul the garbage and that was it. He watched white men make the first little wedge end of a mistake and learned not to tell them what would happen. Sometimes the original mistakes grew to be minor tragedies such as a platoon killed or a boatload of soldiers drowned. But the white man was always guiltless and always ignorant of how the mistake started. Bony merely took care not to be in such platoons or on such boats.

Other Negroes that Bony knew fell into one of two postures. Some became lazy, with a soft cynicism, and laughed at the antics and mistakes that were justified only by white skin. In a way that Bony could never quite understand they achieved a degree of superiority. Others developed a razor-sharp bitterness. These were the ones that perfected the smile so hostile that it could make a second lieutenant just out of UCLA blush with embarrassment or a way of saying "yes-suh" to a Texas captain which would have the sharp astringent sting of insolence in it.

Bony simply watched with a kind of idle curiosity, safe in his cocoonlike wrapping, never asked to participate and never wishing to.

Eventually they sent his work company to San Francisco. They all knew it would be a tour that would only last a few months and then they would be sent to the Pacific. Most of the Negroes melted quietly into the growing population of San Francisco, found girls, favorite bars, barbecue houses, jazz joints. Bony, driven by the raw rasp of intelligence, tried all of these alternatives, but with his second damning feature knew in advance that they were doomed. Knowing that a negative ending was sure it was impossible for him to be insulted or even to feel bad when not a single person in a Negro bar or bowling alley or restaurant would talk to him.

His company was then sent to Honolulu where they worked on the docks loading and unloading materials as a kind of acclimation. Bony was more prepared for Honolulu than were the other men of the company. He had heard it called "the melting pot of the Pacific" and knew that being a Negro in Honolulu would not necessarily be painful, and might in fact be a distinct pleasure. But he also knew, with only the slightest iciness in the middle of his viscera, that he would never make a connection with any of the girls of Honolulu. He was perfectly right. But he was not disappointed.

In midsummer of 1942 the company was loaded aboard a fast APA, surrounded by three or four destroyers that roamed the horizon, and in concert with a dozen other ships of like character sailed for the South Pacific. They were off-loaded in an improvised staging port in Melanesia.

The work which Bony and his company had to do was simplicity itself. Most of the time it was unloading cargo. A ship would pull up alongside the temporary dock which the Sea Bees had built of coconut trees and rosewood and would empty directly onto the dock.

If the cargo was mailbags or canned food or cartridges it was relatively clean. If it was cement bags they worked in a gray haze of cement dust and in a temperature of 110°.

If there were no ships to unload, Bony's company was assigned to the marginal jobs. These were not always necessarily the dirtiest jobs and seldom were they dangerous. For example, they were never asked to do the firefighting that resulted from an aircraft raid or bomb disposal work, nor were they asked to go into the front lines where the fighting took place. Rather they would be asked to move hundreds of cartons of rotting soup and K-rations and sugar. This inevitable debris of war gave off an odor that was beyond belief, or at least it was beyond the belief of commanding officers that white troops could endure it. For days on end they would sort through the mountains of foodstuffs, select out those cartons that were rotting, throw them onto trucks that quickly became slimy with rot, haul them to the lagoon and throw them into the water. In a few days the lagoon started to bubble as the cans and cartons began to disintegrate.

Most of the Negroes in Bony's company bitterly resented the work. Bony did not. The reason was simple; he had expected this type of work from the very beginning.

War is a sporadic thing. There would be days of intense activity and then there would be whole weeks of spare time when there was nothing for anyone to do. During this time they had a chance to explore the life and land of the high island of the South Pacific.

Most of the other men in Bony's company took one look at the villages and the vegetation and decided to spend their time sleeping in their tents.

One of the things that they had explored, and most of them had rejected at once, was the possibility of sexual intercourse with the Melanesian women of the high island. The women were, in hard fact, only slightly different from the women they had known in Harlem, St. Louis and San Francisco, but the difference was critical. First of all, Melanesian women, all of them, were the same deep purple-black as Bony. Secondly, they all had heavy saggy breasts, a musky odor, a skin that was a crust of dust and sweat, and an appearance of utter strangeness. There was not one member of Bony's company that was tempted by any woman on the high island.

For a few months there was a sense of tension on the island simply because of the fact that the Marines and two divisions of the Army were fighting the Japanese on the northern end of the island. A few of Bony's companions in the company, out of some deep-rooted sense of dignity or hostility or aggression, tried desperately to get into the fighting zone. Generally this meant that they wandered into the fighting area with a stolen rifle or carbine in their hand, but without being attached to any organized fighting unit. Several of them were killed, several came back with a hard glint of satisfaction in their eye because they had had a chance to fire a live round at a live enemy.

It did not take long, however, for Bony to realize that when the fighting was over, the port would remain a "staging area." This meant that it would be one of those places where masses of equipment and food and supplies are loaded and unloaded and trans-shipped. With the prescience he dreaded Bony knew that the other members of the company would resent this. Somehow it was a mark of inferiority that they could not share the risks of combat but must endure the endless dull routine of work in a nondangerous area.

It was at this point that Bony's intelligence and his prescience began to play a major part in his life. He would wander to the Melanesian villages, squat down at the edge of the village, and watch the life that took place there. He watched Melanesian women work sago palm pith into a white substance and he tasted it. He came to know what a blob of red clay stuck into a belly-button meant: a warrior. He watched family fights and brawls. He learned the language. He also knew that the Melanesians had become fatally dependent upon the Americans for food and clothing and tobacco. He knew, with his unwanted prescience, how all of this would end.

When Bony returned from his trips to the Melanesian village he would climb into his bunk and listen to the other American Negroes talk about life "Stateside." They talked of gambling, high yellow girls, big paychecks, consuming whole fifths of rich bourbon whiskey on Saturday night, shooting craps, and endlessly of women. Some of the older men, the type who had been Pullman porters, talked slowly and almost shyly of their jobs and family life.

They were on the high island for a year and a half, but Bony was never quite sure when the awful meshing of his intelligence and his prescience told him that it would be a mistake for him to return to the States. Others in his company would fall back into family relationships and friendships and warm boozy Saturday evenings. But for Bony it would be as isolated, spare and thin as it had always been.

At some point Bony started to realize that he

could stay on the high island and live a rich life. Were he to take off his private's uniform and put on a breechclout he would look precisely like a Melanesian. This was true only of him. No other Negro in the company was dark enough to have "passed" backwards into this primitive society.

Once the idea had seized him his intelligence began to flesh out the notion with an almost incredible luxuriance. In the States Bony would be a rejected member of a rejected race. In Melanesia, with ingenuity and foresight, he would be a king among savages.

The beginnings of Bony's plan were really almost unconscious. He began, for example, to learn the dialects which the Melanesians in the nearby villages spoke. In a matter of months he was fluent. The Melanesians were delighted to have an American soldier in uniform among them and they did not notice that his skin was the same color as theirs. American Negroes, to them, were as remote as American white soldiers.

Once he had learned the language the shape of the unstated plan, deeply buried in Bony's mind, started to unroll. Almost as if it were a photograph etched on his mind he could see what life would be like on the high island when the American troops had been withdrawn. Most of the Melanesians were wildly enthusiastic about canned salmon which had been imported by the American Army, and claimed that this was the item they would miss most. Next they would miss tobacco, after that they would miss sugar and tea and hard candy and K-rations.

But Bony noticed that they had an almost passionate intensity about jeeps and mechanical equipment. Also he sensed that they were enormously relieved at the sudden access to medicines that would cure yaws, trachoma and intestinal worms, but it was an enthusiasm which was deeply buried and inarticulate.

One Sunday afternoon when he was on liberty Bony stumbled across a huge hidden cave which had been formed by some accident of ancient flowing lava. The cave was not only well hidden, but it was open at both ends and thus ventilated and quite dry. The next time that Bony had a liberty he took a portable field radio which he had stolen from the dock up to the cave and left it. After that a pattern established itself. Bony began to stock the cave. He filled it with penicillin, antibiotics, Coleman lamps, flashlights, spare parts for radio receivers, odd bits of tubes and wires and a whole workshop of tools. For one period, covering almost two weeks, he transported bit by bit an entire jeep into the cave. He took every part of the jeep except the engine. Why he neglected to transport an engine to the cave he did not explain even to himself, except to argue that it would be impossible to carry so heavy a weight in any case. He also took one carbine, several hundred hand grenades, a hundred pounds of dynamite and six cases of flares.

When victory came in Europe there was a tremendous excitement among the troops in Bony's company. Bony did not share the enthusiasm. He knew that they would not remain much longer on the high island. There were only a few things left for him to do.

Bony saw his future in America with a tiny hard part of his mind. He would always be a skulker at the edges. He would never know the quick flashy pleasures of the high yellow girl or the two-tone convertible nor would he know or be any part of the somber pleasures to which he knew his pure intellect entitled him. Always there would be that tiny hesitation, the quick flashing glance at his aboriginal features and his blue-black skin, and he would be excluded. Somehow he knew with absolute certainty that were he to return to America he would wind up doing one of two things, shining shoes or cleaning Pullman cars after the white-toothed porters had departed.

Bony did not steal the food and the equipment with some conscious plan in mind. Rather he did it to protect himself against that tiny cameo-like memory in his mind.

The day of victory did come. There was a week of extra rations of beer, a systematic rifling of alcohol from hospital stores, a kind of wild hysteria which gripped all of the troops. They did not know how soon they would go, but for each the moments, by some terrible trick, stretched out interminably. Also although there were frequent outbursts of temper and many fights, everyone walked and worked and almost breathed with intense caution. No one wanted to be killed at this point in the game.

Rolling back the troops in the mountains and the packing of supplies took longer than anyone had anticipated. For Bony this was an advantage. In the great confusion of departure no accurate inventories were kept, and theft became a simple matter of appropriating what one wished. Bony picked up tins, cans of paint, a gross of lipsticks that had been sent out for the WACs, books, almost enough equipment to supply a field hospital and instruction books and manuals sufficient to give even a duller person information on how to do various operations.

He carefully avoided complex machinery which would deteriorate in the humid climate or which was dependent upon a supply of fuel.

The day came. Bony's company was ordered to board a ship at 0600 the next morning and the scuttlebutt had it that the ship would sail directly to San Francisco. Bony had looked forward to the day and at the same time he dreaded it; dreaded it with all the swarming fears, the almost mad duality with which the person who is to have a limb amputated regards the lancet.

The next morning Bony got up early. He had thought out carefully what he would do. After brushing his teeth in the washshack, he walked a hundred yards into the jungle with a small bundle under his arm. He took off his private's uniform, undid the bundle, and took out the short lava-lava which the male natives of the island wore. He rolled his own clothes up in a bundle, fingering for just a moment the wallet in the rear pocket of his pants which contained his identification cards, a few dollar bills, and the last links with his old life. Then he put the bundle in a nearby river and heaped a half dozen stones on it.

He then walked slowly back into the camp with the several hundred natives who worked at various chores. Because they came from several different villages none of them thought it peculiar to see a strange native. But there was one moment which burned itself into Bony's mind forever; he was walking with some of the natives when they came face to face with his top sergeant. The top sergeant was a fat, light brown, very powerful Negro from New York, skilled in the ways of manipulating organizations.

"All right, you fella belong this camp," the sergeant yelled. "You fella dis day go chop chop, fella belong me go back America. You fella workum good today."

His eye swept over the group and did not even flicker as it passed over Bony's face. For a wild, and somehow icily black sad moment, Bony viewed the group of natives through the eyes of the top sergeant.

They were a blue-black lot of men, possessed of aboriginal noses, their hair kinky, their teeth gleaming, their eyes slightly yellow in the whites and intensely black in the center. Apelike, simple, amiable, hardworking, ill-educated, friendly.

In some odd way that moment before the top sergeant, the moment when he blended into the Melanesians and out of the American Negroes, had an almost official aspect to it for Bony. He felt like an alien who had petitioned for citizenship, been summoned before the judge and had been ignorantly, unknowingly approved. Bony turned on his heel and swung off with the group of boys to start hauling the bags of the American Negro company down to the wharf. He worked easily with the islanders, laughed at their jokes, moved among his former companions in their crisp khakis, and knew with an iron-hard certainty that he would not be detected.

Late that afternoon the ship sailed. It was the last of the American troops to leave and the Melanesians stood on the dock, quite informally, and without rehearsal staging a sort of farewell ceremony.

One big buck from Alameda, California, stood up on the stern of the ship, and roared down to the Melanesians, "We is giving it back to you boys. The whole god-damned kit and caboodle is yours for nuttin. Live it up. Gift of Uncle Sam."

The Alameda boy had always been the company clown and the Melanesians laughed automatically, although Bony was the only one that understood the joke. They stood for perhaps fifteen minutes as the ship worked out into the roads, put on speed, took a bone in her teeth and began to grow slim.

Then the Melanesians turned and with a wild yell descended on the stacks of discarded supplies which the Americans had left behind. With one collective impulse they went for the food. The tobacco, the most desired item, they had already pilfered or made off with. While they were scrambling through the food pile Bony quickly trotted in a wide circle around the abandoned camp to the motor depot. This was where all of the jeeps, weapon carriers and other machines had been cannibalized and then stored. Days before, Bony had arranged this operation carefully. He quickly wired up dynamite charges that he had distributed around the dump, wheeled over three or four fifty-gallon tins of gasoline, set the charge for three minutes and trotted back to where the islanders were looting the food piles.

Bony was standing among them jabbering, his eyes bulging with excitement like theirs when the explosion went off. They turned, stunned by the shock-waves that hit them and, for a few moments, unable to comprehend what had happened. Then a low moan, like the lowing of cattle, went up from the Melanesians. In real fact most of them had desired more than anything else to have a wheeled vehicle as a souvenir of the American occupation. The scrambling for food was really a diversionary action, most of them did it only because the food was portable. Their real hearts lay with the motorized vehicles.

Slowly, like people hypnotized, their eyes wide with lust and a massive sense of deprivation, they walked towards the burning pyre of vehicles. They watched the explosion as tires blew up on jeeps, as gas tanks exploded on huge trucks, as 4 × 4's tore themselves to pieces, as tent-stake trucks burned to black and charred replicas of themselves that dissolved into black ash at the touch.

It was precisely at this moment that Bony asserted his first slight move in the direction of superiority and dominance over the islanders. He had improvised a song in the general dialect of the island which was a haunting lament that they could not lay hands on the shining and marvelous vehicles that moved men over land faster than the swiftest man could run for even a quarter of a mile. Although the islanders did not know it Bony had, quite deliberately, jerked them back savagely into the nineteenth century. He had also avoided a great deal of commotion. Had each of the Melanesians had access to a jeep or a 4 × 4 or a truck there would have been days of utter madness and civil disorder until the gasoline and oil had run out. Then there would have been a feckless strain between them for the remaining gallons and then quarts and then pints and then cupfuls of gas; frenzied arguments over the strange vehicles. With an intuition as honed as his intelligence Bony had realized that if they were to fight about food it would be a manageable conflict, but a conflict over something as inscrutable as machinery would be bloody.

As he stood and sang his song they looked at him with the strange eyes with which people view a new messiah.

Oddly enough no one among the natives took Bony at anything but face value, a native who said he came from another village, but always slurred the pronunciation of the village so that it struck everyone as being far distant. When the camp had been sacked, when the last overburdened man and women had staggered back with the last case of pork and beans and canned salmon and K-rations, Bony made his entrance into the village which was to be his new home.

The village was located on a low plateau that rose a hundred feet above the ocean and ran in a flat rising green slope for a half mile or so and then towered suddenly into substantial mountains that

were lost in mist. Bony stood for a moment at the
entrance of the village and looked at the women with
their heavy loads. If they were young their breasts
were round and conical, their hips rounded, their legs
short and muscular. If they were older their breasts
hung to their waists, their waists had vanished, and
their mass of kinky hair was run through by long
beautifully carved pins made of bone.

For just a moment, a memory as subtle as a faint
odor flicked across Bony's mind. It was an intersection
in St. Louis in the colored section which was filled
with pool halls, barbecue joints, bars, big flashy drug-
stores. Bony thought of the girls on a Saturday night,
wearing their new dresses, the billiard balls began to
click in the pool halls, the odor of sloe gin wafted
from convertibles drifting up and down the street, the
music from a hundred radios and record players began to play.

This, Bony said to himself, closing his eyes, *is what
you must never remember.* He stood for a moment
shivering in the warm humidity like a man with a
seizure. It was almost a physical act as if by the use
of some unknown muscle he had snatched the memory of St. Louis from his mind. He grinned, turned and
walked into the village promptly.

It went much easier than Bony had expected. During the endless months in the staging area he had
read every book he could about the area and he had
watched. He had questioned a staff anthropologist at
great length and finally stopped only when he was
sure that he knew more than the anthropologist.

The first test was physical. Bony had moved into a
hut which had been abandoned after the head of the
family had died in it and left no heirs. Before going
into the hut he had exorcised it of all evil spirits by
drawing an elaborate design in the dust in front of

the house. But he was no sooner installed in the house
when a tall powerfully built young native appeared
and told him in a voice that was unmistakably harsh
that the house belonged to him.

A knot of curious villagers gathered. Bony thought
about this moment a great deal. Here he stood, facing
a man who, in terms of knowledge, was thousands of
years behind him. Bony had every advantage of information, ingenuity, the vast store of information and
knowledge of the western world at his fingertips. He
could have avoided the physical test by cleverness with
words, but he had decided that it must be met directly.
However, it was Bony's intention not merely to be the
number one man of the village, but to be a number
one man the likes of which they had never seen. Bony
knew any number of tricks of judo or boxing, of par-
alyzing blows to the kidneys, of sharp hard deadly raps
beneath the ear that would allow him to knock the
young native unconscious. But this would only arouse
a kind of dull curiosity in others and Bony would be
exposed to a long series of bouts. He was confident he
would lose none of these, but the mere act of engag-
ing in them would demean him.

"Your name is Wuli," Bony said to the young man.
"This hut was available to the first man who did the
proper incantations. I have done them. You really
want only to challenge me to a fight." Wuli looked
down at his feet, shuffled them in the dust, looked
sideways at his arm and tightened his biceps and
smiled slowly. "I would fight you gladly, but for you it
would be a tragedy. I have special powers."

Wuli looked at Bony, sneered, and then said bale-
fully, "Good. We will test your special powers. We
will fight. The winner will take the hut."

"No, we will not fight," Bony said. "I will give you a

demonstration and if you wish to fight *then*, we will fight."

Bony walked over to a coconut which was lying on the ground a few feet from his hut. He picked it up, brought it back, laid it squarely in front of Wuli. Then he squatted down and stared intently down at the coconut. He raised his hand in a chopping motion, brought it down softly on the coconut as if he were going to split it with the edge of his hand, and did this three times. The crowd stared in fascination and then laughed. A husked coconut can only be split with an axe, and even when husked it is usually broken with a stone or the back of a machete. The crowd thought that Bony's gesture was arrogant and magnificent in a way, but it was also humorous. They were still laughing when Bony brought his hand high in the air and then put it down with a quick flashing hack against the coconut. There was a rasping sound and the entire coconut, husk shell and soft meat was split open into two neat parts. The laughter stopped deep in a score of throats. The crowd shuffled forward, stared down at the coconut, looked sideways at Wuli and gathered closer around the coconut.

"It was a coconut he had prepared by cutting through it before with a machete," Wuli said. "Bring him a new coconut, a green one and he will not be able to repeat."

A young boy in the crowd ran to the nearest coconut tree, quickly bound his ankles together with a coconut palm and went in leaps up the tree. He selected a large fresh green nut that he cut loose and threw down. Wuli walked over, shook it, looked at it carefully and placed it in front of Bony.

Bony smiled at Wuli and then down at the coconut. It was an old trick of *karate,* a branch of judo, which was really very simple. Most humans were so pre-

cisely alike, so ordinary in their strength, so close to
being identical, that any eccentric skill, however slight,
would dazzle them. Bony had learned to develop
the muscles at the edge of his hand, the ability to
swing all of his weight behind those muscles in one
slash. Three times he touched the coconut and the
fourth time he raised his hand and slashed the coconut in two.

This time the crowd shuffled backwards, not a
great deal, but backwards. Instantly Bony was on his
feet, his knees bent, his arms spread wide apart. In
the pose of the classical Melanesian fighter, he
walked towards Wuli. Wuli stared at him in fascination, like a man who had forgotten something. Then at
the last moment he broke into a grin. He turned his
hands palm upward and extended them towards Bony.

"You do have special powers," he said simply. It
was a surrender and everyone that saw it knew it.

It was the closest that Bony ever came to physical
violence. After that his victories were all verbal.

Bony had been right. The villagers in three years of
working for the Americans had lost centuries of skill
and experience. They had planted no crops of sweet
potato, had exhausted the surrounding land of sago
palm, had stopped making fishhooks. For a few
months this did not matter. The abandoned American
food was sufficient. But one by one the families began
to run out of food and an intense bickering began
among those that had food and those that did not.
The cans, the splendid American cans, had at first
seemed without limit. Everyone had eaten profligate-
ly. Cans of beef and green peas and peaches and
yellow corn and butter had been emptied together
into pots and made into delicious stews. No one had
thought the cans would end. But they had and in each
case it was with an awful abruptness. One day a

family would eat until it was bursting. And the next morning there would be nothing. They would walk back to the abandoned American camp and search and perhaps scavenge a few cans and then realize that they faced starvation. It was puzzling and they began to go beyond bickering; they began to stalk one another.

Bony waited until the first blood was shed. He knew that no one would listen until that sobering moment arrived. It came one morning when Wuli returned to his hut to find a neighbor among his few remaining cans of food. Wuli had reached for a U.S. Army machete and hacked blindly at the man. He cut the thief's head almost loose from his shoulders. The thief lived long enough to stagger into the center of the village, blood jetting from the wound in his neck, his hands reflectively trying to hold his head steady. The village gathered and stared.

"He was stealing," Wuli said in a puzzled voice.

"Soon most of us will be out of food and will have to steal," Bony said quietly. "Does that mean that we will wind up like this one?"

"We must raid the next village," a young man said. "They have food."

"And when we have killed them and eaten their food, then what?" Bony asked.

"Yes, then what?" an old man, his hair gray, but with snapping eyes, said. "We must learn to plant again. And to fish."

"Plant what?" Wuli asked. "We no longer have seeds or the tools to cut the earth."

"I will find the seed," Bony said. They turned and looked at him. Since the day he split the coconuts he had not raised his voice in the village. "I will also find the tools with which to make tools. But you must talk to the old people and remember how such things are done."

The old men of the village, there were six of them, straightened up and looked at the villagers. For three years they had been ignored, for age, which had always been valued because of the practical wisdom it brought with it, had been devalued by the artificial prosperity of the war.

"I can teach how to make a fishhook," one of the old men said. "It is slow work, but a good shell hook will last a lifetime."

The other old men began to talk, with pride, of lost arts they could practice. The village listened for hunger is a powerful spur to learning.

That night Bony visited his cave, emptied bags of seed into leaf containers and returned with them to the village. He also brought a handful of iron files to help with the working of the shell into fishhooks. He also brought a block of innocent-looking high explosive along. It looked like a mud cake that had been mixed with wax.

The next morning Bony had the men of the village come to the lagoon. He lit the fuse of the explosive, waited a moment for it to spark and then threw it into the lagoon. The men stood watching, their faces puzzled. Then the water exploded upwards and when it fell back the surface was covered with stunned fish.

"Quick, catch them before they recover," Bony yelled, and ran into the water. They followed him like men possessed, like men following Genghis Khan. They recovered almost four hundred pounds of fish. Bony told them that they could eat only part of it, the rest must be salted.

The village eked out a living until the crops came in, but no one starved. In other villages which had been close to American bases the story was different. They starved and bickered and fought. Some began to make raids, but in the end starvation always faced them. Once such a hungry band had raided Bony's village and he had waited until they were just at the edge of the village and had fired a flare into the air. It went up a hundred feet and burst into a huge red, white and blue festoon. The raiders had paused, looked upward, and turned and filed away.

In a year Bony was the unofficial chief of the village. The real chief was a very old and frail man, but he did nothing without consulting Bony. Everyone knew that when the chief died Bony would take his place.

By the time the chief died Bony had married. He had picked the girl carefully. She was his age and had a lithe elegance. She was, also, precisely the same color as Bony. As part of the elaborate dowry ritual Bony gave the girl's family a dozen bars of soap and six lipsticks. She could use the soap whenever she wished, but Bony told her that the lipstick was to be used only when they were in the privacy of their own hut. It was a happy marriage.

The European power which served as protectorate over the area took a good deal of time in getting around to Bony's village. They had enough problems elsewhere with starving villages, discontented natives and reopening communications. They made a careful study of the village and then returned to their tent.

The last day of their visit the two members of the inspection team called him to their tent. The senior man was a seasoned old-timer who knew the islands well. The junior was on his first tour.

"Rather a skinny chap to be chief, isn't he, sir?" the junior asked. "I thought they always picked one of their biggest and strongest men."

"Sometimes they pick the smartest, just occasionally," the senior said, his eyes still on Bony. He leaned forward and spoke to Bony. "You number one fella here? You talk pidgin?"

"Me number one fella, me talk pidgin," Bony said.

"What fella walkalong this village 'un makeum doctor business?" the senior asked sharply.

Bony shook his head, but his mind was racing. Then he remembered. A week before one of the men had ripped his arm open while setting a pig trap. It was a long deep gash from elbow to shoulder and Bony had cleaned it, dusted it with sulfa powder and pulled the edges together and stitched the wound shut. The senior man had seen the neat stitches.

"No lie, number one fella," the senior man pressed. "Some fella walkalong 'un do doctor business to fella belong village." He gestured at his upper arm, made stitching gestures.

"Me 'da fella do dat," Bony explained.

The senior man's eyes hardened. He bent forward to hear the explanation. Bony said that he had worked for the American troops and among his jobs was to clean up the hospital. Occasionally he watched the American doctors at work, Bony said, feeling carefully for the right pidgin words and then letting them pour out.

"Sounds reasonable," the junior man said in conversational English which most white men are convinced natives cannot understand.

"Something strange about it though," the senior man said. "This village is different from any I have ever seen before. Not big things. But a lot of little ones. No yaws, for example, and they use compost on the maize and taro. Did you ever see a village before with a privy built over the water? Usually they just use the beach at low tide."

"Maybe this boy learned it from the Yanks," the junior man said.

"He must have," the senior man said, finally satisfied. He looked long at Bony. Then he stood up and walked over and tapped Bony on the chest. "Looksee, number one fella. How you lak leave 'da village and walkalong sea in cutter? Long, long, long walkalong 'un come big city belong white man. You go school. Read 'un write. Maybe go big school become doctor."

Bony stood for a long moment. He looked around at the village and saw it through the white man's eyes ... a dozen smoky huts with greasy split bamboo floors, some miserable patches of maize and taro, old women shredding coconuts into wooden pans, a few men fishing in boats off the village. In his mind's eye Bony could also see the city ... the white sparkling city, with streetcars, theaters, restaurants, activity. For the first time his prescience failed him, did not tell him where the alternatives would end. *Perhaps*, he thought, *in their country it would be different.* He licked his lips. He lifted one foot and placed it against the inside of his leg and stood one-legged ... a gesture he had learned from the Melanesians. It was the posture of contemplation, of thoughtfulness.

"Look, you fella, you stand straight when talk white man," the junior man said crisply.

Bony then had his answer. He did not resent the young man's command. It was a valuable piece of information. He looked once more at the village, at the tiny changes and improvements he had made. It was his, the only thing in his life he had made, the only place that folded in around him and supported him. He glanced down at the backs of his hands, at the purple-black skin, the chafed knuckles. He laughed softly.

"This fella belong village," he said and tapped his

chest. "Mary belong me here and pickaninny belong me here. This fella belong village."

The senior man nodded. He was irritated ... partly at his assistant, partly at something about Bony and the village he did not quite understand. Bony turned and walked away.

"They're funny buggers," the junior man said. "Even when they are bright like that one they don't want to get away from the village. Good Lord, you offered him everything a black man could want and he turned it down."

"Maybe not everything," the senior man said softly, almost to himself. He watched Bony walk back into the village, waving to one person after another, giving advice to some. Some unformulated doubt in his mind was eased. "Maybe not everything, by a long shot."

13. The Beach and the Old Way

THE "OUTSIDER" has made a dent on Oceania, but in a very special way. Many of the outsiders are Indians, who flow wherever there is plantation work, chiefly to Fiji. Many others are Chinese, who flow wherever there is trading to be done; the vast majority of little tin-roofed isolated trading shops are owned by Chinese, who maintain a thin tough cobweb monopoly of trading over all of Oceania.

There is a great nervousness about the Chinese in the Pacific. Many of them have lived overseas for generations, sending the bodies of their dead back to China in great ornate coffins, buying a young Chinese girl from their home village. Their children are often educated in Chinese schools. They are clannish, value marriage with other Chinese, work incredible hours, have an earned reputation for dependability and

efficiency. The Chinese probably have more wealthy men than any other racial group in the Pacific. In some places like Singapore and Jakarta or Manila they have built homes and clubs which are plain on the outside, but are decorated in a lavish Chinese style within ... a style so intensely Chinese that it is often in the most execrable taste. The most wealthy of the overseas Chinese try to recapture the almost forgotten splendors of Peking and Shanghai or Canton; as if by making a dream into a building one has captured it. I have been in Chinese homes in Jakarta and Manila that were so jammed full of Chinese furniture and art and figures that the beauty of the individual pieces disappear and one is living in a crowded art shop.

There are also thousands of Chinese who are desperately poor. There are little stores in the Philippines (always called "The Chinaman's," regardless of the real name) which have a tiny supply of Borden's canned milk, Campbell's soup, barrels of different kinds of rice, dried fish and about a half dozen customers a day. In the background, shy and hovering, there is a Chinese wife, and a number of children. It is a thin life. There is also in most cities of Oceania a hard-working group of Chinese proletarians ... the only workers in the Pacific that manufacture things. They make cabinets, iron beds, calico prints, mosquito net, sun glasses ... and everything is cheap.

For all of these reasons the Chinese in Oceania are not much loved. The Filipino or the Tahitian or the Indonesian is caught somewhere between admiration and suspicion. Recently the reaction has been complicated by the rise of the Two Chinas: Red China of the mainland and Chiang's China, locked up in Formosa. Political leaders in Oceania are not quite sure how the overseas Chinese will jump. Perhaps, the

Chinese themselves are not sure. But their intentions are masked. It is next to impossible to get an overseas Chinese into a political discussion. At that point he becomes smilingly vague, almost a caricature of the "inscrutable Oriental."

This nervousness expresses itself in different ways. In Tahiti an aristocratic old native family will resist marrying into a Chinese family and be not quite sure of their reasons. In Indonesia, which has recognized Red China, the government has moved powerfully against the Chinese, forcing them to choose Indonesian citizenship or suffer severe economic penalties.

Japanese in the Pacific are something different. Those who live in Hawaii, for example, do not even regard themselves as Japanese. They mingle on every level of society and recall their racial solidarity only when they want to "get out the Japanese vote." In the rest of the Pacific the Japanese is remembered with a peculiar ambiguity. It was, after all, the Japanese who were the first colored race, the first Asians, to take the white man on in modern warfare and come within a hair's-breadth of defeating him. At the same time the ways of the Japanese, orderly and sometimes tyrannical and often hysterical in crisis, are not attractive to the island dwellers of the Pacific. After World War II the Japanese almost disappeared from Oceania. Now they venture forth occasionally to attempt a fishing venture or a business enterprise. They seldom come to stay. They arrive in a disciplined and purposeful array, accomplish their mission or fail, and go back to Japan.

White men are a very small minority, but they possess inordinate power. They are almost exclusively concentrated on what is known as The Beach.

The Beach is not a place; it is anything new or foreign. Thus all of Suva or Nouméa is The Beach, and so are sewing machines, gin, calico, movies, jeeps, radios and missionaries. Opposed to The Beach is what the Samoans call *fa'a* Samoa, the Old Way. Pandanus mats, poi, taboos, mother-of-pearl fishhooks, tattooing, female circumcision, handmade outriggers are *fa'a*. Christ is The Beach; the *kahuna*, skilled in folk medicine and magic, is the Old Way. Matches and canned salmon are The Beach, and barracuda and rubbing sticks are the Old Way. Every tribe, village and island has a phrase for The Beach and another for the Old Way. The two live in a delicate tension. When they come into conflict The Beach usually wins, although even Hawaii, the most triumphant victory of The Beach, has little enclaves where the Old Way persists in language, food, custom and religion. In New Guinea and New Ireland The Beach has made only small dents.

The most dazzling triumphs of The Beach are the cities and towns of Oceania, which tend to be more intense, exaggerated and convoluted than cities elsewhere. They are usually jammed with Chinese traders, Japanese importers, American anthropologists, Australian civil servants, visiting dignitaries from the United Nations, a swarm of tiny shops, and drifters of almost every race. The economic pressure and the fight for social status are intense. The natives who live in the towns are carefully skimmed from among the most intense, adrenalin-loaded, hyperactive of their people. Their gestures are staccato, violent and persuasive. They talk furiously and they are experts in the hard sell. They are, in fact, a speeded-up caricature of Madison Avenue and Wall Street. I have, for example, never had lunch with a Japanese or Indian or Chinese or native businessman in Oceania without the sensation of being subtly bribed. There is the knowing wink, the call for champagne when beer

would do as well, the sense of double talk. It is, I
imagine, much the kind of rowdy and fevered mood
that prevailed in the Early West of America.

The white men of The Beach form a peculiar community. They are spread over a vast distance and
thousands of islands, but they maintain a remarkable
communication with one another. It is really a community based on gossip. Let a Dutchman on Basilan
take a loss in mahogany and it will be common
knowledge in the Vaima café in Tahiti a week later.
A Frenchman takes a mistress on a tiny island and
her name and characteristics and genealogy are
known to white men in New Guinea and Manila and
Guam. Unlike any other gossip the gossip network of
the Pacific is highly factual. A German in the Galapagos can describe to you the plantation of an Englishman on New Georgia down to the type of silver he
uses, his annual income, what the British Solomon
Islands Protectorate officials think of him. And they
will never have met and are separated by six thousand miles. An example: Dick Gump, owner of the
famous importing store in San Francisco, is building a
house on Moorea. A Frenchman in Bora Bora, hundreds of miles from Moorea and thousands from San
Francisco, made me a quick sketch of what the house
was to be like. When I saw Gump's plans they were
precisely what the Frenchman had drawn.

The gossip of The Beach is not casual. It is something almost palpable that binds the thin sprinkling of
white men together; gives them a sense of community. Become known as a liar or a storyteller and you
will quickly find yourself outside of the community.

The impact of the white man is difficult to assess
accurately because no one is quite sure what the
original Oceania was like. For Americans the evalua-
tion is especially difficult because we are possessed of

a granite-hard streak of romanticism and are also bewitched by a century-old vision of what the Pacific or the South Seas or the Sunny Isles of Paradise or Polynesia was like.

The American vision of Oceania mixes many things together in uncritical proportions. The great salt distances, the scatter of archipelagoes, the word of Maugham and Stevenson and Melville, the harsh paintings of Gauguin, place names like Batavia and Tahiti, the fumes of sandalwood and fresh pepper, all blended into a gauzy version of *The King and I* done to ukulele music among coconut trees, with lovely hula hands and seductive hips swaying in the background. There is a belief that there was a time when the whole vague muddled area was peopled by big fair men and small graceful women. The men were magnificent sailors and the women were magnificent dancers and, in some hidden and unknown way, possessed secrets of love unknown to the West. There was a moderate drinking of something called *kava*, a chewing of betel nut, and eating of poi. Life pulsed slow and languorous.

Then, the vision tells us, the serpent slid into the garden in the form of the white man. Magellan and Cook brought in three Western exports which began the destruction: iron, gin and syphilis. Close behind the explorers came the New England whalers. The skippers were stern and Puritanical and hard, their crews mutinous and highly infective. The whalers were followed by a wave of simple adventurers, hard-case drinkers, gamblers, remittance men and black-birders. Then, we were led to believe, things were made even worse by the arrival of the missionaries. They were men and women with the American Gothic faces, harsh morals, black alpaca coats, ice-cream trousers and high black shoes. Their wives had an irresistible urge to put Mother Hubbards on the women and shorts on the men, and tuberculosis soared. The "misi" after dressing the native taught him to sing psalms in pidgin English, and soon black and tan choirs were chanting:

> Mi fella and mi mary, we belong
> Number One Fella,
> Me no can lose him more, for
> He send Pickaninny Jesu
> Keristio.

There was also a deep-seated folk belief among Americans that the missionary male was not entirely pure in his motives. Either he became infatuated with a Sadie Thompson or some half-caste girl or he turned from the cloth and became an avaricious trader who wound up owning one fifth of Hawaii.

Then, for a long period, the vision becomes thinned out. There was, we believe, a long haul and tug between the missionaries and traders and government bureaucrats and navy strategists seeking coaling stations, but, our vision runs, all this ended with World War II. With a sudden painful jerk Oceania was swept into world history. Islands which had never seen an automobile suddenly became anchorages for huge aircraft carriers, bulldozers tore airstrips in the virgin jungle, natives learned to drive jeeps, savage dogfights filled the sky, and the bodies of Japanese and American sailors drifted up onto strange shores. When it was over, Oceania was a part of the modern world. Her innocence was gone.

Now what is curious about this vision is that, in crude outline, it is not far from the truth. It is true that when Magellan barged into the Pacific the people who were already there had achieved a kind of idyllic balance with nature. In Hawaii there was an almost total absence of viruses and bacteria, with the result that wounds seldom became infected and most people died of old age. The poi-fish-fruit diet of the native was almost perfectly balanced. His sex life was free and easy. He did suffer some handicaps, but many of the very old chose to die simply because living no longer had much zest to it. Most problems were absent or were too easily solved.

It is true that the first contact with white men was devastating. Syphilis raged through the islands like fire along a fuse; in only a few short years after Cook brought the spirochete to Kauai the entire chain was infected. In Fiji the son of a royal chief returned from London with a small cough, and 30,000 Fijians died of measles. In Melanesia whole populations were decimated by nothing more virulent than the common cold.

It is true that the Pacific woman, and her husband and her father, had a somewhat peculiar idea of sex and this led to some extremely odd goings-on. The Melanesians, for example, brought their best women to the beach for the pleasure of the first white sailors they met. The sailors, used to the painted, noisy whores of Marseilles and Southampton, proceeded to mate savagely with the girls. The Melanesians, astonished by such aggressiveness, thought the strangers were preparing to eat or maim the girls and fought to protect them. This misunderstanding was very quickly straightened out, however, and to this day the tradition of sexual license and permissiveness in the Pacific is a part of every Western man's prurient knowledge.

Even the austere sailor Captain Cook could not help remarking the forwardness of Pacific women:

. . . no women I ever met with were less reserved.

Indeed it appeared to me that they visited us with no other view than to make a surrender of their persons.

As for the white man, his passion was so peculiar that a belief grew up among the Polynesians that in his homeland there were only men and that he sailed to the South Seas simply to find women and to enjoy them.

It is true that the ideals of the missionaries often amounted to cool logical clerical madness when introduced among tropical people. When the missionaries in the Marquesas insisted that boys caught sleeping with girls had to marry them, the rule not only upset an ancient custom but badly confused the Marquesans. The magnificent Monseigneur Bataillon, a huge priest with a beaklike nose and cold blue eyes and a white beard, is an example of the missionary who made a harsh empire out of paradise. He broke the backs of the natives by making them haul stones for a huge white cathedral which towered impressively, but senselessly, above the tiny nipa huts of the islands. In the end the great bishop himself was troubled over the Christian impact on Oceania and had to admit that "of the vices hypocrisy remains, of the virtues gayety, simplicity and cordiality having disappeared."

The arrogance was practiced by more than one denomination. A wonderful description of William Edward Goward, the head of the London Missionary Society in the Gilberts, is given in *We Chose the Islands,* by Sir Arthur Grimble:

> . . . he was a stocky, pink-faced, white-haired figure . . . like Bismarck . . . in radiantly laundered ducks, flaming with energy, stubborn as a mule, puritanical as a Pym, arrogant as a cardinal. His village visita-

tions at Beru were royal progresses. Flocks of beefy, white-skirted native pastors, teachers and deacons followed in his train. His parishioners lined the village streets and bowed as he passed. His word was, quite literally, law: he said pagan shrines must be destroyed, and they were destroyed; said the Gilbertese women must wear drawers and drawers for women it was.

It is also true that some of the missionaries could not resist the temptations of the marketplace. The austere New England missionaries to Hawaii and their equally austere wives, after an era of bickering the like of which has seldom been seen, piously took over the economic life of the islands with a hard grasp which is only now being pried loose. Farther south the Abbé Rougier, sent out to save the souls of heathens, wound up owning most of Fanning, Washington and Christmas islands and turning a most impressive profit on the enterprise.

But most candid observers eventually view the missions as Robert Louis Stevenson did: "I had conceived a great prejudice against Missions in the South Seas . . . that prejudice was at first reduced and then annihilated." The missionaries did bring TB and Mother Hubbards and Psalm books in pidgin English and the end of sexual ad-libbing and a slightly preposterous respect for the New England character (some old chiefs look like nothing so much as dark-skinned Calvin Coolidges—white stiff collars, high black shoes, ascetic) and a pervading sense of guilt. But they also did more, notably with medicines and schooling; they even introduced the wheel.

But parts of the myth of the Old Ways are wrong. There were some things about the Old Way which were, and are, so alien to the Westerner that he cannot believe them, even if he sees them. Others were cruel in a way that is so casual and oblivious a manner that they go unnoticed. Such things rarely find their way into print. Either the writer does not see them or he wants to forget them.

Let me offer an example of behavior so bizarre that it violates what the white man knows of reality. This is an episode described by Erskine who visited Fiji in 1849 on H.M.S. *Havannah*. He wrote:

I walked into a number of temples which were very plentiful, and at last into a *bure theravou* (young man's *bure*), where I saw a tall young man about twenty years old. He appeared to be somewhat ailing, but not at all emaciated. He was rolling up the mat he had been sleeping upon, evidently preparing to go away somewhere. I addressed him and asked him where he was going, when he immediately answered that he was going to be buried. I observed that he was not dead yet, but he said he soon should be dead when he was put under ground. I asked him why was he going to be buried? He said it was three days since he had eaten anything, and consequently he was getting very thin; and if he lived any longer he would be much thinner, and then the women would call him a *lila* (skeleton) and laugh at him. I said he was a fool to throw himself away for fear of being laughed at, and asked him what or who his private god was, knowing it was no use talking to him about Providence, a thing he had never heard of. He said his god was a shark, and that if he were cast away in a canoe and was obliged to swim, that the sharks would not bite him. I asked him if he believed the shark, his god, had any power to act over him? He said yes. Well then, said I, why do you not live a little longer and trust to your god to give you an appetite? Finding that he could not give me satisfactory answers and being determined to get buried to avoid the jeers of the ladies, which to a Feejeean are intolerable, he told me I knew nothing about it, and that I must not compare him to a white man, who was generally insensible to all shame, and did not care how much he was laughed at. I called him a fool, and said the best thing he could do was to get buried out of the way, because I knew that most of them work by the rules of contrary; but it was all to no purpose. By this time his relations had collected around the door. His father had a kind of wooden spade to dig the grave with, his mother a new suit of tapa, his sister some vermilion and a whale's tooth, as an introduction to the great god Rage-Rage. He arose, took up his bed and walked, not for life, but for death, his father, mother and sister following after, with several other distant relatives, whom I accompanied. I noticed that they seemed to follow him something in the same way that they follow a corpse in Europe to the grave (that is, as far as relationship and acquaintance are concerned), but, instead of lamenting, they were, if not rejoicing, acting and chatting in a very unconcerned way. At last we reached a place where several graves could be seen, and a spot was soon selected by the man that was to be buried. The old man, his father, began digging his grave, while his mother assisted her son in putting on a new tapa, and the girl (his sister) was besmearing him with vermilion and lamp-black, so as to send him decent into the invisible world, he (the victim) delivering messages that were to be taken by his sister to the people then absent. His father then announced to him and the rest that the grave was completed, and asked him, in rather a surly tone, if he was not ready by this time. The mother then *nosed* him and likewise the sister. He said, before I die I should like a drink of water. His father made a surly remark, and said, as he ran to fetch a leaf doubled up, "You have been considerable trouble during your life and it appears that you are going to trouble us equally at your death." The father returned with the water, which the son drank off, and then looked up into a tree covered with tough vines, saying he should prefer being strangled with a vine to being smothered in the grave. His father became excessively angry and, spreading the mat at the bottom of the grave, told the son to die *faka tamata* (like a man), when he stepped into the grave, which was not more than four feet deep, and lay down on his back, with the whale's tooth in his hands, which were clasped across his belly. The spare sides of the mats were lapped over so as to prevent the earth from getting to his body, and then about a foot of earth was shovelled in upon him as quickly as possible. His father stamped it immediately down solid and calling out, in a loud voice, "*Sa tiko, sa tiko.*" (You are stopping there, you are stopping there), meaning, "Good bye, good bye." The son answered with a very audible grunt, and then about two more feet of earth was shovelled in and stamped as before by the loving father, and *Sa Tiko* called out again, which was answered by another grunt, but much fainter. The grave was then completely filled up, when, for curiosity's sake, I said myself *Sa tiko*, but no answer was given, although I fancied or really did see the earth crack a little on top of the grave. The father and mother then turned back to back on the middle of the grave, and having dropped some kind of leaves from their hands, walked in opposite directions toward a running stream of water hard by, where all the rest washed themselves and made me wash myself, and then we returned to the town, where there was a feast prepared.

I do not know what this meant. I doubt that anyone alive today does. It is so low-pitched an approach to death that it is beyond our knowing.

Take another ritual which is a combination of cruelty and sexual excitement. Among the Polynesians there was a type of dance which was reserved for visiting royalty or an exalted guest such as Captain Cook. There would be the usual type of *tamure*, heavy with sexual overtones, danced to wooden drums and rising in intensity until it reached a frenzied climax. Then, as today, couples would peel off from the main dance, make love in the bushes and return to the party.

As the dance reached its peak the Polynesian aristocrats would announce the special performance. It was the mating of a young virgin girl to one of the most active and virile of the males. To find a virgin girl usually meant that a girl of eleven or twelve would be finally selected. The consummation took place on a low altar of cold stone, with the aristocratic queens pressed in close and shouting advice to the girl and erotic advice to the male to encourage him. Blood would flow, the girl would scream and the audience would bellow with delight. Eventually it would be accomplished.

Now there are those that say that this is understandable, an unfortunate, but inevitable part of primitive society. That is precisely the point. It is not a primitive ritual. It is a very sophisticated ritual. It is done in the full knowledge that sex and violence are linked; that they reinforce one another in some way that we do not yet fully understand. The ritual was done with the understanding that the pain of another can be pleasurable . . . which is a form of malice and far from a primitive notion.

The examples of things that violate the Utopian myth are substantial but repetitious. It is more interesting why these pieces of information did not penetrate to the literature of the South Seas. There are, I think, two reasons. First, the white man went seeking a paradise, believing it was there, predicting it would emerge from the blue seas and it was a self-fulfilling prophecy. The white man underwent a kind of lobotomy of memory . . . he recalled only those things that supported what he wanted to see. He did not lie. He merely forgot.

The second reason is more subtle. It has something to do with the fact that men that have gone to the South Seas have, generally, selected themselves to go. As a group they have been fascinated with themselves and the writers on the South Seas are no exception. Most of the thousands of books about Oceania concern the white man: how he reacts to storms, women, other men, the sun, gin. Occasionally there will be a book that is heavily sentimental about the Polynesians or the Melanesians, but generally the white man in this ocean is obsessed with himself and those like himself. It is only in the last generation that we have really come to know what is inside the heads of brown and black men. What we do know is slight, but it is enough to deflate most of the fiction that has been written about the Pacific dweller.

The last wave of white men to come to the Pacific, however, were not there because they selected themselves. This was the wave of whites, flecked occasionally with a black face, who were Americans and who were there under orders ... soldiers, sailors, Marines, fliers, Sea Bees.

The last wave of Caucasians has by all odds done the most to overwhelm the Old Way of the Pacific. Everything before this was diminutive by comparison. The Americans brought not only men but mountains of equipment and marvels of technology—enormous bulldozers, jeeps, chocolate bars, hypodermics with penicillin, Quonset huts, an unquenchable thirst for souvenirs, hardtop roads and, most tempting of all, talk of an industrial society in which anyone could have everything. Or so it seemed by Pacific standards. Bright, tough intellectual sergeants and second lieutenants from CCNY and UCLA told innocent Melanesians what life was like "Stateside."

The results were sometimes devastatingly comic and occasionally tragic. Take the weird island of Malaita in the Solomons. This dark, wet, hot and beautiful island has the most evil reputation in the Pacific—for head-hunting, cannibalism, simple stubbornness, resistance to the British officials and the head tax. I visited Malaita during the war and saw an American-maintained radar station which was close to a village. The Americans mixed easily with the villagers and the result was a steady flow of Zippo lighters, K-rations, cigarettes and khaki pants and T shirts into the village, as well as a revolution in the Malaitan mind.

One day I was hailed by a jet-black young Malaitan who spoke English with an accent as close to Oxford's as one could come while living on Malaita. He asked me quietly if I could come to the hut in which his father and he lived. The rest of the family had been murdered ten years before in one of the sudden obscure feuds that grip the island.

In their hut I was introduced to the father, who was a blackly handsome man with a great head of intensely curly hair, a broad flat nose and the cool look of intelligence about him. He was chipping away with two small stones at a larger stone about the size of a small melon. I asked him what he was making.

"A stone ax," the son said and smiled. "No. Don't offer him a steel ax. He likes to chip stone. He learned about it while he was blackbirded twenty-five years ago to work in Australia. Looks like a Stone Age savage, doesn't he?"

He did. There was no blinking it.

"Where did you learn English?" I asked the son.

"In Fiji. I went to the school for native medical practitioners there," he said. "Very good training." Then he paused and looked at me shrewdly. "I could be a very good doctor if I went to a regular medical school in the United States."

"That would be hard to arrange, I should think," I said.

"It wouldn't have to be arranged," he said softly.

"When the war is over and all these men start return-ing Stateside I could just mix in with them."

He walked to a coconut hemp bag and took out a full khaki uniform which included a sergeant's stripes. He shucked into them in a few moments and turned around. Instantly he was transformed into an Ameri-can Negro sergeant. When he spoke his voice was a clever imitation of how any sergeant, white or black, speaks.

"Look sharp, eh, Mac?" he asked. "Think I could fake myself past an embarkation officer?"

"No," I said. "You look all right, but the paperwork would catch you."

I was wrong. Years later a strange note came to me. It said simply, "I did fake my way past the embarkation officer, did get into a medical school, did practice in Harlem. Have since moved along. This is a very nice country. My father sent me the head of a stone ax for Christmas last year. The old man has a sense of humor." He did not sign his name.

Wherever the wave of Americans and their equip-ment and their food and their humor touched in the Pacific, they sparked an interest among natives. In-deed America became a kind of glowing model of social organization or, at least, the Sea Bee rough-and-ready egalitarianism did. The prim pukka tradi-tion of the British could not compete with it.

Sometimes the model of America became tragically distorted. Shortly after the end of World War II a strange political movement developed on Malaita. The natives banded together, were harangued by lo-cal leaders, a few of the older leaders were beaten or killed and the new regime took over in village after village. The first thing they did was to call themselves the Marching Rule. The second thing was to divide the village land into precisely equal sections and as-

sign one section to every male adult. Thirdly they
promised that jeeps, food and khakis would soon
arrive from the United States. It took the British
officials several months to eradicate the movement
and even longer to figure out what had happened. It
turned out that Marching Rule was a pidgin version
of Marxian Society, and that some American soldier
or sailor with Communist leanings had spun the Party
line into the uncritical ears of the Malaitans. I have
often wondered if the American who told them of
Karl Marx ever learned the surrealistic results his
teachings enjoyed on Malaita.

In general Americans are aware that The Beach
has slowly corroded the Old Way. They are aware
of the flashing, complicated, speeded-up pace of
change. Already it is difficult to see what is steady
and unchanged, what is a mixture of the Old Way
and The Beach. The cities and towns of Oceania are
splinters of civilization; all roughly identical, but out-
weighed by the area that is still "native."

I am one of those who believe that it is not possible
to know the "native mind" fully. Nor do I believe
claims made by voyagers that "they treat me just like
one of themselves." "They" never do. There is always
a thin opaque membrane between people of different
races and traditions. It can be stretched thinner, with
effort on both sides, to the point where both think
they are looking through it without distortion, but the
opaqueness always closes in again.

There are five kinds of natives in the Pacific: Australian aborigines, Malayans, Melanesians, Micronesians and Polynesians. There is much mixing, but in a
general sense this breakdown is still useful.

Sir Peter Buck, the late eminent Maori scholar and
politician, uses broader categories so that all men fall
into one of three groups: Negroids, Mongoloids and

Europoids. But when he comes to specific archipela-goes he is forced to introduce qualifying adjectives to mark off smaller groups which he wants to describe. Other anthropologists use the grouping that I use in an effort to break the Pacific up into manageable groups. I do not try to describe the Negritoes, the pygmies of the oceanic Negro, for two reasons. First, because they are small in number. Secondly, because their size has made them the losers in almost every battle for land they have fought and they live in the dark inaccessible places of the Pacific and are *sui generis*. We know very little about them.

Like everyone who writes of races I hesitate to use the word "native," but can find no suitable substitute. It means, in my usage, nothing more than indigenous.

14. The Malay

THE MALAYS are the most numerous race of the Pacific. They came out of the long peninsula of Malaya and spread solidly over the thousands of islands of the Indonesian archipelago, over all but a few of the Philippine Islands, along the northern edge of New Guinea, into the southern part of Japan and even into southern Korea.

There is a saying: "The Chinese travels to trade, the Japanese travels as a conqueror, the Malay travels to a cockfight—and always wins the Chinese gold and the Japanese sword." It is true that the Malay will travel for the most puckish reasons: rumors of strange goings on, the chance of seeing a beautiful girl or a pink buffalo, a story of a powerful fighting cock. He may fail to see these marvels, but he will smile and fold himself cheerfully into the new community. And in a strange way he makes it his own: his offspring, whether he marries an Igorot or a Guamanian, will have the rounded symmetry and beauty, the liquid grace, the nervous quick temperament of the Malay.

In Japan once I visited with the family of a distinguished engineer. The husband was from northern Japan and jokingly said of himself that he was typically Mongol: high cheekbones, soot-black and crystal-hard eyes, stiff short hair, a tautly drawn and highly active man. His wife was from the south and with the softer cast of the Malay. Their children were, both physically and emotionally, the mother's.

The music in the house was atonal but oddly soft. The teen-age children gently chided their father for his samurai stiffness and told him to relax. The father felt vaguely guilty over the wartime collapse of Japan and still felt that Shinto was a proper faith, while the children had adopted Coca-Cola, jazz and American slang with unconscious ease. "It the Malay in us that will allow us to adjust to the West," the engineer said. "The Mongol changes more slowly, with more pain."

The Malay is the most adaptable, the most effervescent, the most resilient, the most musical and the most beautiful person of the Pacific. For some reason these qualities call forth the term "childlike" when describing Malays. It happens to be completely inappropriate. It is true that the Malay has an exterior of gentleness, a soft grace. But this personality is complex and intricate. There are strands of intensity, almost of ferocity, beneath this surface. The Malay loves to gamble, to gossip, to wander, but he also has a pride which is granite-hard and when inflamed he becomes one of the most coldly frightening persons in the world.

Old British government reports and books written by learned Oxford professors have conditioned the world to view the Malay as a very peculiar person. In solemn reports there will be whole sections devoted to such things as "The Lassitude of the Malay" or "Can Malays Be Made Thrifty?" or "The Childlike Politics of the Malay." Perhaps for the nineteenth century Malay and the Peninsular Malay these essays were relevant. After all the Peninsula of Malay has one of the most oppressive climates in the world. Temperatures of 150 degrees are often reported and the humidity is always high. The trades are blocked off by mountain ranges. Today air conditioning in

Malaya is somewhat depressing because when one leaves an air-conditioned room the assault of heat and humidity is as direct and abrupt as a slap across the face. White women have been known to faint upon crossing the threshold.

Also the Peninsular Malay was, and is, subject to a punishing death and sickness rate. Malaria is the great killer and, as importantly, malaria is the great weakener. Thousands of Peninsular Malays have the pinched look and the skinny body of the perpetual malaria sufferer.

The Oceanic Malay, the Malay who lives from Indonesia to southern Japan, is a much different specimen. He is possessed of a bounce and verve that would be Gallic except that it is usually lacking in sophistication or cynicism.

There is a stunning, colorful, Breughel-like quality to life among Malays. A Malay village, whether on Bali or Mindanao, is noisy, rowdy and intimate. There is almost no privacy in such a place Everyone lives in nipa huts, which keep out the rain but are no obstacle to sound. The consummation of a marriage, the sounds of dying (and the Malay incidentally dies more quietly than any other person in the world), an argument between man and wife, the progress of a mah-jongg game—all of these attract a rapt audience. Everything, from procreation to death, seems municipalized, a matter for public gossip, for bets, for speculation. A whole village will draw tense as a cuckolding becomes too obvious or a family argument reaches a climax. I once saw an entire village on Mindanao go into collective delirium because one of their members successfully smuggled in from Borneo a load of illegal goods. The smuggler held a party of celebration which was attended by the mayor, the local police chief, a red-faced Irish Catholic priest, as well as everyone else in the village. When the celebration was over and the wine and Scotch bottles were hauled away, the smuggler had spent more than he got for his contraband. The boundaries between civic virtue and personal enjoyment simply do not exist for Malays.

Technically most Indonesian Malays are Moslems and most Filipino Malays are Christians, but both formal religions are taken very lightly. With a cheerful disregard of theological consistency a Malay will go to a mosque for prayers; visit a shaman on the way home and try to learn his future with music and incantations, the divination of leaves and candle flames; squat in front of his own home and laboriously carve into the handle of his bolo the weird head of a tusked cannibal king who is famous in a Buddhist story. When it thunders he will point upward and tell his children the Hindu fable of Kalmasapada, who tried to eat the sun and is so huge that when he flies he darkens the entire sky.

This soft hedonistic life is lived by people who also happen to be the most beautiful in the world. The beauty of Balinese women is legendary. What is surprising is to find thousands of people, scattered over hundreds of islands, possess this identical physical perfection. The Malay woman is small-boned, has a round perfect face with great melting eyes, long black hair, rounded childlike hips. There is something about the way the flesh is laid over the bones, a natural grace of wrist and ankle and gesture, that turns everyday acts into something suggesting a practical ritual. The sight of Malay women pregnant is startling: her body seems too light for the burden it carries. In rural areas, where food is scarce and the diet thin, Malay women take on a fragile look as they reach thirty, even though they do a day's work that would break the back of the average American woman. In the cities where diets are richer the Malay women takes on a soft fat which is not becoming although she loses nothing of her gracefulness.

There is an interesting contrast between Malay women and other women in the Pacific. When the Melanesian woman receives a scratch or wound she casually washes it with salt water and wraps it with a few green leaves. The cut usually festers, heals slowly and leaves a scar. The Melanesian could not care less. Indeed, she spends a good deal of time in inflicting scars upon herself as a cosmetic device. But the Malay has an almost pathological fear of scarring the human body. When a Malay receives a cut it is carefully kept open so that it will heal from the bottom up and come to a neat, and hopefully, an invisible closure.

Whether the Malay woman is on Macassar, Amboina, Balikpapan, Mindanao, Jolo or Tawi Tawi makes no difference. She will have a high regard for her body, will watch the grace of her fingers with delight, will keep herself clean and, if she can afford it, perfumed. It is narcissistic and it is not . . . for the self-regard is quite without self-love.

To fully understand the Malay woman one would have to fully understand the Indian mentality. Most Malays are nominally Moslems or Christians. But before that they were influenced by the Hindus . . . and within every Hindu there is a terrible struggle between the flesh and the spirit. The selfless gurus, the fakirs with withered arms, the ascetic culture heroes are those that have won. Most Hindus are caught in a half-hysterical, dimly understood excitement about the flesh. Their love-making is the most elaborate, perverted, sustained, frantic and studied in the world. This buried memory of Indian sexuality is communicated to all Malay women.

Take the famous Bali dancers for example. The dance seems figured, rigid, calling for extreme control, a rigid twisting of arms, fingers and knees. But behind the control and rigidity there is the strong sensation of sensuality. That is what the control is over . . . sensuality. So the Balinese dance becomes a tribute to precisely what it rejects . . . abandonment. It is no accident that dancing in India came to its greatest development among prostitutes who conveyed in their cool mannered dances some promise of what they could be like when control was lost. In Hindu music, and much of Malay music, there is a thin wail of sexual hysteria.

Whether Moslem or Christian the Malay woman now lives in a peculiar world. The Moslem will often keep his women secluded and out of sight and seemingly ignored. But only seemingly. In real fact the looks and characteristics and desirability of each woman is well known.

It is the Filipino woman, the Filipina, however, who lives today under the most intolerable of pressures. A well-to-do Filipina girl will be aware of three influences on her conduct. The first, and the most subtle, will be the faint underlying sensuality of the Indian. It conveys itself in songs, jokes, primitive phallic artifacts. But this suggestion of a controlled hedonism is overlaid by three hundred years of rigid Spanish tutoring. Then the Filipina, as a young girl, was taught to cast her eyes down, to learn a little, but not enough to become critical, to act fragile and innocent and withdrawn. Marriage was a burden to be borne for the sake of continuing the race. Then the third influence came in the form of the American. The Filipina was told to be free, to live a bit, to have fun, to be "liberated." The American women set her a startling example.

Today the Filipina is suspended between alternatives. She dresses like a Hollywood star, but draws a proper limit. She drinks, but does not dare get drunk. She flirts endlessly, but with a curious hesitation, a suggestion that it is all harmless ... but is outraged if she is taken as harmless. With a blankness that is startling she will start to discuss birth control with Americans ... but will seldom practice it. She talks of female equality, but is aware that in all probability her husband has a *querida* arrangement; a woman tucked away. The mixture of all of these needs should be unattractive, but Filipinas are magnificently attractive. Some day Manila will have a great hairdresser, a great couturier and the equivalent of a Powers model school ... and when this happens there will be a procession of beautiful, black-haired, brown-eyed women that will startle the world.

The Malay man is small of stature, well muscled, exceedingly vain, and has something of the psychology of a modern-day Casanova. Nowhere are masculinity and sexual attractiveness more prized. Even when a Malay becomes a successful businessman, picks up weight and wears conservative suits, he will still show a catlike, predatory and utterly charming mien toward women.

There is a mood among Malays which is known as *lata*. It is a kind of extreme sensitivity to the moods of others. Malays who are frequently in lata are highly regarded as diviners or exorcists, but most Malays possess the mood to some degree. In lata a Malay will seem in some eerie way to become a mirror image of the person to whom he is talking. His lips move as you talk, he grimaces when you grimace, you reach for a bottle of San Miguel beer and he already has it open,

you sense that he has formed the words in his mind
one splinter of time before you say them. The effect is
surrealistic: you feel your mind has been invaded by
another being.

Lata can have some unnerving effects. Swing
around at a cocktail party and ask a minister of state
an abrupt question and he may go lata ... he stam-
mers, improvises, cannot remember even his ministry.
Then he recovers and goes into a smooth and effortless retort. University classes must be conducted at a
different pace than in an American or European lecture hall. The snap question, directed at random to a
student, will often produce an instant blankness, a
failure of memory, an embarrassment. The lata mood
must be drawn along sympathetically. It converts into
confusion and anxiety when handled roughly.

In politics the lata quality is valuable. Politicians
who possess the lata quality can play on a crowd as
surely as Mme. Landowska's fingers stroked the harp-
sichord. The crowd will shiver, sway, gasp in anger,
exhale with pleasure, roar with laughter and fall instantly silent. The result is that in most countries with
a Malay population politics is an intense, finely
wrought, fiery pattern of speech-making—accompanied
by almost complete indifference to the skills of government. When the Malays acquire the ability to run the
boring, day-to-day aspects of government they will
become the politicians of the Pacific.

"The Indonesians are the Irishmen of the Pacific," a
tough ancient Irishman who lives in Jakarta told me.
"President Sukarno is like our Jimmy Connolly who
died a revolutionary hero in 1916. Hands like our
Jimmy had, and a talker too. Oh, what a talker. When
I close me eyes and listen to his voice it's like being
back in the Easter Rebellion. Even though I can't

understand a damned word he speaks. The whole crowd is shivering and me with 'em."

There is a point, however, where the volatile, Breughel-like openness of the Malay turns into something more black and dangerous. At the core of every Malay, whether he is a sultan or a cane cutter, is relentless pride which has a crystal-like fragility. Almost anything can suddenly shatter this intricate, deeply buried pride: a too blatant cuckolding, a short-changing in the marketplace, a steady loss at gambling, an imagined slight. When it happens the Malay goes *juramentado* or amok. His personality is transformed and, quite literally, he has a murderous hatred of everyone. When this happens a dance can become a charnel house, a polling place the scene of bloody chaos, a marketplace a scene of deadly hysterical stalking. The amok is a man possessed. His face goes hard as marble, his eyes glare at some invisible enemy, his lips twist in an awful agony. In the old days he would bind himself in white cloth. Always his hand finds a razor-sharp kris or bolo, and he will start off on a rampage of killing everyone he sees. Eventually he will be killed by the police or his own family or anyone bold enough to face him. The .45-caliber pistol was invented as the only sure means of stopping an amok. A crazed Malay would often run down a stream of .38-caliber bullets and murder the man holding the pistol. The impact of a .45 will halt a running man in full stride and slam him backward.

Today juramentado is extremely rare, but the strange core of pride is still there. Beneath the mercurial, imitative, effervescent exterior of the Malay lies an awesome concern with self, an almost illimitable sensitivity, a brooding. When this intensity is controlled and put to public use, it will surely make the Malays the most relentless and skilled of political personalities.

Before the Malays become statesmen, however, they will have to learn a lesson about a most elusive thing: time. And that will be a mixed blessing. I have been with a group of Filipinos all of them wearing watches and not one watch was wound. They wore them for decoration, not for timekeeping.

Some day they will discover time, but they will also discover its hard relentless quality. Right now a Malay will let each event run as long as it is enjoyable. One does not get that unconsciously cruel invitation "Cocktails, 5 to 7 P.M." which we so often issue ... the suggestion being that before or after that hour one is not welcome. A drinking party among Malays will start with no notion of when it will end. It may end in a few hours. It may storm along boisterously for days, remove itself from the city to the seashore and then to a barrio, may have a lull when politics and graft and world affairs are discussed and then pick up momentum again as someone hears of a cockfight.

This disregard for time is more fundamental than not winding a watch. That is understandable and happens throughout the Pacific, for people there are still used to telling time by the position of the sun. But the Malay has only a kind of gentle blurred notion of historical time. I once spent a weekend with a razor-sharp Indonesian who was superbly trained in philosophy and history and politics. By Sunday afternoon I realized that there was an odd, jumbled, ambiguous quality to our conversation. The host conducted a coherent dialogue, one of the most brilliant I have ever heard. But something about it was skewed. The Indonesian would use Montaigne, Plato, Darwin,

FDR, Sidney Hook, Hegel and Marx to tie up his argument.

"When did Plato die?" I asked him, suddenly suspecting what disturbed me.

"About the time of Darwin, I think," he said and then smiled. "But I do not know when Darwin died. Does it matter?"

Of course it did not matter. His argument was more coherent because of his total ignorance of dates and times. That the deaths of Plato and Darwin were separated by more than two thousand years had not the slightest bearing on what we were arguing. But I had not realized how much Westerners depend on dates and places to pin down our substance, like a lepidopterist who cannot believe that his butterfly is real until he has pinned it to the board.

The Malay will, alas, come to know about time. He will also come to know a good many other things. One hopes that a knowledge of time and logic and statesmanship will not stamp out the burning spontaneity that makes the Malay one of the most attractive humans on earth.

15. Man and Mote

FOR THE FIRST three days Sarah sat and stared. That was all. As if her eyes would never quite soak it all in. When Oliver came in for lunch or tea or cocktails she would turn and peer at him. After the sweep of sea and forest a human seemed very small, as if bleached and dessicated.

"My God, Oliver, that really is the Sulu Sea, those really are coral reefs and white sand spits and all those trees, those magnificent tall trees, are mahogany," she would say.

"Which I make into plywood," he would say, grinning and reaching for her.

"No, really, Oliver, look at it," Sarah would say. "It really is amazing. I never thought there was anything like this. It is so . . ."

Then she would pause, for she knew that some of the things that she said puzzled and maybe even irritated Oliver. She had taken creative writing at Stanford and occasionally Oliver would chide her for being literary.

"It is so what?" Oliver asked her the third day after their arrival.

"All right it's so big and beautiful that it's therapeutic," she said defiantly, but with a smile. "You've been out here before. You've gotten used to it. It makes me feel cleansed, innocent, like a child."

"You are a child," Oliver said. "But I never quite noticed the grime on you. In fact, I married you for your money. And because you were so damned fastidious. Make me a drink."

Sarah made the drink and brought it back. She sat next to him and they looked out at the Sulu Sea. It was such a strange place for two Jews to be. Bangtok Island was a small island, twenty miles long and ten miles wide, that was rich in mahogany lumber. Their house had a commanding view of the Sulu Sea, for it was on the highest hill on the island. A half dozen Moro boats danced across the water.

"What would Old Isidore think?" Sarah asked. She smiled.

"He wouldn't like it," Oliver said. "No place for a Jew he'd say."

They smiled and drank their drinks. Sarah thought of Old Isidore.

Sarah came from the Cracow family of St. Louis. The head of the family was Old Isidore. Young Isidore was his son and also Sarah's father. The Cracows had started with a small chain of cheap women's wear. They ended with a large chain of expensive women's wear . . . and a trucking line and a small electronics firm and a big fortune and a collection of Van Goghs and Gauguins and the first Picassos. Much later they even had Klees and a Mondrian. Old Isidore sat on a dozen boards and when he resigned Young Isidore was always invited to replace him.

Old Isidore was fiercely in love with the midwestern part of America. He was one man who said "the heartland of America" constantly and with pride and without the slightest sense of derision. His children and grandchildren could go to Vassar or Harvard or the Sorbonne, but he managed—subtly when he could, crudely when he had to—that they all returned to work in the Midwest. He cadged them into philanthropies and charities and city councils, not for social advancement but because he really wanted them to love the Midwest as he did. Occasionally he would tell a skittish grandson a few ghetto tales ... brief, black-hued, tragic, blood-tinged tales. Tales of Jewish isolation and pogroms where honest old orthodox Jews lay on the streets of Vienna and Prague with their black hats and long pigtails intact, but with their brains battered out by a mob seized with the pogrom madness. It worked.

At every bar mitzvah that Sarah could remember, the boy would begin his speech and his manhood with a tribute to the richness of Missouri earth, the greatness of the midwestern plains, the opportunities of the new land. He would finish with a fervent wish that he could live his life out in these prairie cities and lands and leave them better than he found them. Old Isidore leaned forward at each of these ceremonies, his black eyes glistening, his old lean body as intent as if he were hearing them for the first time. When he gave the boy the 24-karat gold fountain pen he always said, "Use it for the good of the heartland of America." He was passionately anti-Zionist.

When Sarah met Oliver Layden at Stanford one of the first things that made him attractive and a curiosity was his utter disregard of both his Jewishness and his lack of American citizenship. At first she had suspected him because of the fact that his family had Anglicized their name which had been Kritizky when they lived in Poland. She soon learned, however, that they did not change their name because they were ashamed of being Jews; they changed it because no Filipino could spell or remember that name. This was important for the Kritizkys had fled Poland, made their way across Russia to Harbin, hung on to life in

Shanghai, did coolie work in Tsingtao, sweated and scratched their way to Manila, did deckhand work down to Zamboanga. There they dug their fingernails in and stayed and changed their name to Layden. In twenty years they were plantation owners. Oliver was the only Jew Sarah knew who made his living directly from the soil.

Oliver was attractive. Oddly enough he looked almost precisely like the Stanford boys from Southern California . . . lean, his hair bleached by the sun, casual towards girls, very intense about sports. He was skilled at soccer when he arrived at Stanford, but he quickly became expert at volleyball, surfboarding and tennis. He went out for football when he was a sophomore and the coaches called him a "natural" and privately they were astonished at his skill and were sure he would be a first-stringer. But when the scrimmaging started Oliver lost interest. He tackled low, hard and viciously as he was instructed, he ran with an intuitively evasive lope that made him very hard to tackle, he straight-armed tacklers with a short smashing gesture that was more like a boxer's jab and left the tackler dazed for minutes afterwards . . . but he quit after three days of scrimmaging.

"It's too dull a game," he explained to Sarah. "Drill, drill, practice, practice and lots of pep talks and then you get lost in a great big scramble of guys who are sweating and grunting and over-enthusiastic. And everyone is always 'talking it up,' making like it is a big thing. I guess you have to be born American to like the game. It bores me."

Sarah sat with Oliver in the rooting section for a few games and came to agree with him. It was a tangled, swirling game in which only an expert could detect individual skill. After the first few games they usually took their books up into the hills back of Stanford and studied.

They first made love on a blanket on a Saturday afternoon when the sun was bright and the hills were burnt a deep tawny color. The blanket was under a California live oak and occasionally they could hear a roar from the stadium, muffled and coming from fifty thousand throats, but blended into a strange and somehow exciting and unhuman sound. During one of the roars Oliver looked up from his book, stared at Sarah intently for a moment, and then rolled over towards her. He kissed her and in the same instant ran his hand up her leg, ripped off her shorts and was on top of her. It was over quickly and he was smiling down at her, and to her astonishment Sarah enjoyed it. There had been some pain, distant and remote, but the central sensation had been so consuming and exquisite, so quickly achieved that she was only aware of a great pleasure ... deep in the muscles and the organs.

"You've done that before," she said and discovered for the first time that she was breathing deep fierce breaths and was trembling slightly.

"Yes," Oliver said simply. The expression on his face did not change, did not seem evasive or apologetic or boastful or anything that Sarah had anticipated.

"It's not just exactly what the marriage manuals had prepared me for," Sarah said.

"No. It's better," Oliver said.

She nodded at him and although she did not know it at the time her face was seductive and exciting. Oliver moved again and she responded instantly. A moment later, no longer than a minute, Oliver had rolled free and she was staring straight up into a blue sky that was perfectly empty and endless except for a single slow-floating cloud. It had happened again, that incredible quick swoop of pleasure, that shattering fragment of sensuality. She studied the cloud with an intensity that was crazy and meaningless. She laughed, a deep-throated laugh of pleasure, the simplest laugh she had ever uttered. She waited for the breathing to slow, for the trembling to stop. She felt not the slightest anxiety.

"The marriage manuals are wrong," she said.

"We're going to be married," Oliver said.

"I know," Sarah replied.

It was more difficult than they had foreseen. She took Oliver to St. Louis during Christmas vacation to meet the family. Old and Young Isidore were a bit curious about the name Layden and they questioned Oliver, at first casually and then more forcefully, on the precise circumstances which had led to the change of name. But they were satisfied on that score at some point. One of Sarah's uncles was a rabbi and he, also casually, brought up the question of Oliver's religious practice. Oliver explained that they were the only Jews on Bangtok Island where the Layden plantation was located and for this reason he was vague on many matters of Judaism.

"But is your family Reformed or Orthodox?" the rabbi pushed gently.

"What difference does it make?" Old Isidore said and there was a rasp in his voice. "The boy's a Jew. That's enough. All this business with Reformed and Orthodox and eating kosher is nonsense."

The rabbi shot an offended look at Old Isidore, but knew that the matter was now settled. No one had won an argument with the old man yet and no one really ever expected to.

Sarah watched Oliver closely. At first she was embarrassed at the openness of the questioning, the air of interrogation. But she soon sensed that Oliver did not mind them in the least. He answered calmly, looking directly at whoever asked the question, keeping his answers crisp and short.

"Now about the business of business after you graduate from Stanford?" Old Isidore asked. He smiled at his joke, but Sarah realized instantly that this was the central matter. The old man was tensed up. "We have business in six midwestern cities. Sarah has told you about them. Which business do you want to go into?"

"None. We are going to live on Bangtok and I'll run the plantation," Oliver said.

He smiled and seemed oblivious of the instant tension in the room. The faces of the adults had suddenly gone smooth and expressionless. The women moved their eyes away from Oliver's face and Auntie Joan, the most emotional girl to marry into the Cracow family, rolled her eyes upward in the instinctive gesture which Jewish women make when they anticipate trouble. The men, more deliberately, slowly looked from Oliver to Old Isidore.

"Our businesses are in the heartland of America," Old Isidore said as if he had not heard Oliver's words. "We are in lots of things ... artist supplies, trucking, retail. Maybe soon even a small feeder airline. Almost any job that a young man wanted he could find in the Cracow businesses."

"I'm sure of that," Oliver said. "But I want to live on Bangtok."

The old man stood up and walked directly across the large living room to the door of his study. He turned and motioned to Oliver. They both walked into the study and the old man closed the door. They were in the study for two hours.

When they came out the old man was somehow changed. His posture was the same, erect and straight, his face was the same, Semitic and hard. But his eyes were filled with a cloudlike bewilderment, a muted look of a confusion so vast and fundamental that it seemed almost as if the eyeballs had by some strange way become the milky sightless orbs of those that have trachoma. His head moved around the room, but his eyes saw no one. He waited for a moment and then left the room without speaking.

"Let's go for a walk," Oliver said. He seemed in precisely the same mood in which he had entered the study.

"How did it go with the old . . ." Auntie Joan started to say and then stopped as her husband looked at her.

"We're going for a walk," Sarah said.

They left the house and walked down the well-ordered, neatly laid-out streets of St. Louis.

"What did you talk about?" Sarah finally said.

"Mr. Cracow and I?" Oliver asked. She nodded.

"First, about you. He told me what a beauty you were and I agreed. You are, you know."

Sarah knew. She was tall and slim, had big black eyes, fine bones in her face and a slightly flared nose. Among the young Jewish matrons there was an admiration for her leanness, her black hair, her bearing of pride . . . a kind of inner tautness they admired. Almost all of her mother's friends, themselves plump and weight-conscious, remarked constantly, "Sarah will never run to fat." It was a compliment which meant much more than just the words.

"What did he say then?" Sarah asked.

Oliver paused, looked at a tall new skyscraper and the little black shapes of the window washers forty stories in the air.

"He said you were a wealthy girl and that you had earned not a dime of your money and that you and I owed something to the Midwest which had supplied the money," Oliver said. "He said I owed it to you and your family and myself to plow something of my time and energy and talent back into the land which had been so generous to all the Cracows. He was very serious."

"What did you say?"

"I said that I thought you were beautiful and was glad that you had money, but that I wanted to return to Bangtok and that was what we would do," Oliver said. "I told him that we could live without your money, but I was glad that you had it and I would use it to develop the plantation ... maybe buy some new Belgian machines for the plywood factory, some English trucks for the mahogany-log hauling."

"What else?" Sarah asked. She could not believe that two hours was spent in merely talking about these things.

"That was all. We just kept saying the same things back and forth," Oliver said. "He kept talking about St. Louis and Missouri and Iowa and the Midwest and I kept saying we were going to live and work and die on Bangtok."

"For two hours?"

"For two hours. He is a nice guy, but very persistent," Oliver said.

Sarah realized that Oliver did not understand the dimensions, the intensity, the involvement, the history of the battle that had been fought in the study. Again she had the slight, glancing, almost subliminal sensation that Oliver knew something that the rest of them did not. He was certain in a manner that was nonassertive, indeed almost placid, but was implacable.

"Why are you so determined to live on Bangtok?" she asked.

Oliver shrugged. "You will have to see it. It's an

island, not a beautiful island, but an island and lost in a very big sea and it is the only place that I feel is right for me." He paused, stopped and looked at her. "I can't say it with the right words, but I think you will like it."

"And if I don't?"

"You will," Oliver answered with that low-pitched certitude which was a part of his personality. "It will take some time, maybe, but you'll like it."

As they approached Zamboanga the passages opened up and Zamboanga City itself was something like a diminished Manila. The flight over had been over water which was sweeping and open.

Oliver's house was a surprise. She had expected a long low white sort of building. Instead it was a big lovely intricate structure raised eight feet off the ground by mahogany posts. A broad flight of stairs led up to the veranda which ran completely around the house. Four Filipinos were standing on the steps. Three were house servants and Oliver introduced them to Sarah very quickly. The fourth man took off a finely grained pandanus hat and shook hands with Sarah when he was introduced ... the other three had merely bowed. This man, Oliver explained, was named Salvador and he was the highest ranking Filipino on the Layden plantations.

"Also he is my friend," Oliver said. He jabbed Salvador in the ribs. Salvador jabbed him back and for a few seconds they sparred playfully on the stairs.

"Your husband is a great kidder," Salvador said. "A character."

Sarah was startled at the perfection of his English. He spoke not only flawlessly, but in a colloquial manner. He sounded much more like an American college boy than did Oliver.

Salvador opened the door to the house, bowed

them in and left. Sarah looked around the room. The entire house was made of teak with beams that went up at a very sharp angle and gave the room the impression of great height. The floor had been polished so often that it had a lapidary quality; a deep black glow of color. The wooden wall panels were of carved wood which showed snakes, Moslem symbols, men engaged in battle, men and women making love, a cockfight.

Oliver led her out to the veranda which overlooked the mahogany forests of Bangtok and the Sulu Sea.

"Oh, Oliver, I love it," Sarah said. "The house is like a ship. I mean it's not only built snug and trim like a ship but I have the impression that we are sailing right through the forest."

"The house was built by Moro shipbuilders," Oliver said. "There is not a nail in it ... just thousands of pegs, each one carved to fit its own hole and then pounded firm. In a storm the place creaks like a ship in a high sea."

Sarah was scarcely listening. The whole thing, the house and the forest and the sea and the various colors of the waters and the clouds struck her as nothing visual had ever struck her before. It had a kind of massive symmetry, a sense of unity. Even the half dozen Moro sailboats, each with a triangle sail, seemed part of a composition.

"I'll never go back to St. Louis," she said turning to Oliver. "Not after this."

"You'll get used to it after awhile," Oliver said. "There will come a day when even Manila will seem exciting to you."

"Not me," Sarah said fervently. "This is exactly right for me."

Oliver laughed, reached for her and put his hand

over her stomach. She pushed it downward and waited for a moment. Then she turned and kissed him and again, without removing their clothes, without a word, without a preliminary they were making love on the hard black polished floor.

Ten minutes later he had showered and was back on the veranda.

"Let's go for a ride," he said. "Take a look at the manor."

They walked out and got in the jeep.

The Layden plantation was spread over several thousand acres of the island. Dotted through the plantation were a dozen company villages. Each of them was roughly identical ... a quadrangle of barrackslike buildings with one end of the quadrangle open, a well in the center of the quadrangle and just behind it a flag was flying from a mahogany pole. As soon as Oliver's jeep appeared children came pouring out of doors, mothers stood in doorways and everyone shouted a kind of short chanting greeting which ended with the word "Layden." Oliver then stood up and shouted back at them in dialect, ending his speech with "Mrs. Sarah Layden" and pointing down at Sarah. The Filipinos roared with laughter as Oliver took Sarah's arm and drew her erect.

"What did you say that made them laugh?" Sarah asked as they left the second village.

"It's a Tagalog joke. A kind of pun. It sounds dirty in English, but in Tagalog it is more funny than dirty," Oliver said.

"Oh, come on. Tell me what it means."

"Well roughly it means 'Here is a fine-looking white woman from a great family with much prestige and a long history ... but she, like all of us, opens her legs to make love,'" Oliver said.

"You said that about me?" Sarah asked. Before Oliver could reply she was gasping with laughter. She held on to the edge of the jeep and her eyes were blurred with tears. With her left hand she pounded Oliver's shoulder in mock rage. Finally when she could speak she said, "I thought you were saying 'This is a grand lady who will preside over the Layden plantation and be nice to the peasants. Love the nice lady.'" She gasped again. "That's the first time I ever heard a dirty joke that sounded regal. Are you going to say it at all the six villages?"

"Of course," Oliver said. "It's expected. They would die of disappointment if I didn't say something like that. It's the only time they will ever hear me or any white man say a disrespectful thing about you, but this first time they expect it."

They came to a crew of men who were putting "eyes" from Malaya rubber plants into living Filipino rubber trees. The men did not turn around as Oliver and Sarah approached. They worked with the intensity and dexterity of surgeons, expertly cutting off the original eye, then making a short slit in the bark, inserting the Malayan "eye" and then sealing the wound.

"It is difficult work," Oliver explained. "Some men never learn how to do it. The trees that grow from a successful transplant give almost twice as much rubber as a native tree. Those eyes were smuggled out of Malaya into Bangtok by a gang of Moro smugglers. The Malaya rubber monopoly guard their trees and forbid exportation. Each of those eyes is probably worth a couple of pesos."

Oliver suddenly barked something at the men in Tagalog. They all looked around and smiled. They wiped their hands on their pants, came over and shook hands with Oliver. He introduced them to Sarah, but none of them offered to shake hands. They smiled at her, however, and made a slight bow. Sarah liked them at once. Oliver made a short speech, ended with the same Tagalog joke and the men burst out laughing. Sarah kept her face straight, but the moment they were back in the jeep and moving she burst out laughing.

"Are you going to tell even the men that I open my legs to make love?" she asked.

"Sure," Oliver replied. "Don't get any feelings of wounded pride. It doesn't make them the least bit less respectful. It's just a tradition."

"My pride is not wounded," Sarah said, giggling. "It's just that it's so crazy a thing to say about a new bride. If they could only hear you make that little spiel in St. Louis."

They drove another half mile when Oliver suddenly jammed on the brakes. He reached into the rear seat, lifted a tarpaulin and picked up a short gun. It was an air gun, made in Germany, and it was primed by jerking a short lever below the stock a few times.

"Now, watch this because you'll probably be doing a lot of it," Oliver said. "See that slash in the rubber tree."

It was a long slanting cut in the bark of the tree and it glistened with the white milk that slowly oozed downward. At the bottom of the slash there was a half coconut into which the rubber milk dropped. As she watched she saw three or four drops fall into the coconut.

"I see it, but why the gun?" she asked.

"See at the right of the coconut, that round colored thing," Oliver said and in his voice there was a slight tinge of rage. "That's a Japanese snail. The Japanese imported them for food and the damned things have taken over the islands. They will eat anything ...

rubber milk, cocoa leaves and pods, leaves, any damned thing. There are millions of them around."

"Let me look at it before you shoot it," Sarah said.

They got out of the jeep and walked over to the tree. The snail was huge, as large as an orange. Its shell was a pattern of beautiful striated lines each a different color, ranging from light purple to shocking orange.

"I never knew that snails grew that big," Sarah said. "In a way it's beautiful."

"Oh, my God," Oliver said and there was real anger in his voice. "First of all this is a small one. Second, look at that head."

She moved closer and to one side and suddenly saw the head. It was a moist gray gelatinous lump with two tiny antennalike growths. Its mouth was out of all proportion to the size of the head . . . big, armed with small teeth, grasping. As she watched it put its mouth into the coconut and sucked in the rubber milk.

"All it is taking in that one mouthful is about a sixteenth of an ounce," Oliver said softly. "But multiply this one by a hundred mouthfuls a day and multiply that by three million and you get a result that means a bankrupt rubber plantation. Christ, how I hate the filthy things."

"Are there really that many?" Sarah asked as they walked back to the car. "I mean really millions?"

"Salvador said that in a one-thousand-hectare section he poisoned three million of those bastards in two months," Oliver said. "Their shells made a heap as big as our house."

They climbed into the jeep. Oliver leaned the pump gun against the jeep windshield to steady his aim. There was a slight hissing noise and then a loud crack as the snail's shell exploded. As Sarah watched, the snail's gluelike grip came loose and it slid slowly down the tree like some surrealistic teardrop. Sarah gulped.

"Wouldn't three million rotting snails make an awful stench?" Sarah asked.

Oliver looked at her for a moment. He smiled.

"I keep forgetting that it's all new to you," he said and there was almost something of regret in his voice, as if he did not want to reveal something to her. "Go over and look at the snail."

"What for?"

"Go and look," he ordered.

She walked back to the tree alone. She bent over and looked at the snail. Something had happened. Its head and the hole torn in its side by the slug were red . . . a red, furry, moving red. She bent closer, puzzled. It was a layer of red made up of hundreds of small red ants. It did not disgust her, she felt no nausea. But she had a sharp insight: *if my ears were powerful enough I would hear the rending of thousands of tiny mouths, the gulping of miniscule bits of flesh, a scraping of legs, shouts of outrage as the tiny mouths fight for a good position to gnaw.* She walked back to the jeep. Oliver was watching her intently.

"How do they gather so fast?" Sarah asked.

"No one knows," Oliver said. "It always puzzles me where they hide, how they know when death has come, what they live on between great bonanzas like a mass snail poisoning. When I was a boy I would crawl over the grass for hours with a magnifying glass looking for a red ant and never see one. Then a drop of candy spit would fall from my mouth and instantly it would be red and a few seconds later it would be gone."

They drove along silently for a few miles.

"It's a shame that such a wonderful gentle people

and a beautiful island should have just that one error, that scourge of snails," Sarah said.

"Oh, don't worry, sweetheart, we've got other troubles," Oliver said. "It will just take time for you to see them."

Sarah did not, at the time, really believe him.

That evening they went down to the lumbermill to meet the white executives who ran the offices and were the supervisors for the Layden Corporation. There were six couples . . . two Germans, one Dutchman, two Americans and one Swiss. They were all in the same age range except for the Swiss who was older. All veterans of World War II, all charming, but with the look of the hard-driver about them, all cautious drinkers, but with the air of wanting to take more if their flanks were protected. The wives were attractive and poised, except for the wife of one of the Germans who was cool, tall, elegant, dressed with a simplicity that must have been expensive. Each of the couples occupied identical houses in a compound that was a half mile from the sawmill. Cocktails were served at the home of the Swiss because he was the senior manager.

It was a completely normal cocktail party, like a dozen others that Sarah had been to in the States except for two things: the accents of the Europeans and the distant thin burr of the sawmill.

"Does the sawmill run twenty-four hours a day?" Sarah asked the Swiss.

"Yes, except when there is a breakdown or a shortage of water to float the logs," he replied. "Otherwise it goes steady, steady, steady. In a while you get so you do not hear the sound. It irritates you, yes?"

"No. Not irritating," Sarah said. "It just sounds unnatural out here. I mean a mechanical sound in a place where all the other sounds are natural . . . water running, surf pounding, wind in the trees, the sounds people make."

He looked at her oddly.

"I never thought of that before," he said. "Perhaps you are right."

"There are many sounds here that are not natural," the youngest of the two Germans said. He had short yellow hair, a handsome face, a mood of tension. Sarah sensed that he was combative. "There are radios, jeeps, motorboats. And sometimes the sound of airplanes. Back in the rain jungle there are the ruins of a half dozen Japanese and American fighter planes that were downed when Mindanao was first invaded."

"Oh, of course, I know you're right," Sarah said. "It's impossible to keep mechanical sounds out of a place, but it is so lovely here, so unspoiled that one wishes that it just stayed the way it is. You see I'm in the romantic phase. Everyone tells me I'll get over it soon enough."

For no rational reason she thought of a hiss of air, the cracking of a shell. It took her a moment to recall that it was the air gun and the shooting of the snail. She asked the German for another gin and tonic.

"Why are there no natives among the managers?" she asked Oliver when they were in the jeep driving home.

"I will tell you, but you will not believe me," Oliver said. "Not at first anyway. The fact is that the native has a very soft voice. It is impossible for them to give orders which sound convincing. The next time you are at a cocktail party note how hard and implacable the American and European voices sound. The native can never sound like that."

"How do the natives run an army and a navy?"

Sarah asked. "Surely their officers give orders and are obeyed."

"Sometime you will get the chance to see," Oliver said. "Most effective native officers have stopped being natives and have become hysterics ... they quite literally scream at their men, keep themselves up to a pitch of agitation, a kind of constant outrage so that in the end they *do* come to have a ring of authority in their voices. But it is a terrible life they lead. They have ulcers and coronaries at a frightful rate."

The next day Sarah spent only a few moments admiring the view and then turned to organizing the work of the servants. The house had almost no mechanical appliances except an electrical generator which went on at night to run the lights and the radio. Everything else in the house was done by hand and at a pace that was as soft and slow as an underwater ballet ... the girls wound rags around their feet after breakfast and skated for an hour over the floor, the cook chopped condiments for curry into the tiniest bits with a very sharp French knife ... for three hours ... when a Waring blender could have done the whole thing in ten minutes. The gardening boy chopped at the grass around the house with a long-handled scythe and with an uncanny eye so that every blade was cut to exactly the same length ... occasionally he would stretch out flat on the lawn to make sure it was level.

Sarah found all of this rhythmical. She had no notions of speeding things up or of revolutionizing the old ways on the Layden plantation. The pattern had been carved out for years, bit by bit. The one thing Sarah did want to change, however, was the habit of the cook of always serving one canned American dish with each meal. Dinner might consist of a crab omelet, a roast of native beef, local vegetables and papaya pudding for dessert ... and in the middle of the table would be a plate of canned American pork and beans or a dish of canned salmon or a little stack of canned Texas tamales.

"No more canned American food with meals, Cooky," she told Ah Lee the Chinese cook. "Not unless I order it. Then all right. O.K.?"

"O.K.," Ah Lee said and that night with dinner served a brimming bowl of California canned peaches in heavy syrup.

Immediately after dinner she walked into the kitchen, her jaw set. Ah Lee and the two maids were seated on high stools around a large table in the middle of the kitchen. There were the remains of large fish on a plate in the center of the table. The three of them were eating California cling peaches in heavy syrup. They smiled at her.

"Ah Lee, I told you no canned American food on the table unless I order it," she said sharply. "You savvy."

"Me savvy," he said smiling and Sarah could see nothing of insolence or guile in his eyes. "No Melican-style can food 'ness you say. O.K.?"

"O.K.," Sarah said, surprised at his easy compliance. She had expected some long drawn-out argument, the claim of a misunderstanding. The three of them smiled over spoonfuls of yellow peach and thick syrup as she retreated from the kitchen.

The next day at lunch there was a fresh fruit salad and new baked rolls and a small broiled bonita and a large red chunk of canned corned beef . . . a red chunk of meat, laced with white fat. It rested there, insolent, vulgar, defiant.

Sarah flushed. She explained what had happened to Oliver and found herself trembling with anger by the time she had finished. He looked at a piece of mango on his fork, put it in his mouth and chewed for a moment.

"Look, Sarah, native food can get very monotonous," he said. "They eat rice and fish and sweet potatoes day in and day out. They like the chance to break the monotony with some canned American food. It tastes different to them. But part of the game is that they have to go through the motions of serving it to us first. If we don't eat it then they can. Every Westerner with a cook has to go through the same thing."

"But their own food is so wonderful and it's not monotonous," Sarah said. "I gave Ah Lee a recipe for shrimp curry made entirely out of things he could buy at the native market down in town . . . shrimp, rice, coconut, the condiments. It was wonderful. You said so yourself."

"It was. I liked it," Oliver said and then paused. "But for Ah Lee it is no great thrill. It still has the taste of the Sulu Sea, the paddy field, the native market to him. But Texas tamales. Ah, that is something from another world and so is blueberry jam, and salmon, and tomato soup."

It's so silly with all the wonderful fruits and vegetables," Sarah began.

"Listen a second, sweetheart," Oliver cut in. "Life is the same for these people almost every day. No newspapers or radio sets, no TV, no movies, cockfights once or twice a month." He leaned towards her, talking fast and with urgency. "Ah Lee can sit down tonight in the center of his family, two old aunts, six kids, one wife and a blind father, all living in a nipa hut as big as your bathroom and spin out a wonderful story to them of the glories of blueberry jam and that

god-damned chunk of bully beef. They'll oh and ah
and hiss and admire him and his experience."

The unexpected force with which Oliver spoke,
rather than his words, gave Sarah a quick passing
insight into what he meant. The islands, the untold
thousands of them, were occupied by great placid
streams of people who had flowed over them for
centuries. They gathered in tiny knots, villages and
places smaller than villages, and talked and gossiped.
For a moment she experienced a moment of panic:
she was isolated. It cut through her as sharply and
neatly as a lancet through flesh. Then it was gone,
leaving no wound. Even if she never could understand the natives and the Chinese, she would still
have Oliver and she would have the magnificent
scenery. It would be enough.

She smiled at Oliver. "Let's have some cognac with
our coffee," she asked. "Please."

He smiled back at her and walked over to the
sideboard and brought back a bottle of Martell's and
two snifter glasses. They moved to the veranda. Sarah
leaned towards Oliver and kissed him. Then in some
quick startling manner, the steps of which Sarah
could hardly remember, they were making love half
on the low couch and half on the floor . . . Sarah
savagely digging her bare feet into the glasslike surface of the floor so that she could arch back towards
him, shrieking softly into his ear and then taking it
between her teeth. When Oliver lifted abruptly away
from her, as he always did, she felt surfeit with contentment.

Later however, much later, Sarah knew that the
first sharp edge of the wedge of discontent had been
driven in. Not hard, really hardly noticeable. But the
snail and the block of bully beef were the start. The
next time she walked out on the veranda and looked

at the sweeping view, the green and white of the sea, the towering trade wind clouds she kept her eyes above the forests of rubber and mahogany trees ... somehow the forests now seemed a subtly dangerous place. A place where millions of snails could hide, billions of ants could move in orderly massive silent arrays.

Then in quick succession two things happened which converted the forests from a subtle to a direct menace. She and Oliver were driving to the sawmill when he suddenly jammed on the brakes and reached again under the tarpaulin. His hand came out with a machete.

"Stay in the jeep," he said.

He had run ten steps down the road before Sarah saw it .. a flat hooded head, almost the same color as the vegetation, but weaving while everything else was still. A cobra. The head undulated gently, as if moved by an unseen wind, turned and she saw the eyes . . . two tiny glistening jewels. The cobra saw Oliver and it sank into the grass. Oliver squatted on his haunches, his right hand with the machete held far back, its tip touching the ground. He whistled, a strange hiss of a sound. The cobra's head came back up, could not see the source of the sound and reached higher on a long thick stem of a body. The head coiled smoothly about, the eyes glittering.

Oliver's arm snapped forward and the machete flew towards the cobra precisely like a small whirring propeller. The cobra sensed it coming, began to snap downward into the protective vegetation. The machete hit it just below the head and for an astonishing second the creature poised . . . then the decapitated head fell into the weeds and the stem of the body shot straight into the air, purple blood geysering, hung there rigid for a moment and then collapsed slowly and was gone.

Around her diaphragm and her lungs and up into her throat Sarah felt a terrible pain. She realized that her body had wanted to scream, but that her mind had forbidden it. I will not be hysterical, she said to herself. But her body was still locked in the cramp of an unreleased scream. Sit back, she told herself, sit back and relax. She did and by the time Oliver was back at the jeep, wiping off the machete, the spasm was gone.

"Aren't many of them left these days," Oliver said casually. "Clearing out the jungle for planting destroyed most of them. Then the kids hunt them for fun. And the mongooses we imported to keep the coconut rats under control got the rest. Salvador told me the other day he hadn't seen one in two weeks."

Sarah knew she must say something, must make that complicated sound-making physiology operate. She licked her lips.

"Why didn't you shoot it with the pump gun?" she asked. Her voice was normal.

"A little slug like that, or even a big one like a 30-30 could go right through a cobra and not stop it," Oliver said. "You have to sever the backbone before you really have them. Nick them with a slug and they will just slither away and hole up until it's cured."

Oliver started the jeep and went slowly down the hill, the sound of the saw blades became audible ... first in the teeth and throat and lastly in the ears.

"Do they bite many people?" Sarah asked.

"Not if they can help it," Oliver laughed. "They scramble like hell to stay out of your way. But occasionally a gang of workers walking through the jungle will confuse a cobra and he feels surrounded and strikes out. Or the cobra just makes a mistake ...

misjudges which way to go and slides into your path and then he will strike. But I haven't heard of a cobra striking for weeks."

Weeks, she thought to herself. *Could one calculate the chances of any one individual being struck?* She could not, at that moment.

For the first time since she had been on Bangtok she welcomed the sound and roar and activity of the sawmill. She walked into the great barnlike structure, watched with pleasure as the giant steel claws reached into the water, grasped a mahogany log eight feet in diameter and lifted dripping up to the level where the shiny blades were waiting. A native jerked a lever and the log was shifted onto a sliding carriage, locked down by steel teeth a foot long. The carriage slid forward and the circular blades whined into the green wood. Splinters and sawdust and chunks of bark poured down in a brown jet. The din was enormous.

The carriage jerked back. The steel teeth came out, took a new bite, turned the log over a quarter turn. The carriage shot forward again. Two more trips of the carriage, and the log was no longer part of the jungle . . . it was a massive trimmed rectangle of wood. In thirty seconds more it was reduced to fifty planks of mahogany, each one a few inches thick and forty feet long. The planks slid, sleek and new, down a mechanical ramp to the dock where a fork lift arranged them in stacks.

"I have to go up to the shipping office," Oliver said.

"I'll wait here for a while," Sarah said. Oliver turned and looked at her in surprise. He shrugged. "I'll just watch a few more go through the saws."

"O.K. Come up to the office when you're ready. But stand back a bit. Occasionally the saw blade will hit a nail that someone drove into the tree. Then the saw teeth fly around here like shrapnel."

She nodded and stepped back a few paces, leaned against a protective rail. She was still there an hour and a half later when Oliver came back. He was puzzled.

"I thought you were coming up to the office," he said.

She turned, looked at him dazedly.

"I am ... I mean I was," she said. She looked at her wrist watch. "I didn't realize what time it was."

The second tap on the wedge came two days later. She was playing tennis with Etna, the wife of the blond German boy. The court was just outside of her home and had an excellent surface of crushed and rolled coral. It drained so well that five minutes after a rain squall it could be played on. The court was surrounded by a wire fence to retain the balls. Beyond that was a neat garden of frangipani and bougainvillaea trees trimmed very low and then began the neat rows of coconut trees.

Etna was a good player, but somewhat overcontrolled. Her strokes were accurate and well placed, but delivered with a jerky restraint that robbed them of real power. Sarah usually beat her just by the sheer power of her smashes and the smoothness of her backhand.

They were on the third set and Sarah was serving. She was sweating and she took a linen handkerchief from her pocket and wiped her forehead. Then she threw the ball up, lifted her head back and swung. She knew the instant it left the racquet it would be too long, but her eye automatically followed the ball, watched it hit two feet long and then bounce over Etna's head and high up on the fence. It was then that she saw the motion on the trunk of the closest

coconut tree. For a moment she thought it was a drop
of sweat in her eye and she wiped her hand across
her eyes. But the motion was still there ... a small
black patch that moved rapidly up the coconut tree
towards the band of tin which was put around every
tree to keep the rats from getting to the coconuts.

Etna swung her head around and followed the line
of Sarah's vision.

"It's a coconut rat," Etna explained. "There must be
a mongoose after him. They never go up a tree during the day unless they are being chased."

The rat came to the edge of the strip of tin, put out
a tentative paw and scratched at it. He looked back
over his shoulder.

*From experience he must know he can't get over
the tin,* Sarah thought. *There's no way he can get a
grip.*

Then she saw the mongoose. He came streaking up
the tree, paused halfway and looked up. Sarah was
surprised at how small he was. His body was actually
smaller than that of the rat, but it was more purposeful, more muscled, more tense. The body narrowed to
a small head that moved in swift sure jabs. It was an
elegant creature.

For a moment both rat and mongoose were motionless, looking at one another. Then the mongoose started to flow up the tree in a single burst of motion.
Instantly the rat turned and leaped at the band of
tin, its feet scratching for a hold. The tiny metallic
scratchings carried easily to Sarah's ears. The rat's
nose came to the top of the tin band, carried there by
sheer momentum, he reached a foot upward and
missed the trunk. There was a long steady screech as
he slid back down the tin.

The mongoose and the rat met at the bottom of the
tin strip. There was a short soundless explosion of fur,

claws, teeth; a brown bewildering of bodies. Then the action stopped abruptly. The bodies separated. One of them was red now, red and white, a mixture of blood and ripped intestine. The mongoose held the dead body easily in its teeth, although it must have been a heavy load. The mongoose backed slowly down the tree and disappeared.

"Do you want to take two, darling?" Etna asked. "The rat broke your rhythm. Go ahead, take two."

"Thanks. I think I will," Sarah said.

Her first service came in hard and solid, just caught the line and came up flat. Etna swung and missed.

"Ace," she said admiringly. "You've got a hell of a serve, Sarah."

Ten minutes later they were drinking gimlets on the veranda. Sarah had two and then said, "Good Lord, I'd better have a gin and tonic. I'm dying of thirst. How about you?" Etna shook her head.

Sarah had three more drinks after Etna left. After lunch, for the first time in her life, she fell asleep drunk.

There was one thing that Sarah had learned from Old Isidore. That was self-criticism. That was how she was able to tell that she was frightened of the jungle. After that day with Etna she always let someone else retrieve a ball that went over the fence and into the coconut palms. And she watched the cleared area around the house with a hard eye and the moment a tendril fell across the path she had the gardener hacking it clear.

Her days began to fall into a pattern. She had breakfast with Oliver and then, when he left, she read for an hour on the veranda, occasionally glancing up at the sweep of sea and sky and clouds. She never talked to the servants any more ... they ran the house quite automatically, not even bothering to check the menus with her. At eleven she played tennis with one of the wives of the white executives, carefully rotating them so that everyone was included. Usually there was a cocktail party some place or they gave one. Visiting politicians and businessmen and Japanese and Chinese traders, important ones, were always the occasion for a dinner party. Scattered through the days, at quite unpredictable times, were the intense quick periods of love-making with Oliver. They left Sarah numb with pleasure.

Sarah had been on the island six months when the trade winds abruptly ended. It happened while she and Oliver were serving cocktails to the two German couples and the old Swiss couple on the veranda. Sarah glanced out towards the sea, watched one of the big towering white clouds and suddenly realized that it was collapsing, was already half its size. For some reason she felt a sense of panic. She looked more closely, the gimlet in her hand tilting and dribbling a few drops on her hand. Without looking down she righted her glass. Along the horizon a gray shimmering line was moving towards them ... and as it came the familiar cloud shapes, which had been like marble in the sky for months, began to dissolve, grow small, shrink towards the earth and then finally vanished.

"What is happening out there?" she asked the blond German. She pointed towards the horizon. He stared for a moment and then shrugged.

"Oh, good Lord, it looks like the monsoon," he said to the entire group. "The trades are falling." They all swung their heads around and looked. The women sighed. The German bent towards Sarah. "That gray line is the heat that comes with the falling of the trades. In another half hour this breeze will be gone and it will be hot."

She looked around at the women. They were watching the horizon with the curious abstracted look of people who are thinking of something else, making some future calculation.

"Well, let's enjoy it while we can," Oliver said. He began to pass around drinks. "About another half hour of cool weather."

Sarah drank and talked, but kept glancing out to sea. The whole great sweep of clouds and sea and hills was changing. It had held steady, barely changing for months, magnificent in proportion, a massive symmetry of shape and color. And now it was dissolving, becoming gray before her eyes.

Then the heat came. One moment the breeze was there. The next moment it was replaced by a wet heat that rose straight from the earth. Sarah felt her body sag under the impact. She began to sweat in strange places, the small of her back, the insides of her knees, places she had never sweated before, even when exercising hard. Tiny trickles of sweat ran down her legs and into her shoes. She glanced at the others and noticed that although the men had instantly slipped off their jackets they were also sweating through their silk shirts. And all had sat down, slumped back into their chairs, slowed their movements as if effort were now difficult.

When she looked out to sea her view was gone. Steam was rising from the rain jungle, a slow churning layer of vapor which rose above the tops of the trees and was then burnt away by the sun. The Sulu Sea which had always been cleanly green and white was now a suffering, unbelievable, shimmering gray color. Some relationship between sea and sun was reversed, Sarah thought, and the sea had suffered a defeat. It was dulled, beaten flat, heat waves vibrated upward from the surface.

It started to rain and for a moment Sarah had a sense of relief. The rain had always shot down in hard-driven pellets, instantly dropping the temperature, making a massive widespread spattering sound that was pleasant. But this was a different rain. It came down like a hot fog, falling lightly, making no noise and turning to steam the instant it touched earth. The temperature actually increased. A servant came from the kitchen with a trayful of fans. Everyone took one and began to slowly fan. They went on drinking, seemingly oblivious of what had happened. Sarah resisted the temptation to stare. The women had aged, the face powder and cosmetics washed away, their faces suddenly were gray, their eyes squeezed shut against a kind of subterranean glare that had replaced the bright sunshine. And the men were sweating, their shirts darkening first at the armpits and over the chest, and finally even their pants around the waist turning dark as the sweat slid down their bodies and was gathered by the constriction of the belt.

"How long will this last?" she asked Etna.

"Maybe a few days," Etna said. "Maybe a few weeks. Occasionally a month. Then the trades again and then a hot spell. Off and on for four months. Then the good weather returns."

"What do you do until it does return?" Sarah asked.

Etna looked at her in surprise. "Just what you have always done," she said.

Sarah noticed that everyone drank a good deal more than usual that evening and during dinner they consumed bottle after bottle of Dutch beer. Once Sarah warned one of the maids to be sure more beer was being chilled, but the maid nodded and said Ah Lee had already done that the moment the trades dropped. The meal was curry and everyone except

Sarah ate well, as if in defiance of the heat ... heaps of white rice, then great spoonfuls of yellow shrimp curry, followed by the endless condiments.

When Sarah awoke the next morning she was aware of two things. First, that there was a thin layer of slime under her cheek. Secondly, the heat had changed the entire odor of the island ... she could smell the sea and for the first time it was not crisp, but seemed made up of spoiling, sun-exposed, rotting things. The odor had oozed up the slope from the sea, mixing with the odors of the jungles. She rolled out of bed, walked to the dressing table and poured one palm full of #4711 and splashed it over her face and arms and body. For a moment, but only a moment, it was stronger than the smell of the island. Then the #4711 was gone, lost in the older, stronger, more aggressive smells.

At noon Etna came by to play tennis and Sarah forced herself to go out on the court. But by the time they had rallied for five minutes she shook her head.

"Not today, Etna," she said. "This heat is going to take some getting used to."

Her voice was level, but in fact she was panicked. The court seemed to be in the bottom of a yellowish, shimmering, superheated pit ... the sky seemed literally to have lowered, the jungle to have closed in. She looked up at the sun and it glowed yellow and orange, obscured by steam, but close and powerful.

She took Etna into the house and they drank gin and tonic for a half hour. Then, on impulse, she asked Etna to stay for lunch. They had two more drinks and Sarah asked for beer with lunch. The lunch was salad and a platter of New Zealand lamb tongues and a chocolate cake. Sarah skipped the lamb tongues and took only a plate of tomato salad. But she could not even eat even that for warm tomato was curiously unpleasant, seemed an entirely different vegetable. Etna looked once at Sarah's plate.

"You should eat, Sarah," Etna said. "During the hot season it's important to eat. Just like when you're seasick ... be sure and keep something on your stomach when it's hot."

Sarah obediently took a few lamb tongues and without looking at them began to eat. They were delicious, salt-tasting and firm. They also cut into the rising sense of drunkenness that she felt. She steadied her eyes on Etna's passive gentle face. Sarah spoke quickly, before the surge of alcoholic courage was dissipated.

"Etna, this whole place hates white men," she said. With her hand she gestured and took in the sea and sky and islands. "I can feel it, like a pent-up rage. The whole place just waits to strike back ... termites, ants, rats, the heat, oh my God, the heat, the jungle crawling over everything, sliding into the gardens and over the paths." She took a breath. "And the damned inhuman smells. Don't you have the sensation that the whole thing is coiling up, has been for centuries, and is waiting to strike back? Don't you?"

"At first I did," Etna said calmly. "The first year I was here I used to wake up screaming in the night. Not just a little moan or a nightmare, but a great long scream that would go on for ten minutes with just time out for breath. And Karl would sit up in the bed, light the Coleman, and just wait for me to stop. Then he'd hold me and tell me to just wait, that I'd get over it."

"I'll never get over it," Sarah said. "The whole thing looked so wonderful from St. Louis. A green tropical paradise. And when I first got here. But everything turns out to be rotten underneath, to be what it is not. I was going to return to nature, be a Gauguin, embrace everything that stings and stinks and snaps back."

"Darling, I can't say anything except what Karl said ... you'll get used to it," Etna said. "Maybe it will take a long time, but eventually you will start to ride with it, with the cycle of heat and trades. At some point you start to understand the Malay personality, roll with the weather, get to understand that the jungle is not a black place."

Sarah shook her head.

"No, not ever," she said. "And I'm going to lose Oliver too. He's the last thing left." She looked sharply at Etna. "I want him to be tender and take time with me. But he comes at me like an animal, like something attacking . . . like the jungle or the damned mongoose after the rat. Do you know what I mean? Just a short stalk and a struggle and it's over. At first I liked it."

"I know what you mean," Etna said calmly. "It's the way Oliver was raised. Remember he was the only boy of a Jew on a Malay island. He was raised by the kids on the island and he picked up their ways. He makes love Maori style . . . quick, brutal, silent."

"But why can't he take more time for it?" Sarah asked. She was calmer now. "Just a bit of tenderness and time. That's all it would take. I know I sound like a marriage manual, but it's all I've got left."

"It's the way he was raised," Etna said. "Look, Sarah, these people live in crowded houses, jammed with people, the houses up against one another. They make love when they can ... without privacy, quickly, always knowing that others are listening."

"But we're not living like that," Sarah said. "This house is big. We're alone in it."

Etna looked at Sarah for a long moment. She shook her head quietly.

"The first half dozen times you made love I'll guarantee there were a half dozen natives quietly squatting under your bedroom to listen to how you made love," Etna said, and her voice was hard and convincing. "They wanted to know if Oliver had been changed by the white woman. I knew you made love Maori style two days after you arrived."

Sarah shivered. Some last defense crumbled somewhere. She did not feel disgust or embarrassment, she felt only a searing exposure, a loss of identity.

"Do you want another beer, Etna?" she asked and before the reply came she tinkled the bell for the maid and shouted as the maid came through the door, "Two more Heinekens."

Sarah turned and smiled at Etna and said, "Don't worry, Etna, I'm not going to take to drink. Jews, especially Jewish women, never become drunks."

That afternoon Sarah wired Manila for an air-conditioner and asked that it be delivered by air freight. The cost was $1100.25 and the air freight was $175. It was the only air-conditioner on the island. By the time it arrived Sarah had given instructions for the bedroom to be insulated for sound and had a Chinese seamstress in town design heavy curtains which could be drawn over the windows. When the room was finished it was soundproof, cool, and when the curtains were pulled, quite dark. She illuminated it with large electric lamps which filled every inch of the room with a strong white light.

When the room was finished Sarah's days took on a set pattern. In the morning she no longer played tennis, but leafed through the Sears, Roebuck catalogue and almost invariably ordered something . . . a portable electric hair drier, a transistor radio, a copper chafing dish. She laid up a huge supply of dark glasses, mosquito repellent and anti-sunburn lotions.

The drawers and cupboards began to bulge with the tubes and packages and containers.

Sarah also began to order American magazines. At first she ordered a few of the avant-garde magazines and then *Life* and *Time* and then movie magazines. Finally she even ordered the little magazines on "how to do it;" magazines full of miracles of mechanical ingenuity. By the time she had been on Bangtok a year she subscribed to over fifty American magazines.

Reading the magazines took up her entire morning. She no longer had time for tennis. Her main exercise was to walk around the house and make sure that the jungle was kept cropped back. She never looked up at the boles of the towering coconut palms. She began to gain weight. She took deep pleasure in asking the wives of the managers to come for gimlets and beer and gin and tonic in her air-conditioned room. They would leave the room, after an hour of drinking, and the hot suffocating impact of the air would double their intoxication. Sarah would see her guests to the door and then flee back to the cool rectangle. She would walk into the room with an eager smile on her face. She was always satisfied by the splendid coolness of the room, the evenness of the electric lights.

She left the room only to drive to the sawmill and watch the cutting of the logs into planks. The crew became used to her and even instructed her in the operations of the different machines. She got so she could tell when a blade needed replacing, could identify the characteristic whine of the planer when it ran into a knot of wood and had to be slowed before it burnt up. Around one-thirty Oliver would come out of his office and walk over to the sawmill and when there was a break in the sound call up to her. She would look down at him standing in the haze of

heat, his shirt dark with sweat, and would smile,
throw him a kiss and run down the stairs.

` She would get in the jeep smiling. Every day, at
this moment, she had the same reassuring image in
her mind: the dark, mechanical rectangle of coolness
and blackness that awaited her at the house. She
would reach over and squeeze Oliver's arm. The natives smiled down on them from the sawmill floor.
The jeep drove off quickly into the heat and blinding
sunshine. Sarah did not open her eyes during the ride
back. She kept them tightly closed, holding the memory of the air-conditioned room tight against her eyeballs. That and the anticipation of Oliver and the
love-making.

Today Sarah is thirty-two and she lives in St. Louis.
She has lost the huge bulk of fat she brought back
from the tropics. She is on any number of boards and
committees and leagues. She tells wistful stories of
life in the tropics and has, upon occasion, given lec-
tures on "Life in Southeast Asia." Most people have
the impression that she is a widow.

16. The Micronesian

MICRONESIA means "little islands." The name is somehow endearing. It is evocative of little islands resting on clear blue water. This impression corresponds to the reality, but with a vengeance. The islands are not merely little, they are in some cases tiny and they are flung over a staggering sweep of ocean. Micronesia begins below the equator, swings north and west into the Gilberts and the Marshalls and then the long line of the Carolines and the northward spur of the Marianas. Micronesia ends at the Palaus, not too far from the Philippines.

This is a vast amount of ocean. It reaches through endless miles of latitude to beyond the Tropic of Cancer, it flows east and west for hundreds of empty miles. The scarcest thing in Micronesia is land. Most maps, even very detailed maps, show the area as being empty. In actual fact there are so many dots of land that one can sail from the Ellices to Guam and almost never be more than a hundred miles from a landfall. If one tries it he had better be a good navigator. The landfalls are usually very, very small.

The islands of Micronesia are of three kinds; high islands, atolls and raised atolls. The most typical island is the atoll with a vast lagoon and only the smallest fringe of low land surrounding it. The atoll of

Ulithi is not untypical. It has a vast lagoon, almost 185 square miles of it. During the war the lagoon supplied a magnificent anchorage for hundreds of American Navy ships. The raised part of the atoll, the area on which man can live, however, is less than two square miles.

During the war this led to some peculiar arrangements. If the sailors from the hundreds of ships anchored in the lagoon were given shore leave simultaneously the two square miles of land would have been solid with bodies. The Navy staked out two tiny recreation areas on land; one for enlisted men the other for officers. Ships were given quota of men and officers that could be allowed "shore leave." What this amounted to was permission to stand in a very dense crowd of people which was in a constant milling motion as men worked their way up to the bar, got their beer or hard liquor, and then were pushed back into the maelstrom. On days when the anchorage was full the fringes of the two dense crowds had to stand up to their knees in the warm waters of the lagoon. It was generally recognized as one of the poorest "liberty ports" in the Pacific.

The land, even on the high islands of Micronesia, is generally very poor. The islands, even with the Navy long gone, are crowded, some of them having over two hundred persons per square mile. The land cannot possibly supply food for such a population and the chief source of food is the reef and the lagoon. The shallow waters are worked over as thoroughly as a Japanese rice farmer cultivates his little plot. Within the lagoon the natives spear angelfish, groupers, sharks, squirrelfish, threadfish, Moorish idols, lizard fish, eels and goatfish. In the deeper waters outside the reef they fish for barracuda, albacore, wahoo and swordfish. At low tide the reef is combed for crabs, lobsters, squid, octopuses and sea slugs of various kinds. The giant clam not only yields big chunks of meat, but its shell is a valuable receptacle.

The Marshall Islands are a fair example of Micronesian life. There are thirty-four islands in the group. The total land is only 69 square miles and it surrounds 4500 square miles of lagoon. A third of the islands are unoccupied, usually because there is not enough reef to supply food. The most famous exceptions are Eniwetok and Bikini, which could support a good many people but have been abandoned so that atomic testing can be celebrated in their lagoons.

The Micronesians in these islands are of medium size, of slender build, have dark skin and brown undistinguished eyes, broad flat noses and hair which varies from straight to curly. But natives on other groups will have a slightly different look. On the fringes of Micronesia the natives will be fleshier and their hair straighter and have bigger bodies . . . all signs of an infusion of Polynesian blood. At the western edge of the islands the body shape and color give evidence that the Philippines have been visited or supplied visitors. Through all of the area there is evidence of Caucasian heritage. But despite the differences within Micronesia, and the fact that someone from Palau will differ noticeably from someone from Ralik, almost anyone from Micronesia will be distinctly different from the Melanesians and the Polynesians. Lighter than the former, darker than the latter.

Temperamentally the Micronesians are also somewhere between the Melanesians and the Polynesians. They lack the moodiness of the Melanesian, but are not as outgoing as the Polynesians. They are hospitable and friendly, but there are limits. They do not have the almost imitative quality which allows the Polynesian to cheerfully make a mélange of his life.

The Micronesian has a quality of slight withdrawal; a mixture of pride and parochialism. Like Pacific' natives everywhere the Micronesian has taken to metal tools, steel fishhooks, calico and canned beef. But he has also retained a high degree of self-sufficiency. He still takes a pride in his single-float outrigger which is built with a knife-edged hull and is either hewn from a single log or carefully stitched together out of planks. He is still capable of building the elegant *maneaba,* an exquisitely proportioned meeting hall, although most of the houses are now covered with iron roofs.

There are many islands where the only cultivated soil has been imported by canoe and is carefully husbanded in great pits made of rock. This soil is eked out by adding a compost of leaves, decayed wood and whatever else is capable of decomposition. In these pits breadfruit, bananas and papayas and taro are grown.

For almost a hundred years after their discovery the islands of Micronesia really had only one commodity highly valued by the white man: the female anatomy. The girls of Micronesia, unlike the Melanesians, are flirtatious. Their coquettishness made them famous among nineteenth century whalers which often put into the islands for "rest and recreation." They later developed enough copra in the islands to support a modest trade, but the trickle of white men into the area was small compared to the rest of Oceania. Much later vast quantities of phosphate were discovered on Ocea and Nauru islands and they were worked intensively. In the Carolines bauxite deposits have been found on several islands and those on Babelthuap have been developed.

But the chief importance of the islands has been, and remains, their location. These tiny gobbets of land with their magnificent lagoons have the political asset of simple position. They filled the emptiness of the Pacific; supplied coaling stations and later air strips and staging areas. In time the islanders heard about the Great Powers and realized dimly that they were being traded about for strategic purposes, but it did little to change life on the islands. But World War II marked a stunning change. The Japanese appeared first, and not far behind them came the long gray shapes of Allied warships which poured thousands of tons of hot steel into the ageless coral. The Marines landed in a bloody froth and places like Tarawa and Peleliu leapt from anonymity to a short morbid fame. For a period there was a brisk wondrous time of PX's, chocolate bars, chewing gum and a staggering market for Micronesian gimcrackery.

Then the United States Navy took over most of Micronesia and ran it with a somewhat reluctant hand. It was then that Micronesia's newest commodity was discovered: empty space. This happened to be precisely what the Atomic Age needed and the story of the atomic tests began. Today most of the area is included in something called the Trust Territory which is run by the Department of the Interior for reasons which are not clear to anyone.

The Trust Territory presents some formidable problems. The islands, with a few exceptions, are so small that they can support only a small native population. They are scattered over enormous distances. The natives speak at least eight distinct languages and dozens of dialects. To view the scatter of islands as a political unit outrages common sense. To expect them to become economically fruitful or prosperous in the Western sense is lunacy. The resources are simply not there.

There is also a haunting realization that the centers

of activity such as Guam are leading a highly artificial life. Right now Guam depends on its prosperity for its value as a navy base and as a refueling stop for planes. It also enjoys a flurry of activity when atomic testing is to be done. It is a busy place and looks for all the world like an American suburb occupied, by some accident, only by sailors and handsome brown people. It has the joviality and boosterism of a vast meeting of Rotarians. But it is doomed. Soon its strategic importance will be lost as ICBM's and guided missiles and satellites become the stuff of modern warfare. Airplanes will soon be overflying it as they lengthen their range. It will then have to face the fact that it is the capital of an archipelago which makes no economic sense.

All of this makes the task of the Trust Territory administration rather dreamlike and unreal. No one is certain exactly where the whole thing is going to end. Is it our mission to modernize the islands? If so who pays for it? And what future do they face? Some of the anthropologists attached to the administration have the notion that their task is to bring the Micronesians galloping into the twentieth century. Others, with a harder sense of history and time, wonder what the result will be.

The most tough-minded and reasonable people in all this, I think, are the Micronesians. With a kind of shrewd intuition they know something of limits. I have talked to natives who with almost no formal education sense that there is no basis on which Micronesia can be swept into the "main steam" of history. There is a recognition that to abandon the old way is merely to invite the disaster of becoming permanently dependent upon a way of life that must be propped up from the outside. This is a case where the reluctance to change may be more wisdom than an ingrained reactionary attitude.

For all of these reasons life on most of the islands of Micronesia has a lulling, backwater, calming quality. It is almost therapeutic. The Micronesian blends easily, reflectively, willingly into what nature can do and cannot do. His digestive system, for example, is attuned to high tide. At that moment bands of men and women, usually separated by trees or a sandspit, wade into the lagoon, squat in the water, talk and gossip and evacuate their bowels. The ebb tide provides an efficient and hygienic massive flush toilet. On the surface he will go through the motions of being Christian. In some cases the conversion is genuine and deep. More often it is a gloss that covers a paganism based on the worship of sea, skies and stars.

In Micronesia it is still possible to drink the old root narcotics. It is not popular or approved, but it is done. The drink is made of *sakao*, a small shrub vaguely related to the pepper family. The roots are gathered and the sap is beaten out of them before your eyes and everyone's excitement is barely concealed. Finally the liquid is produced, no more than a small vessel all told. But that is all that is needed. Each person is entitled to three sips.

Three sips are enough. It has a combination of a mixture of Novocain and martinis. Your jaw goes slack and without feeling, but your mind goes soaring. Sakao neatly and pleasantly splits the mind. By the second drink your mind has whirled off into colorful and cosmic regions, the skies open and profound answers come like bolts of lightning to questions that no one has posed. At the same time your lips are working and words come out, but you have little notion of what you are saying.

The only time I drank sakao I had the impression

of orbiting around the atoll. Colors flashed and then took on a fantastic deep quality. Every person in the group stood out distinct and separate and possessed of wonderful qualities of intelligence and generosity and charm. The words they uttered caught at difficult and obscure meanings with a cleverness that was Olympian. Later I was told that I sat and talked quietly and the conversation was quite ordinary.

Micronesia is a place of enormous promise. The banalities of Guam and the gray bureaucratic atmosphere of the schools and welfare bureaus have tamed some of the islands. But all of the drab ingenuity of America will be unable to standardize either the islands or the Micronesians. There is a time, and it is not far distant, when the hundreds of little islands, many of them uninhabited, will be the last places of refuge for those who seek quiet and beauty.

17. The Polynesian

THERE IS one fragment of the Pacific the American believes he knows well: Polynesia. He may not be quite certain of Sumatra and Mindanao or the difference between a *prau* and a gin pahit, but Polynesia he knows. This is the South Seas, Paradise, the Sunny Isles. It is a place of soft winds, surfboards and outriggers, the pink bulk of the Royal Hawaiian Hotel, the scent of flowers. It is a place where beachcombers, defiantly drunken but still white and superior, watch their *vahines* swim in the waves. In some haunting subtle way a vision of Polynesia creeps into the knowledge of all Americans, a vision flawless and jeweled. In Polynesia the defects of America are magically eliminated. The place is warm and sunny. It glows.

My first hint of Polynesia came when I was fourteen. I went to a carnival in Los Angeles which had a

side show called South Sea Mysteries. A deeply tanned girl, wearing a grass skirt made of red cellophane, a flashy artificial lei around her neck and a sequined bra, stepped out through a canvas flap. On the canvas behind the girl were painted brilliant green coconut trees and a circle of nipa huts. As the barker began to talk the girl did the hula. I was mesmerized. I had never seen anything so softly carnal.

"Step right in and see the ancient love dance of the old Hawaiian chiefs," the barker chanted. "There was a time when the eyes of commoners were torn out if they saw this dance, and you can see it for exactly two bits."

My attention swung back to the girl. As a hidden phonograph played "My Little Grass Shack," her hands formed a shack, fish swimming, a moon rising, lovers embracing. She was very good, although I did not know it at the time. Her head was level, her feet never left the floor, her haunches undulated. She was erotic but restrained. She gave the impression of being virginal, but also wanton, which was exactly her purpose. I ignored the fact that her tan began to dissolve under the harsh Los Angeles sun and ran down her face in brown drops.

That day I was hooked by the South Seas or Polynesia or whatever the barker and the girl and the cheap tent stood for. I had a neat, precise and colorful vision of what it was like. There would be tiny clean islands, ringed with white sand and blue surf, and the air would be warm. In this vision the people were somewhat vague, but they would be lithe, brown, carefree, and they would dance. I didn't know then that millions of other Americans were experiencing exactly the same emotion, as the hula craze and movies like *Bird of Paradise* and a few score Hawaiian bands spread the vision broad and wide.

A cold and ununderstanding world kept me from leaving at once for the South Seas, so I turned to the library. The vision grew deeper. In Melville's *Typee* I read for the first time of Fayaway, who became the model for endless South Sea heroines: abandonedly voluptuous, a skin "the color of *café au lait*" a magnificent figure, a slightly fey and doomed look about the eyes, possessed of a deep tribal wisdom that shone through her eyes. In all the books, this beautiful stereotype gave herself willingly to the white man although she knew it would end in tragedy.

Lord Byron, something of a connoisseur of women and of love, wrote a book called *The Island* and made it clear that natural passions could have full expression in these exotic islands. Diderot, the famous French encyclopedist, wrote a rhapsodic book on Polynesia and argued that the "natural" life was far superior to "civilization." I needed no persuading. I plowed through novels, scientific treatises, biographies of missionaries, good writing and bad writing. It was all like diamond dust against a dull jewel: it ground my vision to a lapidary brightness.

Later I was to learn that Melville knew more about whales than about women, that Byron had never been to the South Seas, that Diderot had blatantly fictionalized the voyages of Bougainville. I was also to encounter the numerous works of the professional, nerveless, hard-eyed debunkers of Polynesia. None of this made any difference to me, nor, apparently, does it make any difference to most others who go to Polynesia. The rebuffs, the savage letdowns, the hard surprises are many, but seldom is the original vision altered. Indeed, in a strange way, the foreigner's vision of Polynesia has come to transform the reality of the place.

Of the hard knocks and surprises which the innocent may expect in Polynesia, first is the low-pressure shock of its simple vastness. Spread out a Mercator map and draw a triangle with Hawaii, Easter Island and New Zealand at the three points. The sides will measure 4500 and 4500 and 4800 miles. Polynesia means many islands, but they are tiny fragments scattered through this Pacific immensity. All the islands of southwest Polynesia, taken together, whole archipelagoes like the Marquesas and the Australs and the Cooks, have less land area than the single island of Hawaii.

This is one of the great empty spaces of the world. The huge sea plains stretch away endlessly, identical, heaving, changing color but not shape. The heat is solid and uncompromising. When you come upon an island, an unbelievable lost speck, you ache for it to be beautiful. It usually is although not always in the languorous white sand and coral reef tradition. On Nukuhiva in the Marquesas, for example, there are sheer cliffs at the water's edge which rise over a thousand feet and there are also canyons with walls so steep that one must go by sea from valley to valley. Moorea is beautiful in a monumental, craggy, cold-blue manner. And there are some atolls which are bare and ugly . . . but not many. The high islands are a surprise to the Western eye, but a pleasant one.

Once ashore you will have a job finding a pure-blooded Polynesian. When you do it will be a shock, especially if it is a woman. She has a short jaw; her body is squat and turns to fat rather early. If she is a fa'a Samoa type her feet will be big, callused and tough. It is true that her hair is black and lustrous and her skin is close enough to *café au lait* so that she can sunburn, but her body is designed for work, not for dancing. There is something solid, down to earth, almost utilitarian about the Polynesian woman and the tiare behind her ear and the limpidity of her eyes cannot disguise it.

You are suddenly aware that you have seen this woman before—in the pictures of Gauguin. He was ruthlessly realistic. The heavy-jawed, squat, bent women of his pictures are not a trick of Impressionism, they are simple reality. The kind of lithe, slim Fayaway beauty is very rare among pure Polynesians.

There is another subtly disturbing thing about Polynesian anatomy. I discovered it when I approached a Marquesan reef on which a group of men and women were searching for shellfish. The sun, as always in the tropics, went down abruptly but there was a moment of intense purple light. The figures on the reef turned black—and sexless. I could not tell women from men.

Later I learned that this was a common experience among newcomers to Polynesia. There is a softness of line, a blurring of body distinctions. Both sexes have the same long swimmer's muscles, both walk in the same way, there is an absence of the vigorous gestures we ascribe to males, and the women do not develop the protective mannerisms we associate with femininity.

This is not to imply that Polynesian women lack beauty. Their beauty is of a different kind: a blending of gait and proud bearing, an aura of autonomy, lips that can form into a pout or the most spontaneous of laughs, a body which somehow does not value sleekness but promises almost too much competence in love-making. Gauguin put it well when writing of one of his models and lovers: "She was not at all handsome according to our aesthetic rules. She was beautiful."

There is one word which, in all of its shades and meanings, catches the sense of the Old Way Polynesia and much of the Polynesia now conquered by The Beach. It is the world "simple." There is a great simplicity in the lust of Polynesians for gambling and the cunning with which they can make a gamble of almost anything. They do not gamble as Chinese or Americans gamble; they gamble with a wild plunging abandon, with no sense of probability or odds. Win or lose, they give the same grin. There is also simplicity in the quite unconscious cruelty which Polynesians display towards animals. They will run a horse to a lathering death. A dog with a fishhook caught in its foot will be an object of laughter. I do not recall ever having seen a Polynesian pet a dog or give it food. The dog scavenges for itself.

At the same time you can spend weeks in a crowded Polynesian village and not hear a child cry. When it does the closest woman will instantly sweep it up and comfort it. In many dialects the word for "mother" covers almost every female relative and the child will be treated by any of these women with the warmness that we reserve only for our own children.

In all of Polynesia there is almost no artistic inventiveness. Rather there is a simple repetition of old designs. Tapa cloths, pandanus mats and seashell necklaces are often done in beautiful patterns, but the patterns are ancient, the outgrowth of timeless trial and error. When asked to invent, to create, to experiment in color, the Polynesian is uncomprehending. When given the choice between a magnificently muted tapa cloth and a garish Manchester calico the Polynesian will take the calico and explain his choice: "I like the red. It is prettier. The tapa is dull." This is simplicity itself.

The only working artist I know of in Polynesia is

Agnes Teepee, the vahine of Don Carlos García-Palacios, a Chilean of the most exquisite sensitivities. Agnes paints big bold abstract paintings which are usually suggestive of tropical plants or the reef or the underwater life. Other Tahitians study her work with the most profound boredom until they can spot something in the painting which is recognizable ... a sea anemone, a tiare, the eye of a shark. Then they will walk away satisfied. They seem quite incapable of understanding an abstract notion. They are literal minded in an almost rigid sense.

There is also a vast simplicity in the way the Polynesian regards youth. The Westerner looks back on youth with a terrible urge to recapture it, to possess it, to imitate it. The Polynesian regards youth more kindly, more benignly. I have never heard a Polynesian express the desire to be young again. He folds gracefully into each phase of life knowing it is inevitable. He remembers youth not as something lost but as something he once enjoyed. An ancient will look at Polynesian youth with the languid tolerant eyes of a lion regarding a litter of frisking cubs. They arouse no envy, no curiosity, no puritanical impulse to inhibit or reform.

This simplicity extends to the sex act and explains a basic misunderstanding between the Westerner and the Polynesian. To the Westerner, sex is a dramatic, committing, involving, often frightening thing. For the Polynesian it is a simple matter; as simple as eating or swimming or a prayer or an argument. It need not have consequences. It can be an isolated moment of pleasure. The moment remains discrete, holding no potential of guilt, no web of obligations, need to murmur love words.

Bengt Danielson, who has lived in Polynesia for many years, states that a casual meeting between a

Tahitian boy or girl *always* leads to intercourse. Only two conditions need exist; a bit of privacy and sure knowledge that the boy and girl are not related. In fa'a Polynesia adolescents often spent their nights together in a separate building where the older children gave sexual instructions to the younger. The language of young children when translated literally would make the brain of even the most progressive parent reel. But the sexual words and phrases are used with no desire to shock and never as swear words. The missionaries have ended the common sex huts, but have made almost no inroads into the casualness with which sex is treated.

There are some exceptions. In a few Polynesian societies virginity is highly prized and in the fa'a days it was always assumed that female aristocrats would marry as virgins. The deflowering was done publicly by one of the older chiefs from the bridegroom's clan. If blood did not flow the girl's father would smash in her head with a club. Today this kind of behavior is not expected of aristocrats.

There are still islands on which the wedding is celebrated by allowing all of the male guests that desire it to have intercourse with the bride. Many a popular bride comes through such an experience half dead from fatigue and takes weeks to recover.

One day my wife was sitting on a beach outside of Papeete while I was skin diving. A net fisherman, a big attractive man of about twenty-five, was working the water close to the shore. Perhaps my wife looked lonely. In any case she was alone. The fisherman walked over and said hello to her in French.

"Would you like to make love?" he asked, without any introductory remarks and in a very gentle voice. "I know a place just behind these trees."

My wife explained that she was waiting for me to

come in from skin diving. He looked out towards the reef and then back at my wife.

"He may be out there for hours," he said simply.

My wife still declined. He was not the least offended. He pointed out the private place beyond the trees in case we should like to use it. Then he went back to his fishing.

During the nineteenth century a whole literature developed around the dewy-eyed and innocent South Seas maiden who was seduced by the white man and then abandoned to a life of misery and regret. This was based on a misreading of Polynesian character. First, the girl was not abandoned; she had the family, the tribe, the island to return to. Secondly, she did not put as much into the affair as the white man imagined—she could not, it was a psychological impossibility. Sex does not mean this to the Polynesian. Thirdly, there was no misery to the situation as such. An individual white *tane* (man) might be miserable to live with but his Polynesian vahine could not be made miserable simply because she had lived with him. Once over, the affair continued only in the tortured imagination of the white man.

The girl can be rapt and devoted to a lover, her simplicity and dignity can even be exciting. But what disconcerts the Westerner is to learn that he may well be one of a series of lovers, that he has not bitten deep into her soul, that she does not and cannot see him as the "only" man.

After a time this knowledge, so directly counter to our puritanical, high-pitched and intense attitude towards sex, can make white men miserable. They long to make the relationship more tense and involved. For the Polynesian woman this is impossible. She does not know how to become involved and desperate. The act of love-making in Polynesia is much different from the elaborate love-making of Europe and America. There is very little kissing or caressing, very little concern for a simultaneous climax. It is what the Polynesians call "Maori love" as opposed to the white man's form of love. It is quick, silent and often brutal. At the climax a Polynesian couple will often scratch one another's faces and during one of the daylong feasts called *tamaaraa* a particularly attractive girl may go into the bushes with fifteen or twenty men and have welts on her face for days afterwards. The substitute for what white marriage counselors call "foreplay" is the dance. It is the most directly sexual dance in the world. There is no disguising its intention nor its effect. It is meant to be provocative and stimulating and it is.

Another facet of the Polynesian simplicity is recklessness. For example, every time a tidal wave strikes the Hawaiian Islands, a number of lives are lost unnecessarily. The tidal wave is always preceded by a powerful outward suck of the ocean which leaves reefs and harbor floors suddenly exposed, fish flopping wildly, sandbars steaming in the sun. The Hawaiians cannot resist flocking out onto the reefs, laughing wildly, grabbing for free fish—although they know that in a few moments a wall of water will come sweeping in. When the horizon suddenly tilts skyward and a gray line rises suddenly, they turn and scramble for the beach, roaring with laughter. The silent inexorable rush of the vast wave always traps a few, but despite the keening and wailing for the lost ones, no one thinks of staying away when the next tidal wave comes.

Simplicity also embodies a thin red thread of cruelty, childlike indifference to pain in others. Polynesia is no exception. When Captain Cook's death was avenged by a savage bombardment of a Hawaiian town, the native girls on board clapped their hands with delight, shouted *maitai*—"very fine"—enjoyed the pyrotechnic display which was destroying their friends and families.

In fa'a Samoa, chiefs often ticked off a subject to be buried alive at the base of each corner post of a new royal residence. Records indicate that the victims grinned up wolfishly as the pole came crashing down on them, and that their families roared wildly and went on with the festivities. Prisoners were often bound tightly with tinder-dry coconut fronds and then set alight, and the whole village watched as the human torch ran desperately for the sea. If he made it, fine; if he did not, the first step in preparing the body for a feast had been taken.

In most of Polynesia, The Beach has won a solid victory over the Old Way. Indeed, the victory was won long ago and today it is almost impossible to find a pure Polynesian or an undiluted practice of the Old Way. In some islands the Old Way has virtually vanished, but somehow, in a way which is not clear to anyone, the flavor of the South Seas still comes through. Nowhere is the mystery more puzzling than in Honolulu. By any act of sympathetic interpretation it is not an especially attractive place. The outskirts are ringed with junkyards, used-car lots, small factories and warehouses. The center of the city is badly planned, crowded, noisy, spangled with neon lights. Tract housing crawls hideously up the green mountains and disappears into the perpetual fogs of the Pali. The hotels of Waikiki are international style—tall, sleek, concrete. Enormously tall and enormously profitable, they age quickly in the soft climate, but they will be there forever. The visitor could be in Miami or Dallas or Los Angeles. But somehow the magic of the place still works, and thousands of tourists return to the mainland with the glazed eyes of those who have seen Paradise. Nothing that land developers and commercial bad taste do can destroy two things: the trade winds and the Pacific. The place may be conventional and ordinary, but the soft warm wind and the sparkling sea are there. Apparently they are enough.

The "outer islands" of Hawaii, such as Maui and Kauai, and the Big Island are infinitely more attractive than Honolulu, but most tourists stay riveted to Waikiki. Eventually they will move to the outer islands, but right now they are content to gaze mesmerized at the rhythmic sweep of the waves, drink exotic mixtures of rum and fresh pineapple and floating orchids and enjoy the trades. Nowhere is the vision of Polynesia more distorted, stifled and lacquered. But enough is still there to satisfy the American urge to "see the South Seas."

Once the traveler leaves Honolulu and moves southward to the Marquesas or Tuamotus or Tahiti or Samoa, the victory of The Beach is less visible, but it is still substantial. There are no sleek intercontinental hotels, but there are tin roofs among the coconut thatch. It is true that the most desired import is canned meat (followed by flour, sugar, tobacco and piece goods), but one can still eat a magnificent Old Way meal of broiled fish, a curry of shrimp and octopus and sea snail, breadfruit and a dessert of cool juicy fruits picked from nearby trees. Beachcombers are few and far between, but in Quinn's Bar in Tahiti, for a few francs, you can take a picture of Emil Gauguin, the fat and idle son of Paul Gauguin. It is true that many nipa huts will have a foot-operated Singer sewing machine and an old Victor phonograph, but they will also have the softly beautiful pandanus mats. You will also see jeep springs used as coconut scrapers and watch native skin divers come up from the depths wearing American diving goggles. But push deeper into the bush, or sail to an island that is the least bit isolated, and at once the lacquer is gone. The mark of The Beach is there, but it is still blurred, still faint.

In many ways The Beach has made the reality of Polynesia more like the vision. Take the matter of feminine beauty. As the Polynesian began to intermarry with Chinese, Australians, Portuguese, Americans, Japanese and others, an odd change occurred. The pudgy, squat, waistless girl began to be replaced by a mestizo of more elegant features, a molded jaw, slimmer legs and slighter build. Today throughout Polynesia there is an amazing incidence of girls who possess the beauty invented by Melville's imagination. The fevered men who went to the South Seas inspired by the nineteenth century vision were probably disappointed, but their visits guaranteed that future generations of Polynesian women would look hauntingly like Fayaway.

The vision which the white man took to Polynesia also worked wonders with the hula. In cold fact the hula of the Old Way was a shambling, dreary, and very boring dance which went on for hours, a low-grade folk dance performed to the beat of sticks on hollow logs. Even the missionaries found little to remark in it except its tedium. At the same time Polynesia had a courtship dance which was brutal, direct and highly erotic. It was danced infrequently, but few who witnessed it forgot it.

It was the genius or the curse or the bland ignorance of The Beach that it modified both these dances and blended them. The result is the modern Hawaiian hula, softly sexual but not violent. It is danced to steel guitars and ukuleles and almost any other kind of instrument. It is, by any standard, a great improvement over the original version, and perhaps more important, it is infinitely more compatible with the soft languorous version of the South Seas. But be prepared for the fact that outside of Hawaii the Hawaiian hula is regarded as a joke. In the Tuamotus and the Marquesas and Tahiti the hula is danced the old way. The only time the tamed Hawaiian version is danced is to satirize it. The waving graceful hand motions of the Hawaiian hula will send a group of Polynesians into gales of laughter.

Some aspects of Polynesian life are so deeply rooted that The Beach has not affected them at all. One is always aware, for example, that these are an oceanic people. For Westerners the ocean has an ageless thin edge of danger to it. One sees this in the doleful faces of the wives of Portuguese fishermen and the resignation of seamen shipping out of San Francisco. For us the sea is stern, possessed of a Calvinistic finality.

The Polynesian regards the ocean differently. He loves it. He knows it can be dangerous, but the danger is Olympian, capricious, zestful. A man has a chance against it. The Polynesians will tease the sea, take enormous chances, challenge it to the very edge of impudence.

Even the Hawaiians, who have received the fiercest onslaught of softening Western ways, still possess this calculated recklessness. One place they show it is at Makapuu Beach on the windward side of Oahu. The entrance to the beach is flanked by signs which say, "Danger. Heavy Under-Tow. Off-Limits to Service Personnel." On storm days the wave trains come in with an awesome, towering regularity. They are gray and low at the horizon, but rise to enormous heights as the bottom shoals and turn a bitter green before they dissolve into smoky water. The crash of water is so solid that, standing on the beach, you can feel it as a tiny shock in your teeth.

I went body-surfing at Makapuu with two Hawaiian friends and it was not until we were past the surf line and treading water and waiting for a "big one" that I realized what they intended. Body-surfing is a much more intricate art than surfboarding, because you must catch the wave at exactly the right point, arch your shoulders exactly right, and if you know the art, shoot in to the beach with your body out well in front of the wave. Once mastered, it is not particularly dangerous. But what my companions proposed to do was to ride the storm waves directly towards an outcropping of rock and coral against which the waves shattered themselves into the maddest spume I had ever seen. The trick, they patiently explained, was to duck out of the wave just before it hit the rocks, dive deep to escape the turbulence and swim underwater back towards the surf line. It called for exquisite timing.

They demonstrated for me a few times. Just as the wave was about to shatter on the rocks I saw their feet flash into the air, their bottoms rolled forward and they disappeared. A half minute later their heads popped to the surface just beyond the churning white water.

I could not do it. Technically I understood what had to be done, and I have surfed a good deal. But I did not view the ocean as they did. What they were doing struck me as a kind of insanity. To launch oneself at forty miles an hour, in the grip of a huge wave, directly at a wall of hard rock and coral was beyond my Westernized capacity. In the end I took the long safe glide into the sandy beach.

The Polynesian, on the other hand, has a highly

developed skill at sliding neatly by those parts of
white culture which bore, stifle or restrain him. He has
only the slightest interest in politics. The Malay can
become rigid with nationalistic excitement. Polynesians, with the exception of the Maoris, let politics
alone. Nor does the Polynesian, merely because he
goes to church, really accept the ethical stiffness
and content of Western religion. He can understand a
chief punishing someone for adultery as a *crime*, as
something necessary to maintain a minimum of order.
But he cannot see adultery as *sin*. The difference is
important. All Polynesian gods are Olympian gods:
puckish, capable of mistakes, possessed of human
qualities, forgiving, occasionally drunk. The only part
of Christian religion which Polynesians understand
thoroughly are the Ten Commandments, because
they sound very much like Ten Tabus.

This shrewd and protective selection of white atti-
tudes is nowhere more obvious than at the movies. I
once spent several nights at a hot, tin-roofed, over-
crowded theater in Samoa. Each night I saw the same
film. So did everyone else in the village. The place
steamed with heat, and insects flew like crazy motes
up and down the flickering light from the projector.
The movie was an ancient Western with a classic cast
of good guys, bad guys, fair damsels and wicked
Indians.

The audience ignored every scene except those
that involved shooting, drinking or kissing. In a long
dull scene they called on the local Don Juan to tell of
his latest exploits. He was reluctant, but he was persuaded. He stood in the aisle and did a bawdy hula
and recited his prowess. I was later told that he
delicately left out the names of his amours, but the
audience gleefully chanted them out. In mid-gesture
an Indian appeared on the screen and the Samoan

buck dropped into his seat like a man shot. Every eye
swung back to the movie, the sound of the insects
rose in the silence. At the end of the film, when the
cowboy hero kissed his girl modestly on the cheek,
the entire audience rose and chanted out a piece of
Samoan advice which described in explicit detail
what a man should do with a girl in such circumstances.

Other audiences in the Pacific will sit frozen in
their seats, absorbing every scene, never laughing,
enraptured by the study of a life that might be theirs
in the future. The air is dense with thought, with a
sense of desire. They leave with a sigh. In Polynesia
the audience is irreverent, bawdy, Hogarthian, and
there is not the slightest indication of desire for "the
American way of life."

The currents of Western thought are swirling over
the vast sun-drenched Pacific. In some places they
have dissolved the Old Way forever. In other places
they have made only the slightest impression. But
wherever The Beach makes itself felt, it is also subtly
transformed, softened by the climate and the vast
distances. One has the dim, but sure, knowledge that
the capacity of the Pacific to resist is nearly infinite,
like the reaches of its water.

18. The Aborigine

MAKE A MAN of earth, hone him down to gauntness
and put him in a lunar landscape and you have the
Australian aborigine. He is beyond Neanderthal man
or Java man. He is human, beyond dispute, but of
another planet, another life, another level. He is a
Paleolithic relic.

You will see him first as a shadow, a dark rocklike
quiet shadow, on the edge of the horizon. He stands
with one foot tucked up against the knee of the other
leg, an oddly restful position. Beside him will be a
smaller thinner shadow ... shapeless when sprawled,
but lean and bony when standing and that will be the
dingo dog. They could, when seen only as shadows,
almost be man and child. Both are thin, both are
wary, both are suspicious, both expect no love. Both
scan the landscape in the same canny way, both have
the same innocent hard eyes. Move towards them and
they vanish. Around a rock, down a gully, behind a
tree, but gone.

The anthropologists say he is the simplest person in
the Pacific and the world. He travels light. The possessions of a whole family, a lifetime and sometimes
many lifetimes, of accumulations will amount to no
more than twenty pounds. A stone, worn smooth by

handling and sweat and throwing, no bigger than an apricot will serve as both a weapon and a religious object. A woman's hair is valued not for Byronesque reasons, but because it is the best cordage they will ever have. This is simplicity sure enough. But something is slightly askew about all this, somehow a bit phantasmagoric.

The aborigine probably walked into Australia centuries ago when that continent was connected to the mainland. For a long time he roamed over Australia. He ranged down the coastline, moved up the banks of rivers, followed water wherever it existed. He never developed money, arithmetic, complex tools or villages. No one is sure why. Even when it was possible to build habitations and settle down the aborigine did not. He roamed endlessly and grew lean and spare in the process. When the whites came the space open to the aborigines began to dwindle, but they still wandered. Most of them still do. The difference is that the land they wander is the worst in Australia.

A few aborigines have settled into towns. They are not like American Negroes in a cotton town. There is a haunting difference. The Australian does not *see* the aborigine. They will hover at the edge of a sheep shearing, in the mouth of an alley, in the dark recesses of a warehouse, in garbage dumps. They are paid, but they have no names. They function, but they have no status. The Australian calls them "abo" or, if he is drunk, he roars "boy" or "nigger" or merely waves a hand and the aborigine obeys. They wear cotton pants and shirts, but their long necks and handsome, strongly carved Dravidian heads look too raw for the material. Their eyes peer out from huge bony foreheads and when the whites laugh the black face remains flat. Their eyes slide slowly and unblinking over whites, just short of understanding. The aborigine will humble himself for a pinch of tobacco and then, for no surface reason, will withdraw into a monumental dignity and quiet.

There is no "color problem" in Australia with the aborigine. The Australian does not feel threatened by the aborigine. He does not *see* him. The town-broken abo is a black shadow that can work, so unsubstantial that he is usually invisible. The aborigine pleads *nolo contendere*, "I do not wish to contend," every time his eyes meet those of a white man. He is as dingo as his dog, as undangerous.

Yet, one senses, something is wrong with all this. Behind those deep-sunk eyes and that strangely elegant body there is a rage, a resource, a something. One hungers to see the aborigine in the unbroken state . . . which is very difficult indeed.

One has the eerie feeling that the aborigine had the chance to become "civilized" and rejected it. Australia was once his entirely. Parts of it are a rich land and it could have supported settlements, commerce, folklore, cultivated crops. Everywhere else when the opportunity arose the people have seized upon it. But not the aborigine. He has acquired a microscopic and almost weird sense of the physical world and of the imperatives of existence. Nothing else. It is almost as if the aborigine wants to keep his existence narrowly balanced on a razor edge.

Take a single example. I once sat in a jeep and watched a group of aborigines through binoculars. They knew I was watching and they kept a careful distance.

The moment the jeep motor started they heard it on the dead still air. Moving with an unhurried stride they would cannily trot down a ridge . . . knowing full well that to get closer to that ridge I would have to double back down the ridges for five or six miles to gain on them.

Suddenly, however, their posture changed and the game ended. They went as rigid as black statuary ... six figures, lean and tall and angular, went still. Their heads were in the air sniffing. They all swung at the same instant in the same direction. Even with the binoculars, the 8 × 50 binoculars, they saw it before I. It was nothing more than a tiny distant rain squall, a dull gray sheet which reached from a layer of clouds to the earth. In the 360 degrees of horizon it obscured only a degree ... no more. A white man would not have seen it. The aborigines fastened upon it with a concentration that was beyond pathos.

One of the heads turned and spoke rapidly to the others. They were unmoved. They waited, watching the film of rain without speaking. Another head broke the rapt attention, spoke and even gesticulated. The other five were motionless. Then the squall thickened and began to move in a long drifting slant across the dry burning land. This time there was no need for talking. At once the whole band set off at a lope. They were chasing a rain cloud.

They went after the rain squall as mercilessly as a wolf pack after an abandoned cow. I followed them in the jeep and now they did not care. The games were over, this was life. Occasionally they would, for no reason that I could see, suddenly alter the angle of their trot. Sometimes I guessed it was because the rain squall had changed directions. Sometimes it was to save the minute energy that would be expended in going up and down a gully ... they skirted it. Their gait is impossible to convey in words. It has nothing of the proud stride of the trained runner about it, it is not a lope, it is not done with style or verve. It is the gait of the human who must run to live: arms dangling, legs barely swinging over the ground, head hung down and only occasionally swinging up to see the target, a loose motion that is just short of stumbling and yet is wonderfully graceful. It is, I suppose a barely controlled skimming of the ground. An ounce less control and it would be a shambles; an ounce more form and it would be uneconomical.

They ran for three hours. Finally, avoiding hummocks and seeking low ground they intercepted the rain squall. For ten minutes they ran beneath the squall, raising their arms and, for the first time, shouting and capering. Then the wind died and the rain squall held steady. They were studying the ground. Suddenly one of them shouted, ran a few feet, bent forward and put his mouth to the ground. He had found a depression with rain water in it. He bent down, a black cranelike figure, and put his mouth to the ground.

With a gesture that was more lordly and generous than I have seen almost anywhere the discoverer stood up and beckoned to the closest of his fellows. The other aborigine trotted over and swooped at the tiny puddle. In an instant he had sucked it dry.

The aborigine lives on the cruelest land I have ever seen. Which does not mean that it is ugly. Part of it is, of course. There are thousands of square miles of salt pan which are hideous. They are huge areas which have been swept by winds for so many centuries that there is no soil left, but only deep bare ridges only fifty or sixty yards apart with ravines between them thirty or forty feet deep, and the only thing that moves is a scuttling layer of sand. Such stretches have an inhuman moonlike quality to them. But much of the land which the aborigine wanders looks as if it should be hospitable. It is softened by the saltbush and the bluebush, has a peacful quality, the hills roll softly.

The malignancy of such a landscape has been beautifully described by the Australian Charles Bean. In his *On the Wool Track* he tells of three men who started out on a trip across a single paddock, a ten- by ten-mile square owned by a sheep grazer. They went well equipped with everything except knowledge of the "out-back" country.

> The countryside looked like a beautiful open park with gentle slopes and soft grey tree-clumps. Nothing appalling or horrible rushed upon these men. Only there happened—nothing. There might have been a pool of cool water behind any of these tree-clumps: only—there was not. It might have rained, any time; only—it did not. There might have been a fence or a house just over the next rise; only—there was not. They lay, with the birds hopping from branch to branch above them and the bright sky peeping down at them. No one came. Nothing happened. That was all.

The white men died. And countless others like them have died. Even today range riders will come upon mummified bodies of men who attempted nothing more difficult than a twenty-mile hike and slowly lost direction, were tortured by the heat, driven mad by the constant and unfulfilled promise of the landscape and who finally died. White men, even experienced ones, make a terrible mistake when they believe that they can master such country. The aborigine makes no such mistake. He is utterly lacking in arrogance. He bends with the land and wind and clouds and available food.

The aborigine is not deceived by the land, whether it be salt pan or wind ridges or rolling hills. He knows that the land is hard and pitiless. He knows that the economy of life in the out-back is awful. There is no room for error or waste. Any organism that falters or misperceives the signals or weakens is done. The conditions of existence are as tight, narrow and delicate as they can be drawn. I do not know if such a way of life can come to be a self-conscious challenge, but I suspect that it can. Perhaps this is what gives the aborigine his odd air of dignity. Maybe he appreciates the conditions under which he lives.

Actually seeing an aborigine today is a difficult thing. Many of them have drifted into the cities and towns and seaports. Others are confined to vast reservations and not only does the Australian government justifiably not wish them to be viewed as exhibits in a zoo, but on their reservations they are extremely fugitive, shunning camps, coming together only for corroborees at which their strange culture comes to its highest pitch: which is very low indeed.

I persuaded an Australian friend who had lived out-back for years to take me to see some aborigines living in the bush. It was a difficult and ambiguous kind of negotiation, even though the rancher was said to be expert in his knowledge of the aborigines and their language. Finally, however, the arrangements were made and we drove out into the bush in a Landrover. We followed the asphalt road for a few miles and then swung off onto a smaller road which was nothing more than two tire marks on the earth. The rancher went a mile down this road and then, when he reached a big red boulder, swung off the road. At once he started to glance towards the instrument panel. It took me a moment to realize what was odd about that panel: there was a gimbaled compass welded to it, which rocked gently back and forth as the Landrover bounced about. The rancher was navigating his way across the flatland.

"Do you always navigate like this?" I asked.

"Damned right," he said. "Once I get out on the flat I do. Some chaps that know an area well can make their way by landfalls ... a tree here, a wash here, a boulder there. But if you don't know the place like the palm of your hand you'd better use a compass and the speedometer. Two miles northeast, then five miles southwest ... that sort of thing. Very simple."

I looked around. He was right. The landscape kept repeating itself. I would try to memorize landmarks and recognized in a half hour that it was hopeless. An identical tree shimmered in the distance, a new anthill axactly like the others had appeared, a blinding white salt flat shaped like a question mark was only one of many the same shape.

Finally we approached the bivouac of the aborigines. They were camped beside a large column-shaped boulder. The camp consisted of a single family; a man, his lubra and two children. The sun was not yet high and all of them were in the small area of shade cast by the boulder.

There was also a dog, a dingo dog. Its ribs showed, it was a nondescript color, it suffered from a variety of sores, hair had scabbed off its body in patches. It lay with its head on its paws and only its eyes moving, watching us carefully. It struck me as a very bright and very malnourished dog. No one patted the dog. It was not a pet. It was a worker.

"The buggers love shade," the rancher said. "I suppose because it saves them some loss of body water. They'll move around that rock all day, following the shade. During the hottest part of the day, of course, the sun comes straight down and there isn't any shade."

We drove close to the boulder, stopped the Landrover and walked over towards the family.

The man was leaning against the rock. He gazed away from us as we approached. He was over six feet tall and very thin. His legs were narrow and very long. Every bone and muscle in his body showed, but he did not give the appearance of starving. He had long black hair and a wispy beard. The ridges over his eyes were huge and his eyelids were half shut. There was something about his face that disturbed me and it took several seconds to realize what. It was not merely that flies were crawling over his face but his narrowed eyelids did not blink when the flies crawled into his eyesockets. A fly would crawl down the bulging forehead, into the socket of the eye, walk along the man's lashes and across the wet surface of the eyeball and the eye did not blink. The Australian and I both were wearing insect repellent and were not badly bothered by insects, but my eyes watered as we stood watching the aborigine.

I turned to look at the lubra. I cannot describe her accurately, for she remained squatting on her heels all the time we were there. She, like the man, was entirely naked. Her long thin arms moved in a slow rhythmical gesture over the family possessions which were placed in front of her. There were two rubbing sticks for making fire, two stones shaped roughly like knives, a woven-root container which held a few pounds of dried worms and the dead body of some rodent. There was also a long wooden spear and a woomera, which is a spear-throwing device and gives the spear an enormous velocity and high accuracy. There was also a boomerang, elaborately carved. Everything was burnished with sweat and grease so that all of the objects seemed to have been carved from the same material and to be ageless.

The two children, both boys, wandered around the Australian and me for a few moments and then returned to their work. They squatted on their heels with their heads bent far forward, their eyes only a few inches from the ground. They had located the runway of a colony of ants and as the ants came out of the ground and made the short surface traverse the boys picked them up, one at a time, and pinched them dead. The tiny bodies were dropped onto a dry leaf and the pile was as big as a small apple.

The odor here was more powerful than that which surrounded the town aborigines. The smell at first was more surprising than unpleasant. It was also subtly familiar for it was the odor of the human body, but multiplied innumerable times because of the fact that the aborigines never bathed. One's impulse is to say that the smell was a stink and unpleasant. But that is a cliché and a dishonest one. The smell is sexual, but so powerfully so that a civilized nose must deny it.

Their skin was covered with a thin coating of sweat and dirt which had almost the consistency of a second skin. They roll at night in ashes to keep warm and their second skin has a light dusty cast to it. In spots such as the elbows and knees the second skin is worn off and I realized that they were much darker than they appeared; as if the coating of sweat, dirt and ashes were a cosmetic. The two boys had beautiful dark eyes and unlike their father they brushed constantly at the flies and kept blinking their eyes.

"That smell is something, eh, mate?" the Australian asked. "They swear that every person smells different and every family smells different from every other. At the corroborees, when they get to dancing and sweating, you'll see them rubbing up against a man who's supposed to have a specially good smell. Idje, here," and he nodded at the man, "is said to have great odor. The stink is all the same to me, but I really think they can make one another out blind-folded."

"Here, Idje, you fella like tabac?" he said sharply. Idje still stared over our shoulder at the horizon. The Australian stopped trying to talk a pidgin I could understand, the words came from deep in his chest. He opened a package of Players cigarettes and held it towards Idje.

Idje turned and looked at us and for the first time opened his eyes full. He took a cigarette carefully from the pack and put it behind his ear. The rancher still held the package out and Idje took another ciga-rette and stripped the paper from it and stuffed the tobacco into his mouth. He chewed carefully, his head slightly back. A drop of tobacco gathered in one corner of his mouth, he licked it back with a purple tongue.

"I'll swear that chewing tobacco is more intoxicat-ing to them than gin," the rancher said. "Old Idje will make that one cigarette do all day. Maybe we've loosened him up a bit and he'll perform."

He talked rapidly to Idje. Idje looked out at the horizon and then nodded. He barked something at the boys. They turned around grinning. One of them picked up the dead rodent from the basket. The mother paused from her graceful languid effortless hand motions, which, I realized, were probably de-signed to keep flies from the food basket. The boy trotted to a saltbush about twenty-five yards away and draped the rodent over the topmost twig. He trotted back and he and his brother walked over to a small bundle which I had not noticed. It was made of woven roots and contained a dozen small stones.

"That's how they start the boys hunting," the ranch-er said. "Each boy collects his own stones and prac-tices with them over and over. When the family

travels the kids are out in front, like skirmishers,
making sure that nothing gets away that can be eat-
en. They'll hit little birds, toads, snakes and rabbits,
but if they run across something big they'll freeze and
the old man comes up for the kill. They cut a swath
right through the desert, and a stretch of land which
looks deserted to a white man will yield them ten or
twelve pounds of food . . . roots, bugs, rodents, anything."

The biggest boy bent over the stones and selected a
handful. He was probably twelve years old, but his
arm was longer than mine, very thin and covered
with long lean muscle. His first shot, a blue stone,
whistled out of his hand. It missed the rodent and
snapped a twig from the saltbush. Idje said something
in a low angry voice. The boy nodded. The next shot
went so fast that I could not see the stone, but it hit
the rodent's body with a sharp thud. The boys then
alternated and in a few moments each of them was
hitting the rodent with every stone. The rodent's
body dropped from twig to twig, a few drops of blood
hung like glue and drew out into very long teardrops.

The rancher said something to Idje. Idje called to
the boys. The oldest boy ran out and put the rodent
on top of the bush. Then with a quick geometric
perfect search he gathered the stones. He had memorized where each had fallen and he did not waste a
step, running bent far over and scooping up each
stone merely by dropping his arm.

"Idje will throw the boomerang," the rancher said.
"The first throw will just be a warm-up, he says. It'll
come close, but won't touch the animal."

Idje picked up the boomerang and ran his hands
over it. Something was wrong and he barked at the
women. She reached into the bag and took out a
small piece of yellow fat. She handed it to Idje and

he rubbed his fingers over it until they were coated and then tossed the bit of fat back to the women. Her arm fell languidly, the fingers opened, and the fat fell into her hand. Idje rubbed the boomerang slick.

"He greases it so it will slide out of his fingers without effort," the rancher said. "The slightest drag and it will miss."

Idje was finally satisfied. He reached his arm back and then in a long flowing gesture, which brought his whole lean body forward in a great snap of muscle and cartilage, he threw the boomerang. It sailed far to the left, at first just grazing the ground and then rising to a height of fifteen or twenty feet. At the point of its greatest height it seemed to have almost no speed, but this is an optical illusion. It turned and began to circle back, dropping down in a long ellipse. It skimmed over the body of the rodent, clearing it by perhaps an inch. I suddenly realized it was traveling at a great speed and instinctively ducked. It was knee-high when it was fifteen yards from us and suddenly it rose into the air. Idje took a single step and caught it.

"Now he'll throw and hit," the rancher said. "They always try to hit on the return. I don't know why, but the boomerang seems more accurate on that leg of its journey."

Idje threw again. The boomerang spun out, again seemed to come to a standstill, and then whirred back. This time it dipped just before it came to the saltbush, came up savagely and slashed into the dead rodent, almost tearing the body in half. Idje grunted. One of the boys got up and brought the boomerang and rodent back.

"I'll try to get him to run down some bigger game," the rancher said.

He said something to Idje. There was a harsh exchange of words and I sensed hostility. The aborigine looked at me with a kind of distant cold pride. The rancher said something and Idje's face softened. He nodded his head in approval. He turned and said something to the dog, which instantly stiffened, came up off his haunches and moved a few steps forward. The aborigine turned and began to run, the dingo a few yards in front of him, sniffing the ground.

"What did you say to him?" I asked.

"He didn't want to run, but I told him you were a writer, a storyteller," the rancher said. "They all have a great respect for storytellers. Next to a good smell the thing they respect most is the ability to tell a story or sing a story. With a good storyteller it becomes a passion. Some of these black boys that everyone thinks are so stupid have learned to speak in six or seven different aborigine languages so they can tell stories. Not dialects, mind you, but languages as different as Spanish and English and French. I've been at it for twenty years and I can speak just one abo language."

The rancher obviously respected the aborigines. He pointed at Idje who was diminishing in size, running straight for the horizon in a beautiful graceful trot. The dog had already disappeared.

"Now that looks pretty damned simple, but it's not," the rancher said. "The abo's real weapons are his legs and his dingo ... if he had to he could hunt without his spear. But as Idje trots along he is watching the ground for signs. I've been out with him and in a single stretch of salt flat a half mile long where I couldn't even see a mark on the surface he could identify where a snake had crawled, a frog had hopped. Once a Landrover full of tourists got lost and we hired Idje to track them down. We followed him in another Landrover and he jogged along about five miles an hour for ten hours. Most of the time I couldn't see a thing, but he would point out where they had backed the vehicle and started in another direction. When we found them they were out of gas and water and just starting to get hysterical. Funny thing, though, they never even offered to pay Idje anything. I paid him off with tobacco and bully beef."

"How do they keep warm at night?" I asked. Nights on the desert can get chilly.

"They build a couple of fires up and sleep between them, the whole mess of them curled up into a family ball," he said. "Man, wife and children all curled up so that you can't tell which is which. Damndest thing. By morning they have, without waking up, all rolled over onto the warm ashes." He paused a moment and then went on in a voice that assumed I would disbelieve him.

"Some nights during the winter it will get down to 20° and even when they don't have firewood they survive that temperature. Do you know how they do it?"

"Not a clue," I said.

"Neither do I," he said and laughed. "And neither does anyone else."

"Where do they get water?" I asked, knowing that in this area the rainfall was less than five inches a year.

"During the rainy season they chase the rain squalls and wherever they find a puddle they drink it up."

"What about the dry season?" I asked.

"They have explained it to me, but I can never quite believe it," he said. "First they go to a 'soak,' a depression where water usually gathers and they dig. What they get if they are lucky is wet sand and they put this in their mouths and suck it dry and then spit it out."

"And if they are unlucky?"

"Then they look for shrubs which have water in their roots and they chew on those. There is also a kind of frog which bloats itself on water during the wet season to carry it through the dry. Finding one of those is like finding a little sack of water."

"That doesn't seem like much water," I said dubiously.

"It isn't," he said and then looked at me shyly. "Look, these are funny people. They have trained themselves to live on almost no water. Have you noticed how they conserve their energy? If you ignore the smell and the dirt it's really quite beautiful. They developed the boomerang so that if they miss they don't have to run after their weapon, it comes sailing back to them. And look at those kids catching ants ... they don't waste energy digging, they wait for the ants to come out. Did you see his lubra catch that piece of kidney fat? In her way she is as graceful as those girls I've seen in Sydney in the ballet." He stopped, embarrassed at his extravagance. I smiled encouragement.

"Anything that lives, animal or vegetable, they will eat," he went on. He went on to say that this included kangaroos, emus, snakes, turtles, crocodiles, bugs, spiders. They plant nothing, but they harvest whatever grows. There is even a form of poisonous yam which they treat by pounding on a stone and leaving it for a few years on top of a rock for the sun and rain to purify. With an uncanny memory they will return to a rock which holds a few pounds of yam, deposited three years before.

We heard the dingo yap, a far clear sound, that carried for miles over the stillness. Then there was a shrill series of yaps and the mother and two children looked intently at the horizon. The sounds were mixed, sounded vaguely of struggle. There was a series of short triumphant barks.

The lubra looked up at the rancher and said something.

"It's a kangaroo," he said. "A small one she thinks."

The aborigine grew from a hazy mote, growing larger and more distinct with each stride. The dingo came faster, moving in a straight economical line straight for the camp. When Idje reached us we saw that he had a small kangaroo in his hands, its neck wrung and its skin already half torn off. He trotted into the camp, squatted in front of his lubra. The kangaroo was eaten while it was still warm, torn into bits by forty bloody fingers. The dingo stalked nimbly at the edge, snapping at bits of blood and shreds of flesh. The noise they made was eerie.

We left while they were still eating. The rancher said something and Idje's face came up from the tangle of hands, skin, blood and sound. His lips were smeared with blood. The rancher indicated that he was leaving the box of Players for him. For the first time Idje smiled. He nodded goodbye and said something. Then he slid a bone into his mouth, crunched down on it.

But with bloody grease around his mouth, with his teeth gnashing a bone, with his fingers tearing unseen at kangaroo flesh Idje watched us. Not abjectly, but keenly, as if we were something to be avoided and rejected. The eyes, clotted occasionally by flies, stared unflinchingly at us as we climbed into the Landrover. The muscles in my neck relaxed only when I knew that we were out of sight of those great unblinking eyes.

Later my memory played cruel tricks on me. I

could remember Idje's magnificent posture, the glitter of his eyes, the incredibly hard justice of his life, the awesome tension between life and death in which he constantly lived. Willingly I wanted to forget the stone-strewn desert and the dazzling inhuman flashing of the salt pan and convince myself that only an animal that was less than human could endure it. I honged to fall victim to the strange Pacific malady of calling "childlike" what one does not understand. I wanted to make Idje and his ilk a version of Rousseau's "splendid savage" and forget them.

Reality is not that easy. Behind that promise of rage and understanding and imagination there is a fulfillment. The life of the aborigine, the life within his mind and soul, is intricate and bloody and soaring beyond belief. Only lately has this interior part of the aborigine been plumbed. For generations he was so suspicious of outsiders and whites and strangers that he would talk to them not at all or only on condition that they not repeat what he said until he, the aborigine, was dead. Slowly the picture has emerged. A few trusted and diligent whites have gotten behind the deep-sunk eyes and into the mind of the aborigine. What they have discovered is chilling.

The surface impressions are correct. The aborigine lacks agriculture, tools, domesticated animals, metals, pottery, the wheel, numbers, politics, a tone system, writing and seeds. But their psychic life is bewilderingly rich.

The aborigines have no notion of a supreme deity. Rather their life is filled with demons and daemons of a highly individual quality. Many of them have not yet made the association between sexual intercourse and conception. When an aborigine woman realizes she is pregnant she instantly associates the condition with something in the immediate surround: a tree, a hill, a cloud, a rock. A whirlwind, a roiling cloud of dust, is thought to be especially virile and aborigine women will flee in terror at the sight of one.

The aborigine wife does not decide by herself who is the father. This is done by elaborate consultation among the men of the family and the clan. When they decide which rock or whirlwind or hill is responsible that becomes the sacred name of the child . . . and is never spoken audibly. They have developed an elaborate sign language to communicate this name. To speak it would be to invite disaster . . . but they do not know why. The child is also given a common name which can be spoken freely. The sacred name, the unmentionable name, becomes the Churinga of the child . . . the spirit on which he can rely and to which he can make incantations. It also becomes a physical object, sometimes as small as a minute stone, sometimes as large as a spear. But not for women . . . they are never told the secret of who they possess as a Churinga.

The mind and heart of the aborigine howls with fears, hopes, totems, tabus, compulsions, injunctions. It is complicated beyond the most sophisticated religion of civilized man. There are rites for giving a man the capacity to make it rain. T. G. H. Strehlow describes the rite:

> An old man produced a sharp kangaroo bone. He stabbed my thumb with it and pushed the bone deep beneath the nail . . . the torment was unbearable . . . When the nail had been loosened, he took a sharp opossum tooth, forced it into the living flesh through the base of the thumbnail, and tore the nail off from behind . . . The men chanted: "They rip off the nail, they tear off the nail; blood flows like a river, rushes along like a river." Then they seized my left hand and removed the thumbnail in a like manner.

The ceremony of becoming a man is beyond belief or reason. The penis of the youth is cut open completely along the urethral canal. Forever after the man squats to urinate. But, by some fantastic circumstance, this does not preclude him from impregnating women. Some men, as if possessed by a feral Freudian obsession, return again and again to have the slashing of the penis repeated.

The final ceremony initiation of a young man is a trial by fire in which he must lie down on a fire which is barely covered by green leaves and then must squat on live coals for a half minute. Young men and women toss firebrands back and forth and, in the process, work up a sexual excitement which becomes unendurable and is consummated in a wild clashing of bodies.

All of this is accompanied by songs of the utmost intricacy and length. Skilled anthropologists have filled endless pages merely writing down the songs that are sung during these rites. Family groups, separated by hundreds of miles, will have identical songs and performances, perfectly reproduced, generation after generation.

None of this is particularly novel. Surely none of it is new ... all cultures are complicated. But the Australian aborigine that poor creature agreed to be the most simple in existence, reveals an awful truth. The life of all of us is complicated, subtle, bloody, fearsome, secret. And we struggle with an insane energy to make it invisible to the outsider.

Conclusion

Most of my days have been spent on the surface on the Pacific, on its islands or along its shores. This is no guarantee that I understand it perfectly. It is too vast a place. It also changes ... not as breakneck as the rest of the world, but enough to bewilder. Each person must see it with his own eye and each will see a different thing: a platitude which happens also to be the truth. The Western mind and body are not prepared for the Pacific. There is, for example, an island where the waves hit the sea reef with a regularity which is close to that of the pulsing of the human heart; and in a few days the island, the sky, the sea and one's body all seem to be throbbing in a massive systolic-diastolic universe. It is unbearable. And there are smells and sights which can never become tolerable.

The Pacific is not of the first importance in a geopolitical sense. Its islands are too tiny, its natural resources too scant, its peoples too scattered. There may be a way to bind the Pacific into an empire, but it is a well-kept secret and there are no Bonapartists about who wish to unravel the scheme. There is a realization that the Old Way will probably yield to The Beach, but the pace will be slow.

If war comes, the ICBM's and the bombers will wing over the Pacific—their targets the packed and heavily populated continents of North America and Europe and Asia. Only by mistake will its islands and archipelagoes go up in atomic smoke. If war does not

come the Pacific will gradually change, but it will not
be industrialized, will not know great hotels or su-
perhighways.

Perhaps the by-passed and low-pitched quality of
the Pacific is what gives it its seductive quality. It is
not rich. Only a few of the early explores could die
believing that it was a place of enormous and undis-
covered riches. The fortunes of the Solomons existed
only in the feverish imagination of the great captains. The enormous riches of *Terra Australis Non-
dum Detecta* might be real, but "The southern continent not yet discovered" remains just that. Magellan
and Mendana and Jakob le Maire and Tasman and
Dampier set the vision of riches high, but the reality
brought it low. Spices and gold and quick fortunes
could be made in Asia and the Americas. But the
Pacific islands, in the end, yielded up only bird droppings, copra and scant deposits of non-precious metals.

And still the place is seductive. As the rest of the
world has become homogenized and identical the
Pacific seems more and more to be unique, simple
and pleasant. Here the hard religion of Christ, the
intricate faith of Buddha, the evangelical edge of
Mohammed are softened by the sun and climate into
a gentle tolerance. Sex loses the element of guilt,
which is a mixed blessing for it also becomes more
tepid and less tensing. Privacy is less valued because
it is impossible. Houses are simple because the
coconut hut and the heat allow nothing else.

The Pacific is not paradise for everyone. For many
visitors the pace is so slow, the metabolic rate so
even, the challenge so diminished that the hard com-
petitive Western mind is outraged. Also one's standard of beauty, both feminine and natural, will be
given an endless series of tiny shocks ... and a few

cataclysmic jolts. For the deeply civilized, the unalterably sophisticated, the industrialized man the Pacific holds a low quotient of pleasure.

For the person who can regain an innocent nerve, a tolerance for repetition; for those who can endure a natural beauty which is soaring and massive and vivid to the point of disbelief and a human art which is primitive and bawdy ... for these the Pacific is endlessly intriguing.